PV

WITHDRAWN

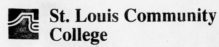

ELECTRICAL CIRCUIT ANALYSIS

ELECTRICAL CIRCUIT ANALYSIS

J. RICHARDSON
Electrical Power Section
Royal Naval Engineering College, Plymouth

G. T. READER
University of Calgary, Canada

ELLIS HORWOOD
NEW YORK   LONDON   TORONTO   SYDNEY   TOKYO   SINGAPORE

First published in 1990 by
ELLIS HORWOOD LIMITED
Market Cross House, Cooper Street,
Chichester, West Sussex, PO19 1EB, England

A division of
Simon & Schuster International Group

Typeset in Times by Ellis Horwood Limited
Printed and bound in Great Britain
by Hartnolls, Bodmin

British Library Cataloguing in Publication Data

Richardson, J.
Electrical circuit analysis.
1. Electronic circuit analysis.
1. Electronic circuits
I. Title   II. Reader, G. T.
621.3815
ISBN 0–13–248097–2 (Library Edn.)
ISBN 0–13–248089–1 (Student Pbk. Edn.)

Library of Congress Cataloging-in-Publication Data

Richardson, J. (James), 1949–
Electrical circuit analysis / J. Richardson, G. T. Reader.
p. cm — (Ellis Horwood series in electrical and electronic
engineering)
ISBN 0–13–248097–2 (Library Edn.)
ISBN 0–13–248089–1 (Student Pbk. Edn.)
1. Electric circuit analysis.   I. Reader, Graham T.
(Graham Thomas)   II. Title.   II. Series.
TK454.R498   1989
621.319′2–dc20   89–39631
                                                    CIP

Table of contents

Part 3 — AC CIRCUIT ANALYSIS

7 AC waveforms

8 AC voltages and currents in linear networks

9 Series combinations of R, L and C

10 Parallel circuit analysis

To our loved ones:

Rosie and Iain; Carol and Sally

Preface

To all students, welcome to the world of engineering, and especially the electrical aspects of engineering. It is a world we, the authors, have chosen to invest our lives and efforts in, and one to which we hope you come with enthusiasm. We strongly suggest that you consider, throughout your studies, whether you find the subject interesting enough for you to go on and to dedicate your efforts to the application of the knowledge you are to acquire.

We are unashamedly proud to be engineers. It is a profession with a long and constructive history which boasts some of the most ingeniously inventive minds as its forefathers. Some of these people you will already know of, although you may not realize it because they have become household names through the use of their names as units of electrical measurement: the Italian physics professor, Alessandro Volta (volt); the German schoolmaster, Georg Simon Ohm (ohm); the French mathematician and scientist André Marie Ampère (ampere); or the British engineer James Watt (watt). Perhaps the outstanding researchers of to-day lie waiting to be acknowledged in a similar manner by future generations.

This book is a text for the student's first venture into electrical engineering. It has been developed from the lecture notes prepared for first year students at the Royal Naval Engineering College who are undertaking degrees in electrical, marine, and aeronautical engineering. The course undertaken by these students lasts a full academic year of thirty weeks or so, and the material presented could be covered at a reasonably leisurely pace in 50–60 lecture hours. Electrical engineering majors should be able to complete the course in one semester, although for the majority of engineering students two semesters will be required.

We believe it is only possible to acquire a good understanding of the principles of electrical engineering by working through as many problems as possible. Thus, not only have we provided many worked examples within a chapter but have given a large number of review/tutorial questions at the end of each chapter. These will help you reinforce the analytical skills learned in the lectures. Engineers, by definition, are problem-solvers, and the sooner aspiring engineers become familiar with the methodology of this activity the better. Although we have taken the greatest care to eliminate errors in the answers provided to the problems, and indeed in the text itself, it is unlikely that they won't occur. If any errors are found please bring them to our attention; and we would welcome any comments you may care to make about the book.

We would like to thank our wives Rosie and Carol for their unbelievable patience and for their help in preparing the manuscript. We would also like to acknowledge the encouragement of Patricia Morrison of Ellis Horwood Ltd in starting on this three-volume series. We hope we have met her expectations, and we trust that students and teachers using this book will find it useful and helpful. Finally, we would like to thank the Dean of the Naval College, Captain G. C. George RN, who provided encouragement and the environment for writing; and to the Ministry of Defence for permission to publish.

Now before we launch into a very brief history of electrical engineering we have a heart-felt message for the students embarking on their studies.

Be proud and excited about your chosen career, whatever it eventually becomes, and never feel apologetic about being an engineer. You are entering a modern adventure, so be enthusiastic and excited, and never lose your sense of humour!

Always remember that engineering can sometimes be a little like the early voyages of Columbus. When you set off you're not quite sure where you are going. When you get there you don't know where you are, and when you return you don't know where you've been . . . Good luck!

J. Richardson
G. T. Reader

July 1989

A short history of electrical engineering

We do not wish you to be distracted from your studies of the principles of electrical engineering by spending too much time considering the history of the subject, but we feel it is important that you know a little about its foundations. A full history of electrical engineering would fill several large volumes and be encyclopaedic in nature. We do not have time for such an indulgence. However, we as engineers must learn to appreciate our past and revere those who laid the foundations for the development of electricity.

All engineers are notoriously dismissive of their own achievements and the impact they have had on society over the last hundred years or so, and electrical engineers are no exception. Yet, perhaps, we are all guilty of underestimating the benefits that 'electricity' has provided us with. Most of the time, only when there is a power cut do we realize how dependent we are on the public electric utilities. Just stop and think for a moment how electrical energy affects your daily life. The first action you took this morning after being woken by your electric alarm clock–radio was probably to switch on the electric light. You went into the kitchen to plug in the electric kettle to make tea, or the electric coffee percolator. After a shower powered by an electric pump and warmed by an electric heater, you used an electric shaver or hair-drier. If you are a big-city dweller you probably went to work by some form of electrically powered transport. At work you may have used the phone or the fax machine, the computer, or any number of electrical appliances. At the end of the working day you returned home and prepared a meal, using the microwave or electric stove, and then watched television or played a CD or phoned a friend living on the other side of the world before turning on your electric blanket which you use to help out the off-peak electrical central heating system. And so on, and so on; it really is difficult to think that it is only just over a hundred years ago that there was no public supply. In fact in Great Britain nine out of ten houses did not have electricity even 70 years ago!

The foundations of electrical engineering are, however, much older than the public supply system. The term 'electricity' was coined some five hundred years ago, probably by Queen Elizabeth I's doctor William Gilbert. The word 'electricity' is derived from the Greek word (elektron) meaning amber. The ancient Greeks observed that when amber, a yellow resin-type substance, was rubbed with wool or fur it was able to attract some light objects such as leaves or pieces of straw. They had in fact seen the effect of an electrostatic force. Also, although they did not realize it, they had observed another type of electrical force, for they had seen that pieces of a black stone they called magnetite would attract each other when brought close together, or sometimes repel each other, i.e. electromagnetic force effects. The Greeks were not the first to notice this, however, Chinese sailors were using magnetic compasses almost a thousand years before the discovery was made in the West. How do we know all this? From books, of course! The writings of Thales of Miteus (600 BC), Theophrastus (321 BC), and the Roman Pliny the Elder (AD 70) mention these observations. The first true, really technical description of the magnetic compass, as far as it is known came from a French military engineer Peter Peregrinus in a letter dated 1269: 'Letter on the Magnet of Peter Peregrinus of Maricourt to Syergus of Foucaucourt, Soldier'. We know nothing about Syergus and little about Peregrinus himself except that it was over three hundred years before anything else was written on the subject. It is interesting to note that the publishing activity of the (UK) Institution of Electrical Engineers is named Peter Peregrinus.

William Gilbert (1544–1603) experimentally repeated these observations and recorded them in his now famous book. *Do magnete, magneticisque corporibus, et de magno magnete tellure*. (On the Magnet, Magnetic bodies, and the Great Magnet) which was written, as the title implies, in Latin. Gilbert took the work of the Greeks much further than they had done themselves. He found that not just amber would attract small objects when rubbed but many other substances as well such as opal, glass, and diamond. He found that other substances such as emeralds, coral, bones, and marble would not attract objects after being rubbed. Gilbert recorded many other observations in his book, and was the founder of the science of electricity. However, although he coined the term 'electricity', the terms 'electrical' and 'electrical science' were first used in 1618 by the Archdeacon of Salisbury, William Barlowa.

The work of Gilbert was the start of the often called first period of electrical engineering. This first period came to an end in 1799 with the invention of voltaic pile and the production of electric current by Alessandro Volta (1745–1827), who at the time was the professor of experimental physics at Bologna. Volta made a pile or battery out of copper and zinc disks separated by disks of moist pasteboard. At last a continuous electrical current could be produced. This relationship between chemistry and electricity became the basis of further important inventions and scientific fields of study and eventually industrial development. Perhaps ironically, Volta's name is now linked with the unit of potential difference, the volt, rather than the electric current. Volta's discovery became known as another form of electricity called galvanic or voltaic electricity. The term galvanic came from the name of yet another researcher, Luigi Galvani (1737–1798). Galvani was professor of anatomy at the same university as Volta, and had investigated the effect of discharges from frictional electric machines on dead frogs. He eventually found that the legs could be made to move with nothing more than two different metals attached across the legs. His experiments included other animals, and he called his new phenomena 'animal electricity', a term that was to persist for many years. The electrical friction machine used by Galvani was invented in 1660 by Otto Von Guericke (1602–1686), the Mayor of Magdeburg in Germany. He built his machine out of a sphere of sulphur which when rotated and rubbed would not only attract light objects but also gave off sparks!

Volta's battery was soon in mass production by William Cruickshank (1745–1800) of Woolwich, England. Sir Humphry Davy (1778–1829) was to continue this work. He developed the process of electrolysis which established the science of electrochemistry as mentioned earlier. By the mid 1700s, Stephen Gray (1696–1736) had identified conductors and insulators; and E. G. von Kleist of Kammin at the same time, as Andraes Cunaeus and Pecter van Musschenbrook of Leiden, found a way of storing electric charge in a device which became known as a Leyden jar. In fact between the major discoveries of Gilbert and Volta many great scientists investigated the phenomena of electricity and added great slices of knowledge to the subject such as the connection between light and electricity, the ignition of hydro-carbons by sparks. Benjamin Franklin's observation that lightning was electrical in nature, and much more; but it would serve little purpose to merely catalogue all these discoveries, and for those who wish to study this period further we recommend the books listed at the end of this section. It can be said that by the end of the eighteenth century many forms of electricity had been observed and a theoretical basis for the subject of electrical engineering had been established.

In the first half of the century two major advances were made possible by the work of electromagnetics of Groat and the American scientist Joseph Henry: electrical telegraphy and electromagnetic induction. Professor Henry, secretary of the Smithsonian Institution, along with Professor Gale of New York University, and Alfred Vail redesigned an unpractical idea put forward by an American artist for an electrical telegraph machine, and Vail designed a code to go with it. Unfortunately, Gale and Vail had signed a contract which ascribed all their inventions and developments to the artist, a man named Samuel Morse! Today, most people remember only Morse and the Morse Code. Morse in fact tried to go even further, and tried to discredit Joseph Henry but did not succeed. At the same time as these ideas were being pursued in the USA. Cooke and Wheatstone were developing another type of telegraphy based on the work of Oersted who in 1820 in Copenhagen had observed that a magnetic needle could be deflected by the passing of an electric current through a nearby wire.

Morse's first telegraph line was opened for public business on 1 April 1845 in the USA, and the first Cooke and Wheatstone line some five years later on the Great Western Railway in the UK. However, it was the Anglo-American David Hughes who invented the printing telegraph that had the greatest success, especially in the USA and Europe. In fact Hughes machines were still in operation in Switzerland until the late 1940s. Telegraphy changed the world of communications and the communications of the world.

In 1804 the third son of a sickly North Country blacksmith became an erand boy and eventually an apprentice bookbinder to a London bookseller. The boy's elder brother paid one shilling for him to join the City Philosophical Society because of his interest in science. Before he was twenty-one, and although he had had little formal education, he had already concluded that there were two 'electric fluids' and had presented lectures on the subject. Sir Humphry Davy was so impressed that he employed the young man as his laboratory assistant and took him on a tour of Europe where he met André Ampère. The young man was Michael Faraday, often called 'the father of electricity'. Electromagnetic induction was discovered by Faraday in 1831, and this established the principles upon which all modern electrical machines — motors, generators, transformers and so on function.

This period was very productive, with Ampère. Ohm, and Oersted all making major steps in the development of electrical knowledge. All these men, like Faraday, were great experimenters, but others developed the theoretical aspects of the subject, notably Kirchhoff, Kelvin and Coulomb. However, it was the work of James Clerk Maxwell (1831–1879), Professor of Experimental Physics at Cambridge University, that produced the foundations of modern electrical theory. In a single theory consisting of four major equations Maxwell unified the work of all those who had gone before him. Although much has been learned since about the relationship between magnetism and electricity, the basic electromagnetic theory of Maxwell remains unchanged. The only major improvement to the theory was provided by Einstein's special theory of relativity.

Nikolai Tesla patented the polyphase induction motor in 1888, and it became the most common means of developing large quantities of electromechanical power. It is still used today albeit in a much improved state. These foundations in electro-mechanical power systems gave rise to the rapid development of both the supply of electrical power through generating stations and the consumption of this power in electrical transport systems and lighting systems. Thomas Edison and Joseph Swan developed the incandescent electric lamp in the 1880s, and this device's impact is apparent to the smallest child who can now flood away his fears at the flick of a switch.

The early power systems came in a variety of forms. There were dc and ac generating systems having both high and low voltage distribution systems. The ac systems came in many different frequencies from 25 to 420 Hz (cycles/sec). This miasma of differing systems called out for standardization, and in 1891 the American Institution of Electrical Engineers conducted a study that led them to a 60 Hz standard in ac generation. The European standard is 50 Hz. The transmission of electrical power over great distances also caused the acceptance of high voltage transmission systems with its inherent reduction in power loss over the transmission lines. The discovery of the ac voltage transformer by L. Gaulard and J. D. Gibbs in 1883 allowed power to be generated at low voltage then transformed up to high voltage for transmission and eventually transformed down to a safe voltage for use by the consumer.

This introduction lays down some of the names and discoveries that formed the nature of electrical system operation from its early years to the present time. We must apologize for not detailing all the revolutionary pioneers and their unrelenting efforts; but this is an introduction, and the studies of, say, Maxwell or Oersted, were so diverse and detailed that they cover the whole field of electrical engineering. We can already see that there are clear areas of electrical engineering specialization that will become potential career areas for all students to consider for their future. Electrical power generation and transmission, electrical motor propulsion systems, telephony and telegraphy, communications, and illumination. This book covers the foundation subjects necessary for any serious student of electrical engineering, and it also gives a springboard to further detailed studies in this clearly indispensable modern field.

A now grown-up child of electrical engineering is that broad discipline called electronics. One of its fathers was Thomas Edison, who discovered the thermionic effect in and patented a thermionic diode in 1883. The modern human being uses electronic devices without thinking about their mysteries or history. An electronics engineer has a myriad range of careers to choose from that encompasses computer engineering, communications engineering, and all the way to power electronics and its control of power systems.

This book deals mostly with the fundamental electrical engineering principles, and thus it is not our intention or purpose to study the history of electronics too closely. All that we hope to have done is to inform the potential electrical or electronics engineer that he is a student of worth and that he has a historical background to be proud of. If you choose to pursue the rewarding life that engineering offers, be content that it is also of worth to others. You make a necessary contribution to the human race.

Students with an ear for English usage should note that the abreviations dc and ac are used as nouns, and adjectival nouns in their own right. Thus we have the somewhat uncomfortable, but fully accepted terms: dc voltage (direct current voltage); dc current (direct current current); ac voltage (alternating current voltage); and ac current (alternating current current). The terms direct voltage (dv) and alternating voltage (av) are not used! The capital letter forms DC and AC are commonly used, with precisely the same meanings as dc and ac. In the present book they are used only where typographically approximate — in some headings and at the beginnings of sentences — in which latter case the forms Dc and Ac are, however, avoided.

Historical background reading:
Percy Dunsheath, *A History of Electrical Engineering*. Faber & Faber.

Part 1
DC circuit analysis

1

Introduction to direct current circuit theory

1.1 INTRODUCTION

In our short history of electrical engineering we found that by the 1800s several forms of electricity were known, although it was not always realized that these different forms were in fact variants of the same phenomenon — electron flow. The development of electricity took place without the scientists and engineers concerned in the development knowing the existence of the electron or the role it played in the production of electricity. Today, we are able to start our studies by considering the electron theory of matter and then to use it to explain the basic laws, conventions, and fundamental science of electrical engineering; but it must be remembered that the theory came after, not before, many of the major developments.

1.2 ELECTRON THEORY

All matter is composed of small particles called atoms†. An atom is made up of even smaller particles. The central part of an atom is called the nucleus, and around this electrons orbit. Both the electron and the nucleus carry an electrical charge. The nucleus is made of two types of particle, neutrons and protons. It is the protons which carry the electrical charge; the neutron is electrically neutral. The number of protons contained within the nucleus is equal to the number of electrons orbiting the nucleus.

The electrical charge carried by each electron and proton is the same, thus a normal atom is electrically balanced, i.e. it is electrically neutral. By convention, the electrical charge carried by the electron is said to be negative (− ve) and that by the proton, positive (+ ve). A schematic illustration of the structure of a typical atom is shown in Fig. 1.1. The diagram is not to scale, since most of the atom consists of empty space because the electrons orbit at a great distance from the nucleus. If we think about an electron as being a sunbather on a beach, then, to scale, the nucleus would be a ship at sea ten miles (16 kilometres) away.

† In a cubic centimetre of copper there will be about 10^{24}, that is, 1 000 000 000 000 000 000 000 000, atoms!

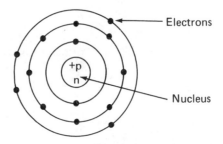

Fig. 1.1 — Typical atomic structure: Bohr's atomic model.

The electrons are kept in orbit by binding forces. Usually, the further away the electron is from the nucleus, the weaker these forces are. If an atom loses an electron, the remaining number of negatively charged electrons are outnumbered by the positively charged protons. Thus, overall, the atom now has a net positive charge. In this state the atom is called a positive ion. If an electrically balanced atom gains an electron, the atom will have a net negative charge, and is called a negative ion. An electron which escapes from its atom is called a free electron; it is the controlled movement of these 'free electrons' which provides electricity.

1.3 ELECTRON MOVEMENT

'When electrons move things happen'

To force the electrons from their orbits an energy input is required, which can be in the form of magnetic, chemical, heat, mechanical, friction, or light energy. We shall be particularly interested in magnetic and chemical energy inputs. The main thing to remember is that if electrons are to be freed and moved, an energy input is required. If the free electrons can be made to move in the same general direction by an energy input, an electric current is produced. Some materials release their electrons more easily than others; such materials are called conductors.

The early scientist found by observation that like charges repel, unlike charges attract. Electrons carry a negative charge, thus they are attracted by positive charges. Thus they can be attracted away from a point having a negative charge (excess of electrons) to a point having a positive charge (a shortage of electrons).

Let us consider a conductor, Fig. 1.2, in the form of a length of copper wire. To achieve a current flow we need to apply a force to the wire so that free electrons will be released and then moved. If one end of the wire is connected to a terminal which has a positive charge, any free electrons will move toward this terminal. If the other terminal is made negative, this will repel the free electrons. However, the terminals will become electrically neutral once the charges have balanced unless more free electrons are produced. If our terminals are part of a cell (commonly called a battery, which strictly means an assemblage of cells), the imbalance will be maintained (by chemical action), as excess electrons will be produced continuously at the negative terminal and attracted to the positive terminal. This is illustrated in Fig. 1.3.

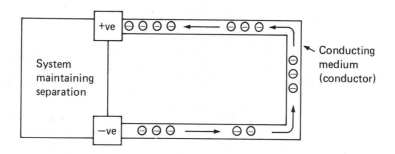

Fig. 1.2 — Electron flow in a conductor.

1.4 ELECTRON CHARGE

The electrons moving along the conductor are carrying a negative charge with them, and it is this charge which gives us an electric current. Many scientists tried to measure charge; one of the most famous, Charles Augustin de Coulomb, has given his name to the unit of charge — the coulomb, which is given the unit symbol, C.†

We now know that the charge on 1 electron is 1.602×10^{-19} C, the smallest amount of charge that can exist. Thus, 1 coulomb is equivalent to the electric charge on 6.24×10^{18} electrons, and is defined as such‡ (see Appendix for other definitions). We can now move on to the definition of electric current.

1.5 ELECTRIC CURRENT

Electric current is defined as the rate of change of flow of charge.§ Current is given the symbol I, and is measured in units called the ampere, after the French scientist André-Marie Ampère.

The unit of current measurement is given the symbol A (usually read as amp or amps). (It is not good practice to call current, 'ampage' or 'amperage'). Fig. 1.4 shows, diagrammatically, the definition of current. We say that the current flowing through an area, Pt.A. is one ampere if one coulomb of charge passes through the area per second. Thus current, time, and charge are related in mathematical form by the following equation:

---

† Electron charge (quantity of electricity), measured in coulombs, has the symbol Q. Note that symbols for *quantities* are printed in *italic*, but that the symbols for the *units* in which the quantities are measured are printed in 'roman' (that is, ordinary upright type). Thus, quantity (charge) Q is measured in coulomb C. Note also that units named after persons do not have capital initial letters, but that their symbols do. Thus, the coulomb has the symbol C, the ampere A, the volt V, and the ohm Ω (capital omega). These letter symbols do not have plural forms: one ampere is 1A, fifty-six amperes is 56A. Printers leave a small space between the numeral and the letter symbol: 7 A, not 7A (which would imply 'sevenamperes'). Letter symbols for quantities or units are not followed by a full stop.
‡ That is, $1 \div (1.602 \times 10^{-19})$.
§ More precisely as the rate of change of flow of positive charge.

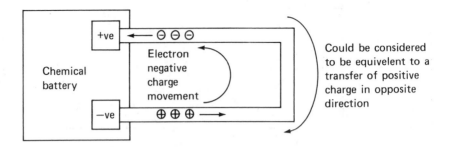

Fig. 1.3 — Electron movement produced by battery action.

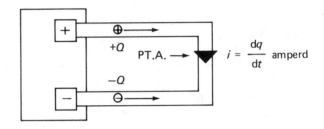

Fig. 1.4 — Current definition.

$$i = \frac{dq}{dt} \ , \quad \text{or} \quad I = \frac{Q}{t} \ \text{amperes} \ ,$$

where i and q represent current I and charge Q. at some particular instant t.†

If over a set period there is no change in the flow of charge, then no current will flow. As the charge flow rate varies, so does the current, as illustrated in Fig. 1.5. However, if over succeeding periods the rate of change of charge flow, dq, does not vary, the current flow will be constant. The relationships between current and rate of change of charge flow are summarized in Table 1.1.

1.6 CURRENT FLOW CONVENTION — THE HISTORICAL ERROR

The most obvious convention for a definition of current flow direction would be that suggested by the motion of free electrons from a negative to a positive location.

---

† Note that time is symbolized by t. The symbol T means temperature. Careful adherence to these conventions is important, since many phenomena are dependent on both time and temperature, and their symbols often appear in one and the same formula. However, later in the book we use T for period of a repetitive waveform, in a context in which there should be no confusion.

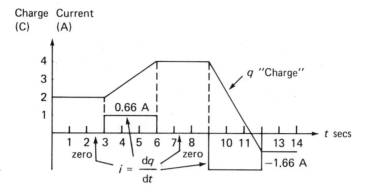

Fig. 1.5 — Resultant current flow with varying charge.

Table 1.1 — Relationship between charge and current

Rate of change of flow of charge	Current
Zero	Zero
Varies	Varies
Constant	Constant

Unfortunately, the founding fathers of electrical science decided that current flowed from positive to negative, exactly the opposite direction. They did not have the benefit of our knowledge of the atomic theory. Fortunately, it does not matter which direction is used, so long as we are consistent in the choice of direction. In this book we shall follow in the footsteps of the original electrical engineers and use their chosen direction which is called conventional current flow. Thus there are two conventions for specifying the direction of the flow of current, as shown in Fig. 1.6.

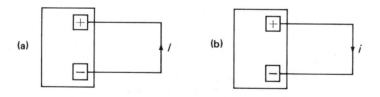

(a) Electron theory convention ($-$ ve to $+$ ve).
(b) Conventional theory convention ($+$ ve to $-$ ve).
Fig. 1.6 — Current flow conventions.

We have selected the older convention (Fig. 1.6b) for two main reasons: first, the majority of publications, especially engineering ones, use conventional flow rather than the electron theory convention favoured by physicists, and second, and perhaps more importantly, most electrical equipment markings reflect the conventional direction. Thus, for example, if we connected the positive and negative terminals of an electrochemical battery and, between the two, place in the circuit a current measurement device, called an ammeter, the instrument would indicate that current was flowing from the positive to the negative terminal as shown in Fig. 1.7. (Reverse

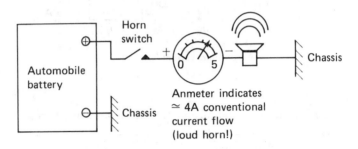

Fig. 1.7 — Conventional current flow.

connection would move the pointer anticlockwise, hard against the instruments endstop.) In other words, we could say that the vast majority of positive and negative markings on electrical equipment are the wrong way round!

1.7   ELECTROMOTIVE FORCE

We have discussed what an electric current is, and which of the two conventions we are to use to describe its flow direction. We know that a current flows as a consequence of the unidirectional movement of electrons between two locations which have different electrical charges. We now need to consider again what causes the conditions that prompt this flow of electrons. You will recall that (section 1.3) an external force/energy source is required to produce the charge difference which is necessary prerequisite if current is to flow. The external energy can be in a variety of forms; but whatever the original source, once the difference in charge is created the energy supplied is transformed into potential electrical energy which itself creates as electromotive force. This force is usually referred to as an 'ee-em-ef', and written emf or EMF. This quantity, electromotive force, has the symbol V (short for voltage); it is measured in volts, V. The symbol E has, in the past, been used for this quantity; but E is also used for electric field strength, measured in volts per metre. Some earlier authorities distinguished the two uses by printing the electric field strength symbol as **E** (that is, in heavy type). However, confusion is avoided by using V for emf and E for electric field strength. The 'bible' in the field of quantities, units, and symbols is Kaye & Laby's *Tables of physical and chemical constants*, now (1989) in its 15th edition. Your college library should have a copy.

It is this emf which causes current to, flow.

1.8 ELECTROMOTIVE FORCE AND POTENTIAL DIFFERENCE CONVENTION

In (system 1) Fig. 1.8 we show two separate electrons, one moving toward a

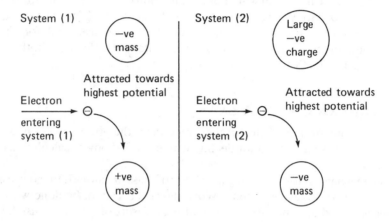

Fig. 1.8 — Force on an electrical charge.

positively charged body and the other (system 2) toward a negatively charged body. But how can this be? So far we have learned that electrons flow from negative to positive, so why is an electron shown moving toward negatively charged body? The reason is that, only to the electron, does the attracting body have to appear to be positive, or in other words less negative. Consequently, if we connect together two negatively charged bodies with a conductor, current will still flow; the electrons will move toward the body which is relatively the more positive or less negative of the two. This is an important concept, especially when we deal with the electrical quantity potential difference.

We have seen that in order to drive the electrons in the preferred direction and cause a current flow in our conductor we need a force, an electromotive force, emf, measured in volts (V). If the conductor were disconnected, no current would flow, obviously. Nevertheless, the potential for electron flow and current flow still exists. We say that between two charged bodies, for example battery terminals, a potential difference (p.d.) exists. The unit of measurement for potential difference between two points is also the volt. The word voltage is used to describe both emf and p.d. There should be no confusion if you remember that potential difference and electromotive force are different in that one describes the potential existing for electron flow (p.d.), whereas the other describes the force actually causing an electron flow (emf).

Fig. 1.9 indicates how we shall conventionally declare what is considered to be a positive emf or voltage, and consequently what we shall consider to be a negative emf or voltage.

$$enf_1 > emf_2 > emf_3 \ .$$

Remembering what we have just said about potential difference and the direction of current flow, see if you can work out the direction of the potential differences shown in Fig. 1.9 and place them in order in terms of magnitude. (The answer is given at the end of this chapter). In this figure, for clarity, we use, emf for the quantity electromotive force, and V for the quantity potential difference, both of which are measured in volts (V).

1.9   POWER AND ENERGY LAWS

One of the major uses of electrical engineering is the production of power, thus we need to establish a method for dealing with electrical power calculations. Consider Fig. 1.10.

If a mechanical force F acting on a body of mass M causes it to move a distance S, we say that work has been done. Work, however, cannot be done without energy being used, and the amount of work done is a measure of the energy used, and energy is the capacity for doing work. It is relatively straightforward to appreciate the concept of mechanical work; when we push a body and it moves we have had to do 'work' to get it to move. Thus we can say, if anything moves then work has been done, and this requires energy. The mechanical system has the following energy or work done equation.

$$\text{Energy (Joules)} = \text{Work done} = \text{Force} \times \text{Distance}$$

$$= F \times S \ \text{(newton-metres)} \ .$$

The electrical system has a similar equation, for when electrical current actually flows under the influence of an emf some of the potential electrical energy is dissipated, that is, work is done. It would require energy to move the $+$ve charge $+Q$ towards the $+$ charge mass.

$$\text{Energy (Joules)} = \text{Work done}$$

$$= \text{Force} \times \text{Charge}$$

$$= EMF \times Q \ \text{(volt coulombs)}$$

The relationship between energy and power is the same, whatever sort of system we are looking at, and it is defined by the equation given below.

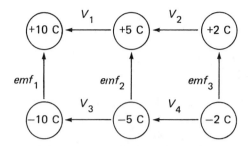

Fig. 1.9 — Electromotive force (emf) and potential difference.

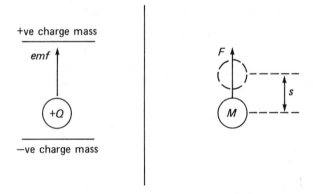

Fig. 1.10 — Force on an electrical charge (with its mechanical equivalent).

$$\text{Power (watts)} = \frac{\text{Energy}}{\text{Time}} \qquad \frac{\text{(joules)}}{\text{(seconds)}}$$

Power is the rate of doing work, so in more precise mathematical terms:

$$\text{Power} = \frac{d}{dt}\,(\text{energy}) \ldots \text{(joules/sec) or (watts)}$$

If our electrical system is operating with a constant emf, the equation for power can be written as follows, recalling the equation that related current flow I to charge Q.

$$\text{Power} = \frac{d}{dt}(V \times Q) = V \times \frac{dQ}{dt}$$

$$= V \times I \quad \text{(volt amperes)}$$

It is worth noting that the units of energy which we have defined as 'joules' may also be defined as watt–seconds if we recall the equation for power, or work done. However, in the International System of Units (SI)† it is the joule that is the unit of energy. Nevertheless, in electrical engineering you will encounter, quite frequently, another energy unit, the kilowatt-hour (kWh). One kilowatt-hour is equivalent to 3.6 million joules, that is, 3.6 megajoules (MJ), which is a convenient unit to use when dealing with large energy quantities and is extensively used in the power generation industries.‡'

1.10 POWER SOURCE AND LOAD CONVENTION

We have discovered a convention for current, electromotive force, and potential difference. We now need to have a similar convention to define power sources and power loads. A power source delivers energy to create an emf and a charge difference such that there is electron flow in the direction shown in Fig. 1.11. The

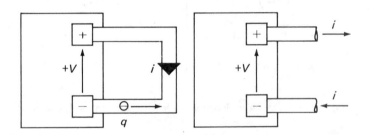

Fig. 1.11 — Power source diagram.

current produced '*i*', is considered to be conventionally flowing out of the positive terminal and into the negative terminal.

A power load requires electrical energy, hence current *i* is considered to be conventionally flowing out of the negative terminal and into the positive terminal

---

† You may care to ask your college library for *Changing to the metric system*, National Physical Laboratory, Her Majesty's Stationery Office, now (1989) in its 5th edition. It includes a historical background to successive (and sometimes unhelpfully parallel) systems of units, and an explanation of the Système International d'Unités (1960) whose use in science and technology is highly desirable. The system recognizes, however, the probable, understandable, and indeed useful survival of certain familiar units (such as the kWh), wqhich conveys more meaning to the domestic electricity consumer than does the megajoule: one hour's use of a one-bar electric fire, or 3.6 megajoules?!).

‡ Your domestic electricity meter measures kilowatt-hours, and those are what you pay for. Your gas meter measures cubic feet, but you pay for therms (but that is another story!).

when our system is absorbing power (Fig. 1.12). The power load/source convention is shown in Fig. 1.13, for conventionally flowing current. The voltage/current conditions are shown for the two situations. Note how they must and do comply with the definitions of votage and current conventional directions.

1.11   THE ELECTRIC CIRCUIT

We have considered what electricity is and some of the basic quantities associated with electricity such as current, electromotive force, charge, and potential differ-ence. We have studied these matters as they are the building blocks for our study of what is the main constituent of electrical engineering — the circuit. All of us knowingly or unknowingly use electrical circuits — in the home, in the automobile, at work, and at school. By putting an electrical plug in a socket we have 'completed' the circuit — so what is an electrical circuit? An electrical circuit is a complete electrical pathway which allows not only electrons to flow from a negative to a positive location, that is, a current flow, but also allows this flow to be maintained by an electromotive force.

The source emf causes the electrons flowing into the positive locations, let us say terminals, to be returned by a direct route to the negative terminals and thus complete the pathway. (Remember that the description we have just given is using electron theory convention.) Of course, when we put the plug into the socket, although we say we have a circuit we don't have a circuit of the type just described until we switch the system on. Until the switch is turned on, no current will flow and the electrical pathway will not be complete. We define these two conditions as a closed circuit — an unbroken pathway, and as an open circuit — a broken pathway, see Fig. 1.4. Thus switches are said to be 'on' or 'off', or 'closed' or 'open'.

We shall also encounter in our studies a third general type of circuit condition called the short circuit.

1.12   RESISTANCE TO ELECTRON FLOW

Let us consider Fig. 1.15 which depicts the flow of electrons (represented by ●) through a material. We know that to produce 'electricity', that is, current flow, we need to generate free electrons. We said that materials whose atoms can be readily made to release an electron are called conductors. Conversely, materials whose atoms do not easily release their electrons are called insulators. Whether the material is a conductor or an insulator, any electrons flowing through the material will be subjected to a buffeting effect from fixed and neutral atoms within the material and from the repulsion effects between the free electrons themselves, as illustrated in the diagram. In others the flow of electrons, and hence the flow of current, will be restricted; the term we give to this obstruction is resistance.

About 200 hundred years ago, when scientists were carrying out experimental investigations into the 'new' phenomenon of electricity, they found that with the same conductor, when they changed the value of the emf, the value of the current also changed. In 1827, a German schoolmaster, Dr George Ohm, published a book in which he described his experiments with emf and current, and concluded, in effect, that the electromotive force divided by the resistance is equal to the strength of the

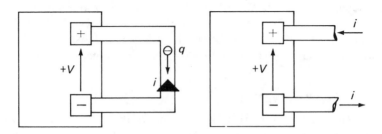

Fig. 1.12 — Power load diagram.

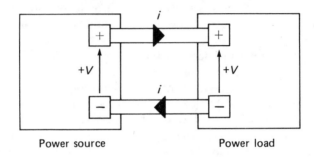

Fig. 1.13 — The power load/source convention.

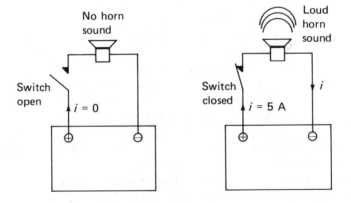

Fig. 1.14 — Example of an open and a closed circuit.

Cross-sectional area A m^2

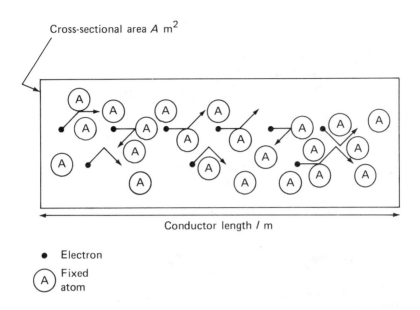

Conductor length l m

● Electron

Ⓐ Fixed
   atom

Fig. 1.15 — Electron flow through a conductor.

current. The type of result Ohm achieved is shown in Fig. 1.16. This conclusion by Ohm was, and still is, extremely important. We know it as Ohm's law, and it can be expressed as follows:

emf = resistance × current

$$V = R + I .$$

Resistance, as indicated, has been given the symbol R, and the unit of resistance is called, not surprisingly, the ohm and is given the Greek capital letter omega Ω.†

In these early experiments it was also found that the resistance of the conductor was independent of the current flowing through it, but that the same emf did not produce the same value of current with different conductor materials or even with the same conductor if its dimensions were changed. This means that our current flow through a conductor is liable to experience a resistance to movement due purely to the material's physical properties.

Experimental observations in the last century led to a series of deductions regarding what governs the resistance of a material. It was found that the electrical resistance of any material, such as a conductor, depends upon four factors:

† In the discussion of electrical circuits, it must be noted that R (in upright type) means the resistive element (the resistor) and R (italic) is the quantity (resistance). It is undesirable, and potentially confusing, to call a resistor a resistance. However, it is often difficult or impossible to maintain the R, R convention, for the resistor shown as R in a circuit diagram is usually discussed in the text in terms of its resistance R.

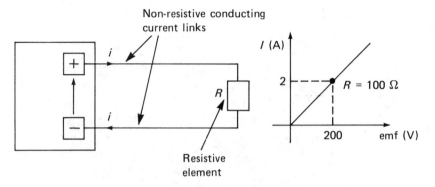

Fig. 1.16 — Emf versus current for a conducting material.

(1) Cross-sectional area
(2) Length
(3) Type of material
(4) Temperature

If we increase the cross-sectional area of a conductor, the electrons are given a wider path to traverse and hence will meet with less resistance. Thus, with a material at a constant temperature and with a fixed length:

$$\text{Resistance} \propto l/A$$

where A is the cross-sectional area of material. The unit used to express this area is (metres)^2.

If we increase the length l of the material, then the individual free electrons will experience a longer flow path and hence a greater resistance. Thus, if we keep our material at a constant temperature and fixed cross-sectional area:

$$\text{Resistance} \propto l$$

If we change our conducting rod from one material to another, say from copper to aluminium, the resistance of our conductor will also change. At a constant temperature this means that resistance of a material has three controlling variables, length, area, and material type. All these factors can be combined into the simple formula:

$$\text{Resistance} = \rho \times \frac{l}{A} \; .$$

The mathematical constant of proportionality, ρ (rho), which takes account of the type of material used, is called the material's resistivity: a simple reorganization of the above formula tells us that it must have units of ohm–metre. Usually the resistivity of the more common electrical materials is very low, and is therefore usually measured in micro-ohms-metre. Great care has to be taken, therefore, when carrying out calculations, to ensure that the correct units are used. The average values of resistivity for the more common conductors are given in Table 1.2.

Table 1.2 — Average resistivity values

Material	Resistivity	
	$\mu\Omega$m	$\mu\Omega$mm
Aluminium	0.0285	28.5
Brass	0.06–0.09	60–90
Copper	0.0173	17.3
Iron	0.1	100
Lead	0.219	219
Mercury	0.958	958
Silver	0.0163	16.3
Tin	0.0114	11.4

The relationships we have just discussed were deduced from experimental observations that used materials available at the time.

In the present century many more materials have been discovered or produced which do not conform to these observations. One very important class of such materials are the semiconductors. In simple terms these materials will let electrons flow readily in one direction, that is, like a conductor, but less readily in the opposite direction, that is, like an insulator. We know from our studies so far that electrons will flow in a general direction, which means that the majority will flow one way but some may not. Thus a semiconductor can act like a conductor and insulator at the same time.

Consider Fig. 1.17, which is a similar plot to Fig. 1.16 but for a semiconductor material. It shows how current changes with respect to voltage applied in a semiconductor, and it is quite clearly a nonlinear relationship. The semiconducting material is obviously resistive, but the resistance is not constant over the full range of applied voltage. We can see this more clearly if we plot the instantaneous value of resistance on a graph as in Fig. 1.18.

Thus we must be aware of the fact that the resistance of a material is not always constant and can vary for a whole variety of reasons both external and internal. We shall now look closely at one of the major external influences upon the resistance of materials, temperature.

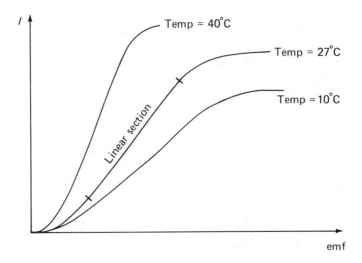

Fig. 1.17 — Semiconductor emf — current relationship.

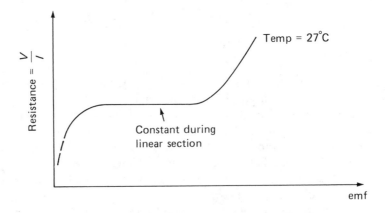

Fig. 1.18 — Resistance against applied voltage.

1.13 THE EFFECTS OF TEMPERATURE ON RESISTANCE

We have said that one of the observed effects on the resistance of a material is that of temperature. If we changed the temperature of a pure metal conductor such as copper and plotted the measured value of resistance against temperature we would obtain the type of graph shown in Fig. 1.19, which illustrates how as the temperature of a copper conductor rises, its resistance increases. This result is typical of all pure metals, because as the material's temperature rises its atoms begin to vibrate and hence cause a greater obstruction to the flow of electrons by reducing the available flow path for the moving electrons (current).

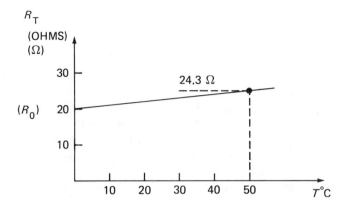

Fig. 1.19 — Temperature versus resistance for a copper coil.

Thus the temperature rise manifests itself as an increase in the material's resistance. The linear relationship between temperature and resistance suggested in the above graph is generally true for metal conductors within the normal range of operating temperatures, and such materials are said to have a positive temperature coefficient. There are materials, however, notably insulators and semiconductors, for which the resistance decreases at elevated temperature, and for which the relationship between temperature and resistance is not linear.

The temperature–resistance relationships for two such materials, carbon and silicon, are shown in Fig. 1.20. Materials which decrease in resistance when their temperature is raised are said to have a negative temperature coefficient.

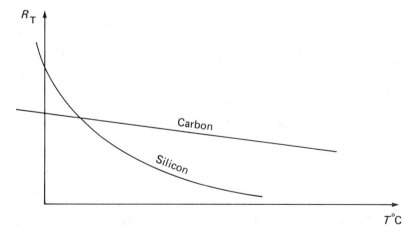

Fig. 1.20 — Temperature–resistance profiles for carbon and silicon.

We shall now develop appropriate formulae so that we can calculate the effects of temperature upon resistance. Let us reconsider the graphical plot for the copper conductor, Fig. 1.19. The graph is a straight line, and we know from elementary mathematics that the law of such a line is:

$$y = mx + c \ .$$

The vertical axis, y, is the resistance of the material at any temperature, T, and we shall denote this, R_T. The horizontal axis, x, is any temperature, T, and the value of c is the value of R_T at the point where the line crosses the y axis, which in our example is when $T = 0°C$. The only factor left to define is the slope (gradient) of the line, m, $\delta R/\delta T$. The Greek letter alpha, α, is the generally accepted and recommended symbol. Thus we can rewrite the equation of the line:

$$R_T = \alpha \delta T_0 + R_0 \qquad \qquad \text{Note } \delta T_0 = \text{change in temperature above } 0°C.$$

The term α is called the temperature coefficient of resistance, and relates how a given resistance will increase when the temperature is raised. The value of α depends upon the value of the resistance at $0°C$. The term δT_0 is the change in temperature between $0°C$ and the temperature of interest. If engineers and designers were to make use of the equation given above for R_T, in its presented form, they would need an extremely large data book listing the value of alpha for all possible resistance values of a material plus a similar data book for all the other materials. This is unpractical, so we redefine the temperature coefficient in the following way:

$$\alpha_0 = \alpha/R_0 \ .$$

We can now simply list one value of the temperature coefficient of resistance for each material and rewrite the R_T equation as:

$$R_T = R_0 + R_0 \ \sigma_0 \ \delta T_0$$

or

$$R_T = R_0(1 + \alpha_0 \delta T_0) \ .$$

Thus our temperature coefficient of resistance α_0 (alpha nought) is now purely dependent upon material type, and is independent of the quantity of material R_0. The units of α_0 are ohms per ohm per $°C$. Typical values for common electrical materials are given in Table 1.3.

It is important to know the temperature at which α is defined, for data are provided which list these coefficients at $15°$ and $20°C$. This is done for convenience since these temperatures reflect common ambient values, i.e. the usual average

Table 1.3 — Temperature coefficient of resistance at 0°C

Material	α_0 (°C at 0°C)
Aluminium	+ 0.0040
Annealed copper	+ 0.0043
Brass	+ 0.0010
Carbon (graphite)	− 0.0005
Hard-drawn copper	+ 0.0043
Iron	+ 0.0066
Nickel–chromium	+ 0.00017
Silver	+ 0.0041

daily temperatures.† It is also more convenient to measure resistance at these ambient temperatures. Thus, for example, at a room temperature of 20°C, the temperature–resistance relationship for our copper conductor is as given in Fig. 1.21.

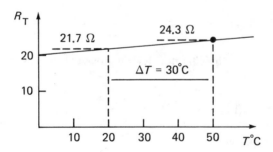

Fig. 1.21 — Temperature-resistance relationships for copper at 20°C.

As before, we can define an equation for resistance based on the straight-line equation, that is:

$$R_T = R_{20} + \alpha \delta T_{20} \ ,$$

(where R_{20} = resistance at 20°C, and δT_{20} is the difference between the temperature required and 20°C.) Redefining α in the same manner results in:

† 20°C (68°F) is standard temperature for the calibration of electrical measuring instruments and the making of electrical measurements.

$$\alpha_{20} = \alpha/R_{20} \ ,$$

then

$$R_T = R_{20}(1 + \alpha_{20}\delta T_{20}) \ .$$

Valves of α_{20} for different materials are given in Table 1.4. This completes the

Table 1.4 — Temperature coefficient of resistance at 20°C

Material	α_{20} (°C at 20°C)
Aluminium	+ 0.00370
Annealed copper	+ 0.00396
Brass	+ 0.00098
Carbon (graphite)	− 0.00047
Hard-drawn copper	+ 0.00396
Iron	+ 0.00583
Nickel–chromium	+ 0.00169
Silver	+ 0.0397

presentation of material in Chapter 1. We now consider some worked review questions.

Answers to section 1.8 (Fig. 1.9)
V_1 & V_2 are both positive.
V_3 & V_4 are both negative.
$V_1 > V_2$ & $V_3 > V_4$

WORKED EXAMPLES

Example 1.1
Q. In a time of half a minute, 31.2×10^{18} electrons move past a point in a conductor under the action of a battery. What will be the average current flow?

A. We know that current flow is the direction of unidirectional electron movement, and the value of this current can be calculated if we know the rate of change of the flow of charge. This fact is expressed mathematically in equation (1.1), $i = dq/dt$. We have not, however, been told the amount of charge, but we have been told the number of electrons passing through the area under consideration. Thus, if we knew the charge each electron was carrying then it would be simple to determine the total charge. We have in fact already stated that a charge of 1 coulomb is equivalent to the charge on 6.24×10^{18} electrons:

$$q = Q = 31.2 \times 18^{18} \times \frac{1 \text{ coulomb}}{6.24 \times 10^{18}}$$

$$= 5 \text{ coulombs}$$

From the current and charge equation $i = dq/dt$, where $q = 5$ coulombs and $t = 0.5$ minutes,

$$i = 5/0.5 = 10 \text{ coulombs per minute.}$$

The SI unit of current is the ampere, but it does not follow that when we calculate the value of a current the units will necessarily be the ampere. We have to ensure that the right units are used. In this particular example the time was given in minutes; an ampere is equivalent to coulombs per second. Thus we must use seconds as our time unit if the answer we obtain is to be in the correct SI unit. Thus:

$$i = 10/60 = 0.1667 \text{ amperes} \qquad \text{i.e. coulombs/sec.}$$

It may seem that we have laboured the point of units in this trivial example, but the point we are making of using the correct units is not trivial; it is very important — remember, always use the correct units.

Example 1.2
Q. How much power would be required to light a factory with 2000 electric lamps if every lamp requires a current flow of 1.5 at 240 V?

A. We have to choose which one of the electrical power equations in section 1.9 is the most useful to us for the solution of this problem. We know the current, I, and the emf, and if we look at the equation set, then the obvious choice is the one that relates Voltage & Current to power.

For one lamp,
$$\text{Power} = EMF \times I = 240 \times 1.5$$
$$= 360 \text{ W}$$

For 2000 lamps,
$$\text{Power} = 2000 \times 360 = 720\,000 \text{ W}$$
$$= 720 \text{ kW } .$$

Example 1.3
Q. The cross-sectional area of a copper conductor is 15 mm². Calculate the resistance of 1 km of the conductor at a constant temperature.

A. We are given the length and area and have to find the resistance. If we look at the equation given in section 1.12 we can see that to determine the resistance we need one further piece of information — the copper's resistivity. We can obtain that from Table 1.2.

Therefore:

$$R = \frac{l}{A}$$

And:

$$\sigma = 0.0172 \ \mu\Omega m = 0.0172 + 10^{-6} \ \Omega m$$

$$l = 1 \ km = 1000 \ m$$

$$A = 15 \ mm^2 = 15 \times 10^{-6} \ m^2 \ .$$

We now have all the elements of the resistance equation, and all the parameters have been converted to the correct units! Thus:

$$R = \frac{0.0172 \times 10^{-6}}{15 \times 10^{-6}} \times 1000 \ \Omega$$

$$= 1.15 \ \Omega$$

Example 1.4

Q. Determine the resistance of a length of copper cable at 125°C if the measured resistance of the cable at an ambient temperature of 20°C is 6.1 Ω.

A. We have derived two equations for determining the effects of temperature on resistance. One was based on a reference temperature of 0°C, the other on 20°C. Obviously to answer this question we need the latter equation:

$$R_T = R_{20}(1 + \alpha_{20}\delta T_{20}) \ .$$

We are given the value of R_{20} for the copper cable and can calculate that δT_{20} as $(125 - 20)C^0$. Thus all we need is the temperature coefficient of resistance from Table 1.4.

$$\delta T_{20} = 105°C, \ \alpha_{20} = 0.00396 \ ,$$

$$R_T = 6.1(1 + 0.00396 \times 105)$$

$$= 8.636 \ \Omega$$

REVIEW QUESTIONS AND TUTORIAL EXAMPLES

(1.1) Define an electric current and explain what is the difference between conventional current flow and electron theory current flow.

(1.2) With a current of 1.5 A flowing, how long will it take to transfer 450 coulombs of charge? (300 seconds).

(1.3) Explain the difference between electromotive force and potential difference.

(1.4) What p.d. exists across a conductor of resistance 12 Ω, when a current of 2.5 A flows through it? (30V)

(1.5) Name five common sources of electricity.

(1.6) What charge is transferred when a current of 10 A flows for 2 minutes? (1200 C).

(1.7) Draw a circuit containing a source and a load and label the diagram, showing the direction of current flow based on conventional theory.

(1.8) Determine the current required to provide energy at the rate of 120 J/s from a 240 V supply. (0.5 A).

(1.9) What is resistance? In a circuit what happens to the current if at a constant emf the resistance is doubled?

(1.10) What is the resistance of an electrical heater if it carries a 10 A current when connected to a 240 V supply? (24 Ω).

(1.11) State Ohm's law and derive an expression for the resistance of a material at any temperature if it has a linear positive temperature coefficient of resistance.

(1.12) A factory is supplied with power at 240 V. The factory load consists of four electric motors each taking 4 A, and 250 electric lamps with a 60 W rating at 240 V. Determine the total current required. (78.5 A).

(1.13) A dc generator supplies 250 A of current at 220 V. What is the generator's power output in kilowatts? (55 kW).

(1.14) A coil of nickel wire has a resistance of 1 kΩ in air at an ambient temperature of 20°C. The nickel is immersed in a liquid and left until its temperature stabilizes, at which time its resistance has fallen to 0.88 kΩ. If the temperature coefficient for nickel is 0.006 Ω/Ω/°C, estimate the temperature of the liquid. (0°C).

(1.15) State four factors which affect the resistance of a material. If an aluminium conductor is doubled in length and its diameter halved, how will its resistance change?

(1.16) Find the resistance at 20°C of the following annealed copper wires:

(a) 10 m long, 1 mm^2 cross-sectional area.
(b) 25 mm^2 cross-section, 200 m long.
(c) An old conductor which is 3 miles long with a cross-sectional area of 0.2 in^2.

((a) 0.173 Ω, (b) 0.138 Ω, (c) 0.646 Ω).

(1.17) The resistance of a piece of copper at 0°C is 46.07 Ω. What is its resistance at 20°C, if the temperature coefficient of resistance for this particular copper is 0.00426/°C at 0°C? (50 Ω).

(1.18) A conductor has a resistance of R_a ohms at T_a°C. If its temperature coefficient of resistance at 0°C is α/deg C,† find an expression for the resistance of the conductor, R_b, at a temperature of T_b°C.

(1.19) If the resistance of a certain wire, 800 m long, is 32 Ω, what would be the resistance of a ¼ km of the same wire? (10 Ω).

(1.20) The field coils of a motor have a resistance of 120 Ω at 15°C. After a run at full load the resistance increases to 135 Ω. Calculate the average temperature of the coils if $α_{15}$ is 0.00401 Ω/Ω/°C. (46.2°C).

(1.21) The field winding of a dc motor is connected directly across a 440 V supply. When the winding is at a room temperature of 17°C, the current is 2.3 A. After continuous operation for many hours, the current has reduced to (1.9) A, whilst the supply voltage is maintained at a constant value. If the winding material has a temperature-resistance coefficient of 0.004 26 per °C at 0°C, calculate the average temperature of the winding. (70°C).

---

† 'deg C' is sometimes used to indicate a temperature *interval*; thus 1 deg C is the change of temperature between the two temperatures 18°C and 19°C. However, this distinctive usage is becoming less common.

2

Kirchhoff's laws, Resistor combination laws, and loop analysis

2.1 KIRCHHOFF'S VOLTAGE SUMMATION LAW

Kirchhoff's voltage summation law is a derivative of the conservation of energy laws.

Energy in = Energy lost as heat

$$V_{total} \cdot I \cdot t = V_1 \cdot I \cdot t + V_2 \cdot I \cdot t + V_3 \cdot I \cdot t + \ldots + V_n \cdot I \cdot t$$

But I and t are common to the input supply and the circuit resistors, therefore (see Fig. 2.1):

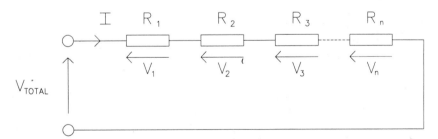

Fig. 2.1 — Resistors in series.

$$V_{total} = V_1 + V_2 + V_3 + \ldots + V_n \ .$$

An alternative way of stating the voltage summation law is to say that the sum of the voltages around a closed loop must equal zero, or

$$V_{\text{total}} - V_1 - V_2 - V_3 - \ldots - V_n = 0.0$$

2.2 RESISTORS IN SERIES

The voltage summation law can be combined with Ohm's law to produce a rule about resistors in series.

$$V_{\text{total}} = I \cdot R_{\text{total}} = I \cdot R_1 + I \cdot R_2 + I \cdot R_3 + \ldots + I \cdot R_n$$

Therefore:

$$R_{\text{total}} = R_1 + R_2 + R_3 + \ldots + R_n$$

2.3 POTENTIAL DIVIDER THEOREM

The voltage across any single resistor can be calculated directly from the total voltage applied without recourse to openly calculating the total current, by the reorganization of the formulae given above.

$$V_1 = I \cdot R_1 = \frac{V_{\text{(total)}}}{R_{\text{(total)}}} \cdot R_1$$

Therefore:

$$V_1 = V_{\text{total}} \times \frac{R_1}{R_{\text{(total)}}}$$

or, in general:

$$V_n = V_{\text{total}} \times \frac{R_n}{R_{\text{(total)}}}$$

2.4 POWER SUPPLIES IN SERIES

When supplies are connected in series their total effect can be, to all intents and purposes, considered as a single supply, as suggested in Fig. 2.2.

If there is no load on our string of supplies, there will be no current drawn from the supplies and hence no voltage dropped across the resistances R_1, R_2, etc. Thus if

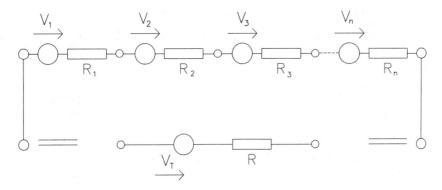

Fig. 2.2 — Power supplies in series (with allowance for supply resistance).

the terminal voltage is measured without the draining off of current we can deduce or measure the effective total emf presented by the series of supplies, using Kirchhoff's voltage summation law.

$$V_{total} = V_1 + V_2 + V_3 + \ldots + V_n \ .$$

If we now remove the condition that created the emfs by either stopping the generators or discharging the batteries, we can deduce or measure the total effective resistance of our series of supplies as suggested in Fig. 2.3.

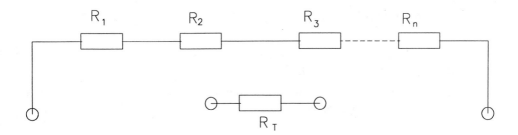

Fig. 2.3 — Power supplies in series without emts.

It can be easily seen that:

$$R_{total} = R_1 + R_2 + R_3 + \ldots + R_n \ .$$

2.5 KIRCHHOFF'S CURRENT SUMMATION LAW

Kirchhoff's current summation law is a derivative of the conservation of energy law,

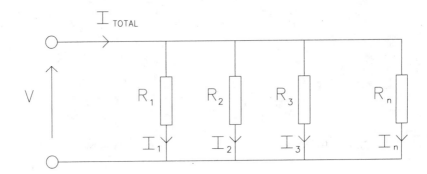

Fig. 2.4 — Resistors in parallel.

and can be deduced as follows.

Energy in $=$ Energy out as heat

$$V.I_{total}.t = V.I_1 + V.I_2.t + V.I_3.t + \ldots + V.I_n.t$$

But V and t are common to both input and resistors:

$$I_{total} = I_1 + I_2 + I_3 + \ldots + I_n$$

2.6 RESISTORS IN PARALLEL

Kirchhoff's current summation law and Ohm's law can be combined to produce a rule about resistors in parallel:

$$I_{total} = \frac{V}{R_{(total)}} = \frac{V}{R_1} + \frac{V}{R_2} + \frac{V}{R_3} + \ldots + \frac{V}{R_n}$$

Again V is common, so:

$$\frac{1}{R_{(total)}} = \frac{1}{R_1} + \frac{1}{R_2} + \frac{1}{R_3} + \ldots + \frac{1}{R_n}$$

2.7 CONDUCTANCE

The inverse of resistance (conductance, G) is given a name of its own to allow simpler solutions of parallel circuits to be achieved.

$$\frac{1}{R\,(\text{ohms})} = G\,(\text{siemens}) \qquad \text{or} \qquad \frac{1}{\text{Resistance}} = \text{Conductance}$$

Thus our parallel components can be summated by using the inverse of resistance to produce a much simpler formulae:

$$G_{\text{total}} = G_1 + G_2 + G_3 + \ldots + G_n$$

Ohm's law can be revised to include an appreciation of conductance as shown in Fig. 2.5.

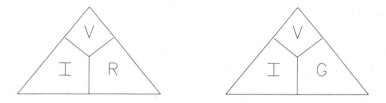

Fig. 2.5 — The Ohm's law triangle.

$$V = I \cdot R \qquad\qquad V = \frac{I}{G}$$

$$I = \frac{V}{R} \qquad\qquad I = V \cdot G$$

$$R = \frac{V}{I} \qquad\qquad G = \frac{I}{V}$$

2.8   CURRENT DIVIDER THEOREM

The current through an individual resistor limb can be deduced by using a combination of Ohm's law and Kirchhoff's summation of currents law (Fig. 2.6a):

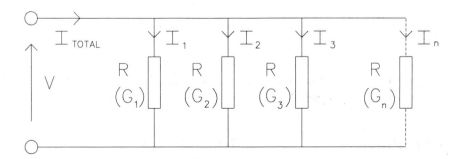

Fig. 2.6a — Resistors/Conductors in parallel.

$$I_1 = V \cdot G_1 \quad \text{but} \quad V = \frac{I_{(total)}}{G_{(total)}} \; .$$

Therefore:

$$I_1 = I_{total} \cdot \frac{G_1}{G_{(total)}} \qquad \text{(compare to potential divider)}$$

or in general:

$$I_n = I_{total} \cdot \frac{G_n}{G_{(total)}}$$

A common formula developed for current division, using resistance, is that used to determine the current division between 'two' limbs or branches of a network. Fig. 2.6b shows the circuit that this forms, and we can see that the current has two path

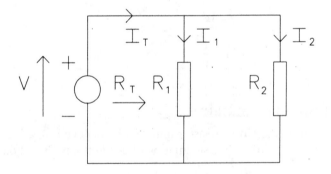

Fig. 2.6b — Current division through two limbs.

options, I_1 and I_2. Now the voltage applied can be calculated from the three expressions given below:

$$V = I_T \cdot R_T = I_1 \cdot R_1 = I_2 \cdot R_2 \; , \quad \text{where } R_T = R_1 \| R_2 \quad (\| \text{ means in parallel with }),$$

that is

$$\frac{1}{R_T} = \frac{1}{R_1} + \frac{1}{R_2}$$

or

$$R_T = \frac{R_1 \cdot R_2}{R_1 + R_2} \qquad \text{(use factorization)}$$

Now

$$I_1 = \frac{I_T \cdot R_T}{R_1} = \frac{I_T}{R_1} \times \frac{R_1 \cdot R_2}{R_1 + R_2} \, ,$$

thus

$$I_1 = I_T \times \frac{R_2}{R_1 + R_2} \, ,$$

and similar deduction gives:

$$I_2 = I_T \times \frac{R_1}{R_1 + R_2} \, .$$

This means that we can see the current dividing in a ratio determined by the size of the resistance of its opposite limb divided by the combined resistance of both limbs. This result is commonly quoted as the current division formula, but it is clear that it works only for a two-limb division and is not applicable for three or more limbs. The conductance formula, however, does allow for any number of multiple limbs, and is thus preferred by the present authors.

2.9 POWER SUPPLIES IN PARALLEL

If we are going to connect power supplies in parallel (Fig. 2.7) then it would be fair to assume that we already know that their individual emfs and internal resistances are. The following technique for deducing the overall effect of connecting these supplies in parallel is a theoretical approach that requires the short-circuiting of the power supplies. In a practical approach this would never be attempted since damage to the supplies might result. This is not, however, a problem when we only 'imagine' the effects.

The overall internal resistance of our parallel combination is deduced, using a similar approach to the one used in serial combination. We imagine the individual supplies to be devoid of emf and redraw the circuit as in Fig. 2.8.

It is obvious that

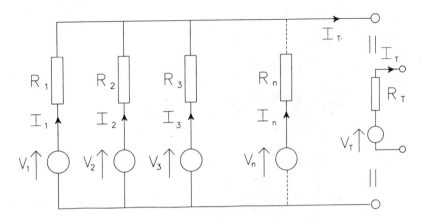

Fig. 2.7 — Power supplies in parallel.

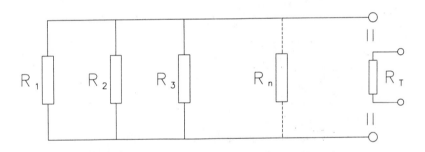

Fig. 2.8 — Power supplies in parallel (emfs zero).

$$\frac{1}{R_{(\text{total})}} = \frac{1}{R_1} + \frac{1}{R_2} + \frac{1}{R_3} + \ldots + \frac{1}{R_n}$$

or

$$G_{(\text{total})} = G_1 + G_2 + G_3 + \ldots + G_n \ .$$

Fig. 2.9 is the effective 'model' that we are suggesting can be deduced for the whole set of parallel supplies. If we short-circuit the output terminals, then a short-circuit current will flow that is limited only by the size of the total effective emf.

$$I_{s/c} = \frac{V_{(\text{total})}}{R_{(\text{total})}} \quad \text{or} \quad V_{\text{total}} = I_{s/c} \cdot G_{\text{total}} \ .$$

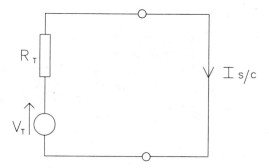

Fig. 2.9 — Suggested equivalent circuit for parallel supplies.

If we now consider the full set of parallel supplies we can deduce the short-circuit current as follows.

$$I_{s/c} = I_1 + I_2 + I_3 + \ldots + I_n \; ,$$

but

$$I_1 = \frac{V_1}{R_1} \quad \text{and} \quad I_2 = \frac{V_2}{R_2} \quad \text{and} \quad I_3 = \frac{V_3}{R_3} \; , \qquad \text{etc.} \; ,$$

giving

$$I_{s/c} = \frac{V_1}{R_1} + \frac{V_2}{R_2} + \frac{V_3}{R_3} + \ldots + \frac{V_n}{R_n}$$

which can be calculated by using the already known values for V_1, R_1, etc. This means that we now know $R_{(total)}$ and $I_{s/c}$, and we can now use these to deduce the effective parallel supplies $\text{emf}_{(total)}$ or V_T.

$$V_T = \text{emf}_{(total)} = I_{s/c} \cdot R_{(total)}$$

Although the short-circuit current is used in our calculations it must be pointed out that at no time during our calculations has there been any practical measurement that would require our applying such a radical electrical test.

2.10 LOOP ANALYSIS

The loop analysis method of circuit analysis allows us to calculate the numerical value of all the currents flowing in the circuit limbs.

We shall employ most of the laws deduced so far, but the 'procedure adopted' is the main piece of new information contained in this section.

The end result of our electrical circuit analysis will be a set of simultaneous equations containing the limb current as unknowns.

Circuit current declaration

The first step is to overwrite our circuit diagram (Fig. 2.10) with a suggested set of

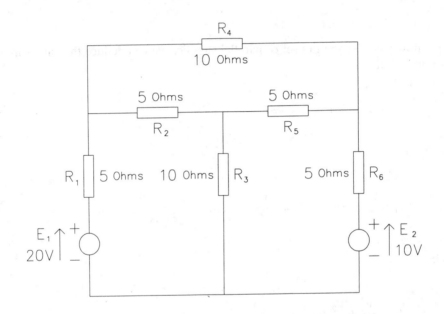

Fig. 2.10 — Circuit for loop analysis.

currents (Fig. 2.11). The touchstone for the optimum number of current variables is that they must not exceed the number of circuit meshes. Our circuit has three meshes, hence three current unknowns. It is advisable to allocate the current directions in such a way that they conform to the already stated conventions on power supplies. If a reasonable doubt exists, there is no need to worry since the analysis technique will account for errors in assumed current direction by producing a negative result.

Application of Kirchhoff's voltage summation to meshes

The next step is to apply the convention concerning power loads to all resistors and hence generate a voltage pattern for the circuit (Fig. 2.12).

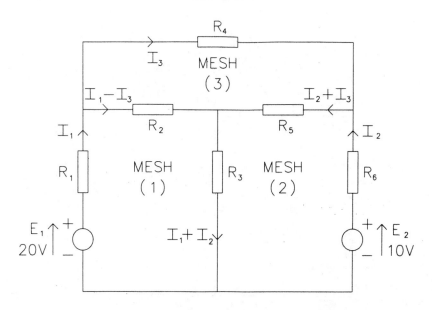

Fig. 2.11 — Circuit for loop analysis (with currents).

We can apply Kirchhoff's voltage summation laws to all three meshes to begin the generation of our simultaneous equations.

LOOP (1)

$$E_1 = V_1 + V_2 + V_3$$

or

$$20 = 5 . I_1 + 5(I_1 - I_3) + 10(I_1 + I_2)$$
$$20 = 20 . I_1 + 10 . I_2 - 5 . I_3 \qquad\qquad (2.1)$$

LOOP (2)

$$E_2 = V_3 + V_5 + V_6$$

or

$$10 = 10(I_1 + I_2) + 5(I_2 + I_3) + 5 . I_2$$
$$10 = 10 . I_1 + 20 . I_2 + 5 . I_3 \qquad\qquad (2.2)$$

LOOP (3)

$$0.0 = V_2 - V_4 - V_5$$
$$0.0 = 5(I_1 - I_3) - 10 . I_3 - 5(I_2 + I_3)$$
$$0.0 = 5 . I_1 - 5 . I_2 - 20 . I_3 \qquad\qquad (2.3)$$

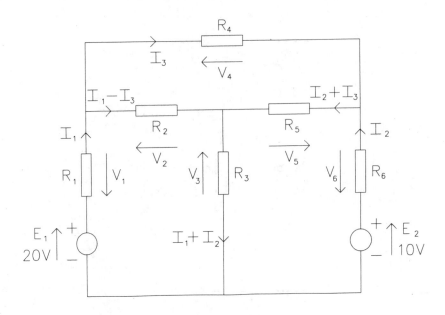

Fig. 2.12 — Circuit for loop analysis (with voltages).

Solution of simultaneous equations
Multiply equation (2.2) by 4 to get:

$$40 = 40 . I_1 + 80 . I_2 + 20 . I_3 \tag{2.4}$$

Add equation (2.4) to equation (2.3) to get:

$$40 = 45 . I_1 + 75 . I_2 \tag{2.5}$$

Add equation (2.1) to equation (2.2) to get:

$$30 = 30 . I_1 + 30 . I_2 \tag{2.6}$$

Multiply equation (2.6) by 2.5 to get:

$$75 = 75 . I_1 + 75 . I_2 \tag{2.7}$$

Subtract equation (2.5) from equation (2.7) to get:

$$35 = 30 . I_1 \ ,$$

giving

$$I_1 = 1.1666' \, A$$

Substitution back into any of our equations yields a complete final result for all three unknown currents.

$$I_1 = 1.1666' \, A \qquad I_2 = -0.16666' \, A \qquad I_3 = 0.3333' \, A$$

To check these results simply put them into the original equations and the voltages chould be correct.

WORKED EXAMPLES FOR CHAPTER 2

Example 2.1

Q. Determine the voltage V_{in} in Fig. 2.13.

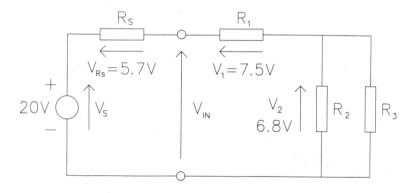

Fig. 2.13.

A. V_{in} can be written down from two separate loop equations:

(a) $V_{in} = V_1 + V_2 = 7.5 + 6.8 = 14.3 \, V$

(b) $V_{in} = V_S - V_{Rs} = 20 - 5.7 = 14.3 \, V$

Example 2.2

Q. Determine R_{in} for both Fig. 2.14a and 2.14b.

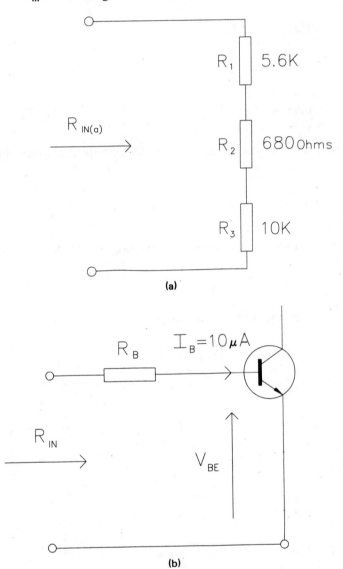

(a)

(b)

Fig. 2.14.

A.
$$R_{in(a)} = R_1 + R_2 + R_3 = 5600 + 680 + 10\,000 = 16.28\,k\Omega$$
$$R_{in(b)} = R_B + V_{BE}/I_B = 50\,k\Omega + 0.7\,V/(10 \times 10^{-6})\,A = 120\,k\Omega$$

(Note the use of Ohm's law to develop effective resistance across the electronic device — a transistor.)

Example 2.3

Q. Determine V_{out} in Fig. 2.15a and write down the value of V_{out}/V_{in}. Also

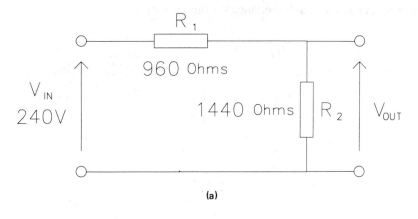

(a)

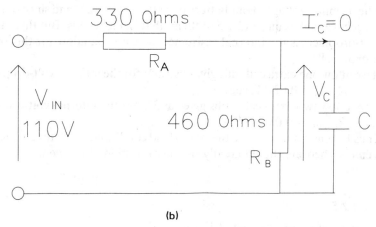

(b)

Fig. 2.15.

determine the voltage across the capacitor, in Fig. 2.15b, if it is drawing no current.

A. For circuit (a) $V_{out} = V_{in} \times \dfrac{R_2}{R_1 + R_2} = 240 \times \dfrac{1440}{960 + 1440}$

$$= 144 \text{ V}$$

and $\dfrac{V_{out}}{V_{in}} = \dfrac{144}{240} = 0.6$

For circuit (b) $V_C = V_{in} \times \dfrac{R_A}{R_A + R_B} = 110 \times \dfrac{460}{330 + 460}$

$$= 64.05 \text{ V}$$

Example 2.4

Q. Determine the number of 1.5 V cells necessary to provide the load resistor R_L with a current of at least 6 A at 12 V terminal voltage (see Fig. 2.16). Also determine the maximum cell internal impedance for this condition.

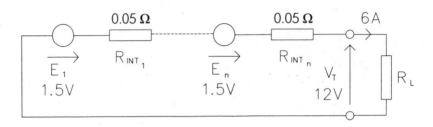

Fig. 2.16.

A. The terminal voltage of our battery of cells must be 12 V and since our cells are of 1.5 V each we shall require 12/1.5 of them, that is, eight cells. But this will not allow for volt-drop across the internal resistance, so we must allow for this by including some extra cells.

If we allow one extra cell, this gives us 1.5 V for the internal volt-drop across nine cells, i.e. $R_{int(9)} = 0.027' \, \Omega/\text{cell}$.

If we allow two extra cells, this gives us 3 V for the internal volt-drop across ten cells, i.e. $R_{int(10)} = 0.05 \, \Omega/\text{cell}$.

Thus 10 cells would achieve the stated load condition. In a later chapter the use of Thévenin's Theorem should greatly simplify this kind of problem.

Example 2.5

Q. Determine I_X for both Fig. 2.17a and 2.17b.

A. In both circuits (a) and (b):

Total current in = total current out ,

therefore   (a) $5 + 6 = I_X + 3 + 2$

$I_X = 6 \, \text{A}$

and   (b) $36 + 12 + 20 = I_X + 100$

$I_X = -32 \, \text{A}$.

(Note $I_{X(b)}$ is actually entering the junction.)

Example 2.6

Q. Determine R_{in} in both Figs 2.18a and 2.18b.

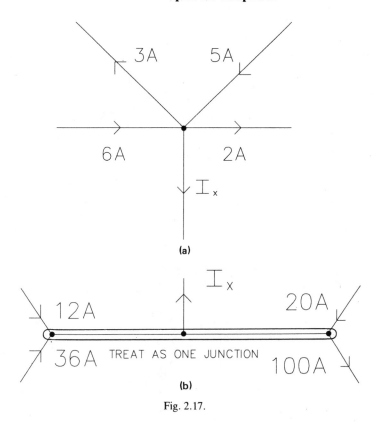

Fig. 2.17.

A. We should use conductance for more than double combinations,

therefore   (a) $G_{in} = G_1 + G_2 + G_3$

$$= 0.2 + 0.25 + 0.333'\,\text{mS}$$

$$= 0.78333'\,\text{mS}$$

that is, $R_{in} = 1.2766\,\text{k}\Omega$.

For circuit (b) we can use the product over sum rule.

therefore $R_{in(b)} = R_g \| R_{FET}$ (where $R_{FET} = 5\,\text{M}\Omega$) (Ohm's law)

$$\frac{1 \times 5}{1 + 5}\,\text{M}\Omega$$

$$= 833.33'\,\text{k}\Omega$$

The electronic device is a field-effect transistor (FET).

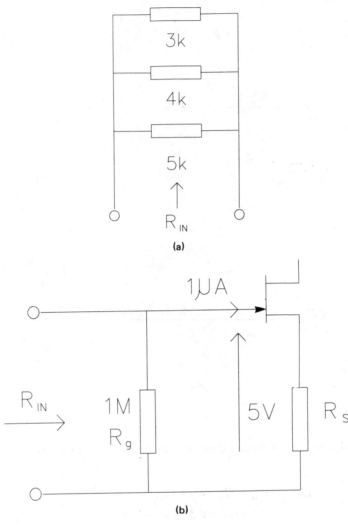

Fig. 2.18.

Example 2.7

Q. Determine I_X in both Figs 2.19a and 2.19b.

A. In both circuits we must find the supply current I_S first, which is calculated from V_S/R_T.

$$R_T = R_1 + R_P \text{ in both circuits, but } R_{P(a)} = 3\,\text{k}\Omega$$
$$\text{and } R_{P(b)} = 1.5\,\text{k}\Omega$$

Therefore $R_{T(a)} = 8\,\text{k}\Omega$ and $R_{T(b)} = 6\,\text{k}\Omega$

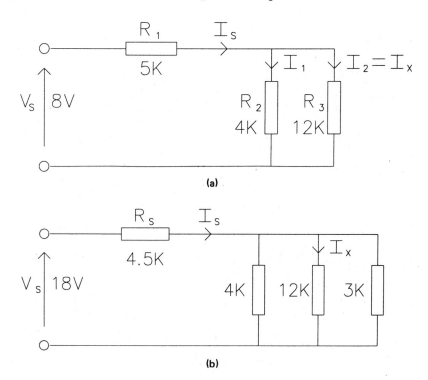

Fig. 2.19.

therefore $I_{S(a)} = 1\,\text{mA}$ and $I_{S(b)} = 3\,\text{mA}$.

For both circuits we can say

$$I_X = I_S \times \frac{G_X}{G_P} = I_S \times \frac{R_P}{R_X} \ ,$$

Therefore $I_{X(a)} = \dfrac{1 \times 3}{12}$ and $I_{X(b)} = \dfrac{3 \times 1.5}{12}$

$$= 0.25\,\text{mA} \qquad\qquad\qquad = 0.375\,\text{mA}$$

Example 2.8
Q. Find the effective battery emf and internal resistance presented to the load
resistance R_L in Fig. 2.20.

A. $R_{\text{eff(int)}} = R_1 \| R_2 \| R_3 \| R_4$ or $G_{\text{eff(int)}} = G_1 + G_2 + G_3 + G_4$

Therefore $G_{\text{eff(int)}} = 0.1 + 0.125 + 0.25 + 0.2$

$$= 0.675 \cdot \text{mS} \qquad (R_{\text{eff(int)}} = 1.4815\,\text{k}\Omega)$$

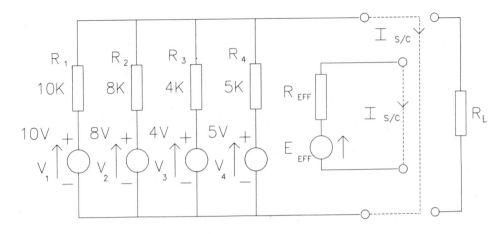

Fig. 2.20.

Now $V_{eff} = I_{S/C} \times R_{eff}$

and $I_{S/C} = V_1/R_1 + V_2/R_2 + V_3/R_3 + V_4/R_4$

$$= 4\,mA.$$

therefore $V_{eff} = 4\,mA \times 1.4815\,k\Omega = 5.926\,V.$

REVIEW QUESTIONS AND TUTORIAL EXAMPLES

(2.1)   Explain, with the aid of a suitable diagram, how temperature affects the resistance of a metal conductor. Using your diagram and any other information develop an equation which relates the resistance of the conductor at an elevated temperature above 20°C.

(2.2)   Three coils have measured resistance of 8, 12, and 15 Ω. Find the equivalent resistance when they are connected (a) in series, (b) in parallel. (35 Ω, 3.64 Ω).

(2.3)   A circuit consisting of three resistors of 4, 6, and 12 Ω is connected to a battery of emf 1.5 V. If the emf remains constant and the internal resistance of the battery can be assumed to be equivalent to a resistor of 1 Ω in series with the battery, how many coulombs of change are passed through the resistors in 1 minute if they are:

(a) connected in series. (3.9 C).
(b) connected in parallel. (30 C).

(2.4)   State Kirchhoff's two laws and explain their meaning, using appropriate diagrams.

(2.5)   Derive an expression for the equivalent resistances of three resistors R_1, R_2, and R_3 when connected in (a) parallel (b) series. A $20\,\Omega$ resistor is connected in parallel with a resistor of unknown resistance. This circuit is then connected in series with a device which dissipates $0.6\,kW$ of power when a current of $10\,A$ flows through it and the parallel combination from a source emf of $100\,V$. What is the resistance value of the unknown resistor? ($5\,\Omega$).

(2.6)   Calculate the conductance of a circuit that passes a quarter of an ampere when an emf of $5\,V$ is applied. If the conductance is increased to $100\,mS$ and the emf remains constant, what will be the current flow. ($0.05\,S$, $500\,mA$).

(2.7)   It is required to pass a current of $10\,A$ through a $2\,\Omega$ resistor. The power supply is in the form of accumulator cells each of emf $3\,V$. If we assume that the internal resistance of the accumulators is $0.1\,\Omega$, how many accumulators will be needed if they are to be connected in a single series block? (10).

(2.8)   State the potential divider theorem. Sketch the circuit for two resistors used as a potential divider and derive the equations for the volt-drop across each resistor in terms of the supply emf.

(2.9)   A potential divider consists of two resistors of $37\,\Omega$ and $88\,\Omega$. Calculate the volt-drop across each resistor if the supply emf is $75\,V$. ($22.2\,V$, $52.8\,V$).

(2.10)   A circuit consists of three parallel resistors of 5, 4, and $6\,\Omega$. A current of $2\,A$ flows through the $5\,\Omega$ resistor. What is the total current flow in the circuit? ($6.17\,A$).

(2.11)   Three resistors of 16.8, 6.3, and $4.2\,\Omega$ are connected in parallel. If the total current taken is $4.6\,A$, find the currents through each resistor. ($0.6\,A$; $1.6\,A$; $2.4\,A$).

(2.12)   A parallel circuit consists of three resistors of resistance 3, 9, and $12\,\Omega$. The current through the $9\,\Omega$ resistor is found to be $8\,A$. What is the current through the other two resistors, and what is the total current supplied to the circuit? ($24\,A$, $6\,A$, $38\,A$).

(2.13)   A resistor of $3.6\,\Omega$ is connected in series with another of $4.56\,\Omega$. What resistance value must a resistor placed across the $3.6\,\Omega$ resistor have so that the total cicruit resistance is $6\,\Omega$? ($2.4\,\Omega$).

(2.14)   A coil of a copper alloy having a resistance of $4\,\Omega$ at $15°C$, is connected in parallel with a maganin resistor of $4\,m\Omega$. When the total circuit current is $50\,A$, what will be the current flowing through the copper resistor? ($50\,mA$).
    If the ambient temperature is raised by $40°C$, find the percentage change in the

current flowing through the copper resistor if the total supply current remains the same. The temperature coefficient of resistance for the copper alloy is 0.0043 per °C at 0°C. (13.9%). (Note: Check manganin out in the library, use any good engineering encyclopedia.)

(2.15)   A resistor of 8Ω is connected in parallel with one of 12Ω, and this circuit limb is connected in series with a 4Ω resistor. A p.d. of 10 V is applied to the circuit. The 8Ω resistor is then moved to be across the 4Ω resistor. Find the p.d. required in the second case to send the same current through the 8Ω resistor as flowed in the first case. (30 V).

(2.16)   Two conductors of equal resistance are connected in series across a 120 V dc supply. In total 1000 W of power are dissipated. A further conductor of the same material and physical dimensions is now connected in parallel with the two other conductors. What will be the power dissipated in each conductor? (500 W, 500 W, 1000 W).

(2.17)   In the series-parallel circuit shown in Fig. 2.21, calculate (a) the potential difference across the 4Ω resistor, (b) the supply voltage. (45 V, 140 V).

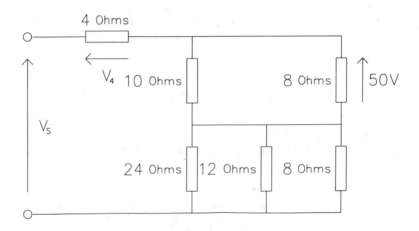

Fig. 2.21 — Series–parallel circuit.

(2.18)   Three resistors of 4Ω, 16Ω and 6Ω are connected:

(a) the 4 and 6Ω resistors in parallel, with the 16Ω in series,
(b) the 4 and 16Ω in parallel, with the 6Ω in series.

Show that in the two cases, the currents in the 4Ω resistor are in the ratio 3:8 when the circuits are connected across the same applied emf.

(2.19)   In the bridge circuit shown in Fig. 2.22, calculate the current flowing through

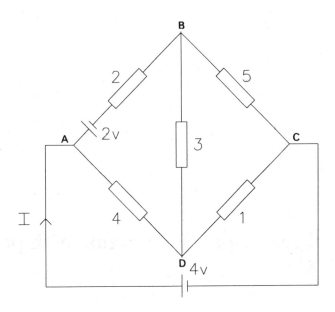

Fig. 2.22 — Bridge circuit.

each resistor. ($i_{AB} = 0.372$ A; $i_{BC} = 0.25$ A; $i_{CD} = -0.896$ A; $i_{DA} = -0.776$ A; $i_{BD} = 0.12$ A).

(2.20)   Find the resistance of the circuit shown in Fig. 2.23. (1.25 kΩ).

(2.21)   Two similar coils each of resistance 100 Ω are connected in series across a 200 V supply. What is the resistance value of the resistor which must be placed in parallel across one of the coils such that the voltage across it is 95 V? (950 Ω).

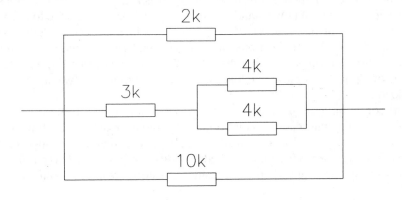

Fig. 2.23.

3

Analysis of series–parallel circuits with power loads

3.1 WHAT IS REGULATION?

In this chapter we are going to study more complex resistive circuits, and we will make use of two important analytical approaches embodied in two circuit theorems called (a) **Thévenin's theorem**†, and (b) **Norton's theorem**. These theorems are particularly useful when we deal with circuits which include a power load.

In most practical applications in which power is generated and used, the system can produce a range of powers and accept a range of loads. We have to account for these situations in our analyses. One means by which we acknowledge that the variation of power has implications for our circuit analysis is the use of the concept of regulation. This term is used to define the difference between the output terminal voltage of a power supply as the loads on the system ranges between 'no-load' and 'full-load'.

The condition of 'no-load' exists when no current is drawn from the supply, i.e., an open circuit, whereas the condition of 'full-load' exists when the maximum permissible current is drawn from the supply. The percentage change in output voltage from no-load to full-load is called the voltage regulation. This parameter will be particularly important when you consider transformers later in your studies. The

---

† This theorem is also called Helmholtz's theorem.

concept of regulation† is illustrated graphically in Fig. 3.1, where the changing load is represented by a variable resistor, R_L.

Regulation is mathematically defined as follows:

$$\text{Regulation} = \frac{V_{T(o/c)} - V_{T(\text{full-load})}}{V_{T(o/c)}} \times 100\%$$

where V_T is the terminal voltage.

In the example shown in Fig. 3.1 the regulation is calculated as follows:

$$\text{Regulation} = \frac{400 - 350}{400} \cdot 100\% = 12.5\%$$

It should be noted that in some textbooks and manufacturers' handbooks the denominator of the regulation equation is sometimes given as the supply terminal voltage at full-load.

The next factor we have to consider in our build-up to the study of more complex circuits is the constant current generator.

3.2 CONSTANT CURRENT GENERATORS

In all of the electrical circuits considered so far we have used power supplies formed from a constant emf generator coupled with a series resistance to represent the internal resistance of the generating device, although we have sometimes chosen to ignore this resistance in our calculations. All practical techniques of electrical generation present the electrical energy produced in this form; that is, we obtain a generated emf as a result of atomic particle disruption (electron flow), and when this emf is used to push current through an external circuit the terminal voltage of the generator is reduced, indicating an internal resistance.

We have just looked at a method for quantifying this, i.e. regulation. In the perfect situation the regulation would be 0%. When the load resistance is very much greater than the internal resistance‡ of the emf source, the internal or source resistance is considered to be negligible, and all the source voltage is assumed to be applied to the load. We have in effect the constant voltage source we have previously mentioned. Thus a constant voltage source, as its name implies, is thought of as a source of voltage whose value does not change with changes in load. All electrical energy sources do not comply with this constant voltage representation, for certain electronic devices can produce a current which remains sensibly constant as the load resistance varies. This phenomenon gives rise to the concept of the constant current generator.

---

† Often referred to as 'voltage regulation' or 'percentage regulation' as well as just simply regulation.
‡ The term internal resistance is frequently associated with battery sources of emf. There are other emf sources, and to discriminate betwen these and batteries the term source resistance is used.

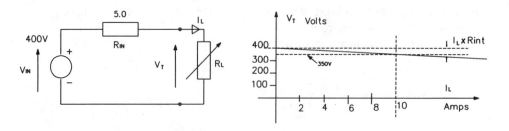

Fig. 3.1 — Power supply with variable load.

Let us illustrate this by considering Fig. 3.2 which represents the output stage of an electronic amplifier driving a load, for example your hi-fi amplifier driving your audio speakers.

As can be seen from the diagram, which gives a typical V_{out} versus I_{out} plot for an electronic amplifier, for a fixed V_{in}, the output current, I_{out}, remains almost constant regardless of the output voltage V_{out}. The electronic device is directly controlling the amount of output current flowing in the load circuit. In the same way as we have a method for representing a constant voltage source on a circuit diagram, we have a method for representing a constant current source which clearly indicates the current controlling effect of the electronic device. Consider the circuit shown in Fig. 3.3.

The constant current generator has two elements. One element represents the current being controlled, AV_{in} and the second element represents the device output ('internal') resistance, R_{out}. This circuit model shown, in Fig. 3.3. will be of more interest to us in a much later part of studies when we deal with electronic circuits.†

At present we wish to concentrate on the simpler dc circuits of the constant current form. This means we will be using the constant current generator model shown in Fig. 3.4.

We shall first of all look at the concept of regulation in a constant current circuit as opposed to the constant voltage circuit regulation we have already dealt with.

3.3 REGULATION OF A CONSTANT CURRENT CIRCUIT

Whether the power source is constant current or constant voltage, the definition of regulation is the same. We can show the comparability between the two ways of representing a power source by considering a deliberately chosen circuit, Figs 3.5(a) to (c).

The definition of regulation is the same regardless of whether the power source is considered to be constant emf or constant current, thus:

$$\text{Regulation} = \frac{V_{T(o/c)} - V_{T(full\text{-}load)}}{VT(o/c)} \cdot 100\%$$

† This book is the first of a three-part series, and we shall consider electronic circuit analysis is detailed in the second and particularly the third books in the series.

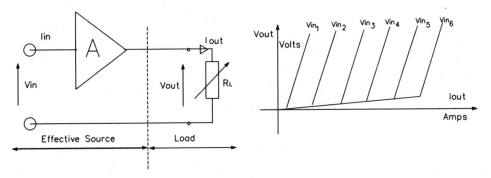

Fig. 3.2 — Amplifier output stage driving a load.

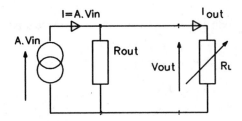

Fig. 3.3 — Constant current generator circuit representation.

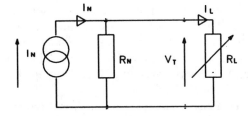

Fig. 3.4 — DC constant current generator model.

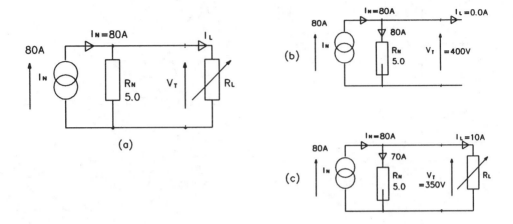

Fig. 3.5 — (a) to (c) constant current circuit analysis.

From the data given on Fig. 3.5 we can calculate the regulation:

$$V_{T(o/c)} = I_{in} \cdot R_{in} = 80 \times 5 = 400 \text{ V}$$

$$V_{T(full-load)} = 70 \times 5 = 350 \text{ V}$$

$$\text{Regulation} = 12.5\%$$

You will note that the value for regulation is the same as in the constant voltage example we considered. This is not surprising, since the two circuits were in fact the same! We analyzed the circuit first of all by modelling the power source as a constant emf with a series resistance, and secondly as a constant current generator. In both cases we calculated the regulation and found that whatever approach we used we arrived at the same value. This means that we have two models for any source of electrical energy.

The first model that we chose to represent our energy source was an emf in series with a source resistance. This is in fact the most commonly found electrical source, hence the emf generator is the most commonly used model. The second model was a current generator in parallel with a source resistance. This is the form of energy source that most electronic devices present to their loading elements, and hence is commonly used in electronic circuit analysis.

Now that we have established the two general circuit models for the analysis of circuits containing power sources and loads we shall turn our attention to the circuit theorems we mentioned earlier.

3.4 CIRCUIT THEOREMS

The analysis of dc circuits encountered so far has been relatively straightforward. However, the analysis of the more complicated circuits, especially those containing both series and parallel elements and power sources and load, has entailed a great deal of repetitious calculation using Ohm's law and Kirchhoff's laws.

The solutions obtained are often for only one set of conditions, for example one load value, and the process has to be repeated if, for example, the circuit performance was required for a number of different loads. In many instances parameter values have had to be calculated which in themselves do not really interest us, but which we have had to calculate in order to achieve the desired result.

In most electrical circuit analysis we are usually only interested in the value of a single particular current or voltage and how it changes with varying circuit conditions. Using the techniques we have already tried the process can become long, tiresome, and somewhat boring in the analysis of complicated circuits. It would be a distinct advantage if there was a method of short-cutting this type of analysis and reducing the length of the calculation process whilst maintaining the accuracy of the solution.

Fortunately, methods exist which meet our requirements, allowing quick and accurate solutions to be obtained for quite complex circuits. The first method is based on Thévénin's theorem, which we can use to isolate any single resistor in a circuit network and reduce the entire remaining portion of the circuit to an equivalent single emf source and a single resistor. This is a very important theorem, and it can be applied both to direct and alternating current circuits. We shall consider the development of the Thévénin circuit model in some detail. There is also an equivalent constant-current generator circuit model based on a second theorem, that of Norton, and we shall consider this model as well in due course.

3.5 DEVELOPMENT OF THE THÉVÈNIN MODEL (FIRST PRINCIPLES)

Let us first of all consider a typical circuit which we would analyze by the loop or mesh method, Fig. 3.6. According to Thévénin's theorem, if we were interested in the

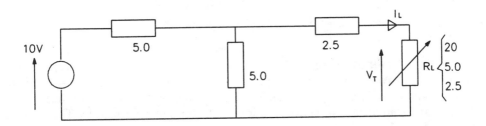

Fig. 3.6 — Linear dc circuit for analysis.

single resistor R_L, in this case the load resistor, then we can replace the rest of the circuit by a single source of emf and a single resistor, as shown in Fig. 3.7, in which V_{th} is the 'Thévénin voltage.

With the type of circuit shown in Fig. 3.6 we would normally be interested in the current, I_L, flowing through the load R_L, and the volt-drop V_T across the load. We

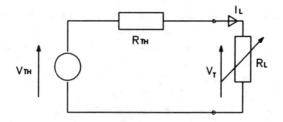

Fig. 3.7 — Proposed circuit from Thévénin's theorem.

could determine the values of these parameters for the three given values of R_L, using loop analysis. If we† did that we could use the data to build up the regulation profile as shown in Fig. 3.8.

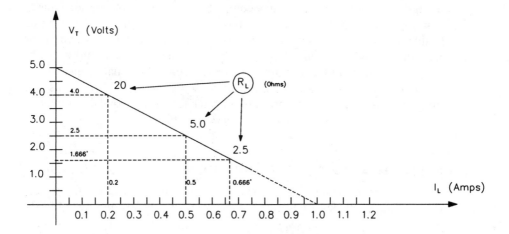

Fig. 3.8 — Regulation profile for the circuit in Fig. 3.6.

Let us look at the loading condition, $R_L = 5\,\Omega$, more closely,the same regulation profile could have been obtained from a 5 V source and a current of 0.5 A flowing through an internal resistance of 5 Ω. Thus we could give these values to the source voltage and source resistor shown in Fig. 3.7, the circuit suggested by Thévénin's theorem.

If the loading test was repeated for all the given values of R_L we would generate a regulation graph in every way similar to that obtained for the real circuit. This means that we have developed an equivalent circuit for the network under examination that represents its actions upon our load resistor in every possible way. This 'Thévénin' model of our circuit is significantly easier to analyze with respect to our load

† You make care to try!

conditions, and it should be obvious that if this is true for the circuit given in Fig. 3.6 then it is probably true for all linear dc circuits.

3.6 DEVELOPMENT OF THÉVÉNIN MODEL (GENERALIZED THEOREM)

We have satisfied ourselves that the use of the Thévénin theorem is soundly based for the particular example chosen, and have inferred that it is generally applicable. Thus we are now in a position to consider the general application of this particular circuit model. (see Fig. 3.9).

If we are to use this model, we shall need to know how to determine the two important model parameters:

V_{Th} = Effective source emf (called the Thévénin source)

R_{Th} = effective source resistance (the Thévénin resistance)

Remember that the Thévénin theorem requires that apart from the resistor of interest all the remaining resistors and voltage sources are to be replaced by the single Thévénin source and resistance. Let us start by determining the voltage of the Thévénin source.

Determination of Thévénin voltage

The determination of V_{Th} is achieved by the following technique.

(a) Disconnect the resistor of interest (R_L)
(b) Calculate or measure the open circuit terminal voltage, then
(c) V_{Th} must equal $V_{o/c}$.

Determination of Thévénin resistance

If we return to the suggested equivalent circuit Fig. 3.9 we can identify two possible methods of determining R_{Th}.

(a) Reduction of emf method

If all the emf sources are effectively removed and replaced by their effective source resistance then we will be left with a circuit which contains resistance only, Fig. 3.10. The circuit will contain only the effective source resistances plus all resistors other than the one of interest already removed from the circuit. We need now only calculate or measure the resistance between terminals A and B of the open circuit to determine the effective Thévénin resistance. That is,

$$R_{Th} = R_{o/c} \text{ (all emfs set to zero)}$$

(b) Short-circuit method

If we create a short circuit between terminal A and B, then a short circuit current $I_{s/c}$ will flow, Fig. 3.11. By the application of Ohm's law to our equivalent circuit we get

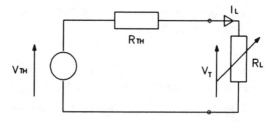

Fig. 3.9 — Thévénin model for any linear dc circuit.

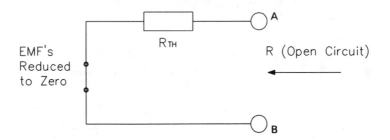

Fig. 3.10 — R_{Th} by reduction of emf method.

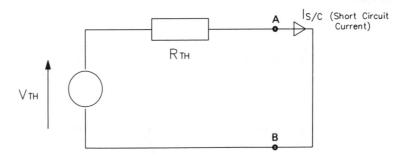

Fig. 3.11 — R_{Th} by short-circuit method.

$$I_{s/c} = \frac{V_{\mathrm{Th}}}{R_{\mathrm{Th}}} = \frac{V_{o/c}}{R_{\mathrm{Th}}},$$

therefore:

$$R_{\mathrm{Th}} = \frac{V_{o/c}}{I_{s/c}}.$$

We can further illustrate the application of the technique, or Thévéninizing as it is sometimes called, by considering worked examples.

3.7   WORKED EXAMPLES OF THÉVÉNIN'S THEOREM

Example 3.1
Consider the circuit shown in Fig. 3.12. The problemm in this case could be the

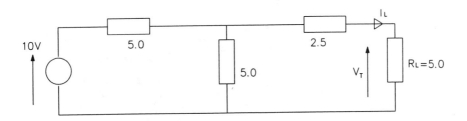

Fig. 3.12 — Linear dc circuit for Thévéninizing.

determination of the load current I_L. As outlined above, the first step is to calculate the Thévénin emf.

(a) Thévénin voltage determination of $V_{o/c}$
We have to remove the resistor of interest, R_L, so that we are left with the circuit given in Fig. 3.13. We can see that the open-circuit potential difference $V_{o/c}$ is equal

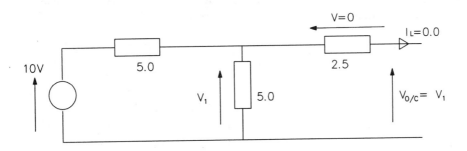

Fig. 3.13 — Determination of $V_{o/c}$.

to V_1, the potential difference across the vertically drawn 5 Ω resistor. The voltage drop in the circuit across the two 5 Ω resistors is 10 V, and, using either the potential divider concept or the fact that the volt drop across the two resistors must be the same, by inspection of the circuit:

$$V_{Th} = V_{o/c} = 10 \times \frac{5.0}{5.0 + 5.0} = 5.0 \text{ V}$$

(b) Calculation of the Thévénin resistance R_{Th}

We will calculate R_{Th} by using both the methods we have already considered. We remove all the emfs from the circuit (Fig. 3.14) and calculate the resistance of the

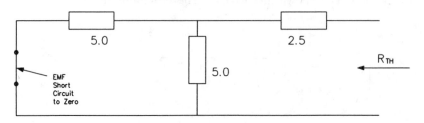

Fig. 3.14 — Reduction of emf method.

remaining circuit. In this case the internal resistance of the source is considered to be zero. Thus we have a series-parallel network with the two 5 Ω resistors forming a parallel limb in series with the 2.5 Ω resistor, i.e. a resistor network such that:

$$R_{Th} = 2.5 + 5\|5$$
$$= 2.5 + \frac{5 \times 5}{5 + 5}$$
$$= 5 \, \Omega$$

We will now find the value of R_{Th} by using the short-circuit method. Consider Fig. 3.15, We recall that

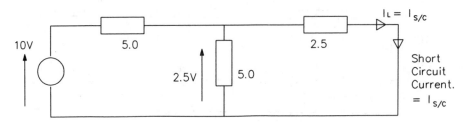

Fig. 3.15 — R_{Th} by the short-circuit method.

$$R_{Th} = V_{o/c} \div I_{s/c}$$

The open-circuit voltage $V_{o/c}$ has just been calculated to be 5 V. We now need to calculate the short-circuit current $I_{s/c}$. This will be the current flow through the 2.5 Ω resistor. The volt-drop across the 2.5 Ω resistor will be that across the 5 Ω resistor which forms the vertical middle limb of the circuit, and it is this volt-drop we must determine.

The right-hand side of the circuit contains a parallel resistive limb which we can make into an equivalent circuit limb containing a single resistor in series with the 5 Ω resistor. Thus,

$$R_{equiv} = 5||5 = 1.667 \ \Omega \ \text{(right-hand limb)}$$
$$R_{total} = 1.667 + 5 = 6.667 \ \Omega$$

The current flowing through our circuit is therefore

$$I_{total} = 10/6.667 = 1.5 \ \text{A}.$$

Thus the volt-drop across the equivalent right-hand circuit is,

$$V_{equiv} = 1.5 \times 1.667$$
$$= 2.5 \ \text{V}$$

Thus the current flowing through the 2.5 Ω associated with the original short-circuit is

$$I_{s/c} = 2.5/2.5 = 1 \ \text{A, and} \ R_{Th} = 5/1 = 5 \ \Omega$$

Finally, we can calculate the current through the resistor of interest, i.e. the load resistor.

(c) *Calculation of current flow I_L through load R_L*
We have sufficient circuit information to draw the equivalent Thévénin circuit, Fig. 3.16 It is relatively easy now to calculate the current that will flow through the load

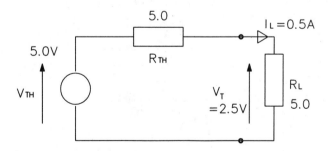

Fig. 3.16 — Thévénin equivalent circuit.

resistor when it is reconnected:

$$I_L = \frac{V_{Th}}{R_{Th} + R_L} = \frac{5.0}{5.0 + 5.0} = 0.5 \ \text{A}$$

We know that this is the correct answer as we previously calculated the value of I_L in a worked example, by direct use of Kirchhoff's laws. The use of Thévénin theorem is straightforward once you have become familiar with the process. This familiarity can be achieved only through problem-solving, and thus we will attempt one more worked example before directing you to try the review questions and tutorial problems.

Example 3.2
Q. Determine the voltage across the 10 Ω resistor in Fig. 3.17.

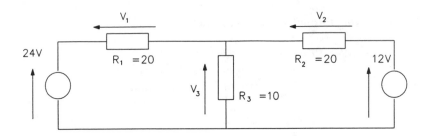

Fig. 3.17 — Circuit for worked example 3.2.

Firstly we remove the 10 Ω resistor and measure the open-circuit voltage $V_{o/c} = V_{Th}$. See Fig. 3.18. We can see that V_{Th} is given by

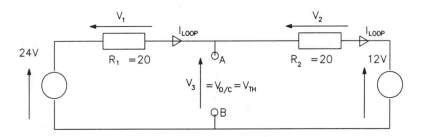

Fig. 3.18 — Circuit for worked example 3.2 (load removed).

$$V_{Th} = (24 - V_1) \text{ V or } V_{Th} = (12 + V_2) \text{ V.}$$

Now $V_1 + V_2$ must equal the total emf applied across the two 20 Ω resistors, and since the two emf's are in opposition this means that the Σ emf across the resistors = $(24 - 12) = 12$ V. Thus the current flow around the loop is:

$$I_{\text{Loop}} = \Sigma \text{ emf}/\Sigma R = 12/20 = 1.2 \text{ A}.$$

This means that $V_1 = 1.2 \times 20 = 6$ V, and $V_2 = 6$ V giving $V_{\text{o/c}} = V_{\text{Th}} = 18$ V.

We will use the reduction of emf method to find R_{Th}, thus Fig. 3.18 is redrawn with the source voltages short-circuited, as in Fig. 3.19. By observation, $R_{\text{Th}} = 20\|20$ $\Omega = 10 \ \Omega$. Thus we can finally rebuild our example circuit, using our generated equivalent circuit as shown in Fig. 3.20.

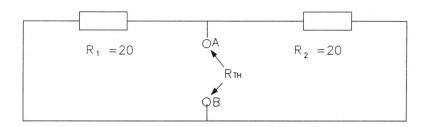

Fig. 3.19 — Circuit for worked example 3.2 (determination of R_{Th}).

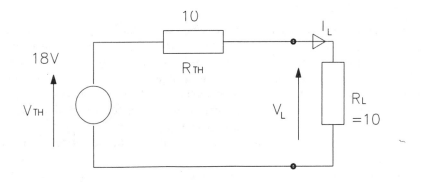

Fig. 3.20 — Thévénin model.

It is easy to determine the voltage across the 10 Ω load resistor by using the potential divider theorem.

$$V_{\text{L}} = 18 \times \frac{10}{10 + 10} = 9 \text{ V } .$$

Aide memoire
To summarize our approach to Thévéninizing a circuit we can identify three procedural steps:

(a) Calculate the open-circuit terminal voltage of the network.
(b) Redraw the circuit diagram with each emf source replaced by a short-circuit in series with its own internal resistance, if any, and each current source replaced by an open-circuit in parallel with its internal resistance.
(c) Calculate the resistance of the redrawn network as seen from the output terminals.

We have mentioned Thévénin theorem several times now without actually stating the theorem formally, thus for completeness we will provide a formal definition:

Thévénin's theorem
Any two-terminal network containing resistances and emf sources and/or current sources may be replaced by an equivalent circuit consisting of a single voltage source in series with a single resistor. The emf of the equivalent circuit — the Thévénin voltage — is the open-circuit emf at the network terminals, and the series resistance — the Thévénin resistance — is the resistance between the network terminals when all sources are replaced by their internal resistances.

3.8 NORTON'S THEOREM

Thévénin's theorem is particularly useful when we are analyzing circuits containing constant voltage sources, that is, emfs, although it could be used when the resistive dc circuits contain constant current generator sources as well. However, for those circuits which contain such constant current sources it is usually more convenient to use Norton's theorem. Norton suggested what effectively is the same approach as Thévénin, but Norton's equivalent circuit model theorem seeks to replace the bulk of the circuit to be analyzed with a current generator source rather than a constant voltage source. However, as with the Thévénin approach, the Norton model could be applied to a circuit containing emfs.

In practice the designer/analyist will choose the more convenient model†. Usually it will be the Thévénin version if emfs are involved and the Norton version if current generators are involved. Of course, many of the circuits we may wish to analyze will contain both constant voltage and constant current sources, in which case the choice between which one of the models is used is simple; we use the one that is easier! The problem is, of course, that you have to realize which one is the easier, and that skill comes only with experience of problem solving.

If you remember that in circuit analysis we have a Thévénin voltage and a Norton current, this should serve as a very useful guide as to which model to use in the majority of cases: emfs–Thévénin; current generators–Norton.

---

† There are other circuit models, and the designer/analyst may not choose either the Thévénin or Norton models. Thus, when we talk about choice in this particular context we are implying that the designer/analyst has only these two models available.

Let us this time start by giving a formal definition of Norton's theorem.

Norton's theorem
Any two-terminal network containing resistors and current sources and/or emf sources may be replaced by a single current source in parallel with a single resistor. The output from this current source is the short-circuit current at the terminals, and the parallel resistor has a resistance value equal to the resistance between the terminals when all sources are replaced by their internal resistances.

The definition is very similar to that of Thévénin's theorem, and the basis for the subsequent circuit model is also similar. Therefore, we do not need to develop the Norton model in the same way as we did the Thévénin model.

We shall start our study of the Norton circuit model by considering a circuit we have already analyzed by using Thévénin. Consider Fig. 3.21 which repeats the circuit shown in Fig. 3.12 but with the Norton equivalent circuit alongside.

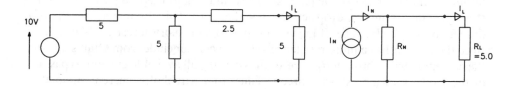

Fig. 3.21 — Linear dc circuit with Norton equivalent.

Whereas we had a Thévénin voltage source, V_{Th}, we now have a Norton current generator, I_N, sometimes simply called a Norton Generator, and in the place of the series Thévénin resistor, R_{Th}, we have the parallel Norton resistor, R_N. To analyze the circuit by using the Norton model we will need to determine I_N and R_N.

3.9 DETERMINATION OF NORTON GENERATOR ELEMENTS
The elements we need to consider are identified in Fig. 3.22, we will look at the determination of the Norton current, I_N, first.

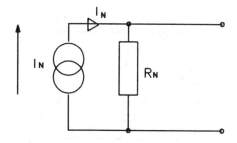

Fig. 3.22 — Norton generator elements.

(a) Determination of I_N
We disconnect the load-representing resistor and form a short-circuit as shown in
Fig. 3.23. If we neglect the resistance of the connecting conductor between the

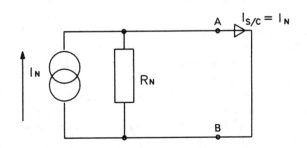

Fig. 3.23 — Norton model with output short circuit.

terminals, the resistance of the path AB is $0\,\Omega$, thus regardless of the current flowing
through path AB the volt-drop across AB will be zero. This also means that the volt-
drop across R_N is also zero. If the volt-drop across the Norton resistor is zero, then
since the resistor has a finite resistance value we can conclude from Ohm's law that
the current flowing through R_N is zero, thus causing all available current to pass out
of the model into the external circuit. Thus from Kirchhoff's current summation
laws,

$$I_{s/c} = I_N$$

(b) Determination of R_N
R_N can be determined by the open-circuit method or the removal of sources
technique. The first method requires the measurement or calculation of the open-
circuit voltage and the use of Ohm's law. The second technique requires the removal
of all the sources of current and their replacement with their respective internal
resistances.

R_N from open circuit method
We disconnect the short-circuit between terminals AB of Fig. 3.23 to leave the circuit
shown in Fig. 3.24. The current generated from the Norton current source, I_N, will

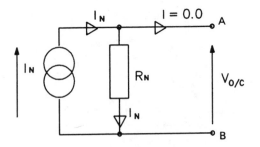

Fig. 3.24 — Open-circuit determination of R_N.

now all flow through the Norton resistor R_N. Thus the volt-drop across the resistor will be the open circuit voltage, that is,

$$V_{o/c} = I_N \cdot R_N,$$

therefore

$$R_N = \frac{V_{o/c}}{I_N} = \frac{V_{o/c}}{I_{s/c}}.$$

Note: if we compare our definition results for R_{Th} and R_N we can see that they are exactly the same. This compatibility between the Thévenin and Norton equivelent circuits will be exhaustively examined after this introduction of the Norton model.)

R_N from removal of sources technique
In this technique all the sources are removed and replaced by their internal resistances. In many instances these will in fact be neglible, and only the resistors in the rest of the circuit will be of concern to us. Thus the circuit of interest to us will be as shown in Fig. 3.25.

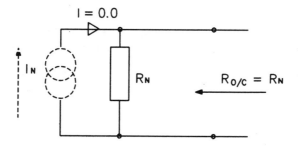

Fig. 3.25 — Removal of sources technique.

When all current are removed from the circuit to be analyzed, then, obviously, there is no possibility of a current flow. When no current flows in a circuit it can and should be considered to be an open circuit. Thus when Nortonizing a circuit the current sources are replaced by an open circuit in parallel with the internal resistance of the current source. Any voltage sources in our Nortonized circuit will be replaced by a short circuit in series with its internal resistance. The resistance of the remaining circuit as seen from the two terminals will then be the Norton resistance. Thus with all sources removed and replaced by their effective source resistances,

$$R_N = R_{o/c}$$

Again, we note that this definition of R_N is a repeat of the definition of R_{Th}. To illustrate the use of the Norton generator model we will look at some worked examples.

3.10 WORKED EXAMPLES, USING NORTON'S THEOREM

Worked example 3.3

We will use the circuit shown in Fig. 3.26. To obtain the Norton equivalent circuit we have to determine I_N and R_N.

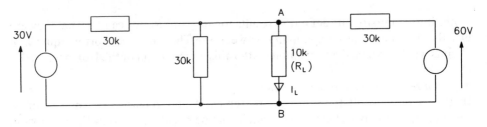

Fig. 3.26 — Circuit for Norton analysis.

Norton current

The Norton current I_N is equal to the short-circuit current, $I_{s/c}$. We can therefore redraw our circuit to show the effects of performing this theoretical action. Fig. 3.27

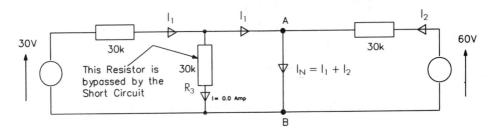

Fig. 3.27 — Circuit for Norton analysis ($I_{s/c}$ test).

shows the circuit with the suggested short-circuit. The circuit diagram shows how this short-circuit can be considered to have eliminated R_3, and we can now also see that the short-circuit current is made up of one element from the left-hand source (I_1) and another element from the right-hand source (I_2). Now,

$$I_1 = \frac{30\ \text{V}}{30\ \text{k}\ \Omega} = 1.0\ \text{mA and } I_2 = \frac{60\ \text{V}}{30\ \text{k}\ \Omega} = 2.0\ \text{mA}$$

Therefore $I_N = I_{s/c} = 3.0$ mA.

Norton resistance
We will use the reduction of emf's method to find R_N, and the circuit is redrawn in Fig. 3.28 in the form that allows us to achieve this.

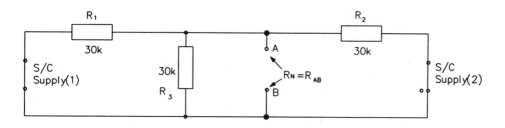

Fig. 3.28 — Determination of R_N.

$$R_N = R_{AB} = R_1||R_2||R_4 = 30 \text{ k}\Omega||30 \text{ k}\Omega||30 \text{ k}\Omega$$

gives $R_N = R_{AB} = 10$ kΩ.

Calculation of current flow through load
We can now draw our Norton equivalent circuit for the network, with a current source, I_N, a *parallel* Norton resistor R_N, and a load resistor R_L. Thus our final circuit is shown in Fig. 3.29.

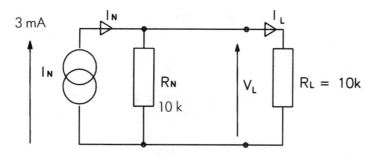

Fig. 3.29 — Norton's equivalent circuit.

Using the current divider concept formula we can readily determine the load current, I_L. The circuit resistance

$$R_p = R_L||R_N = 5.0 \text{ k}\Omega$$

and

$$I_L R_L = I_N \times R_p$$

Thus

$$I_{\mathrm{L}} = \frac{I_{\mathrm{N}} \times R_{\mathrm{p}}}{R_{\mathrm{L}}}$$
$$= \frac{3.0 \times 5.0}{10.0} \; \mathrm{mA}$$
$$= 1.5 \; \mathrm{mA}.$$

Worked example 3.4

Q. Calculate the load current for the circuit shown in Fig. 3.30 when $R_{\mathrm{L}} = 12 \; \mathrm{k\Omega}$,

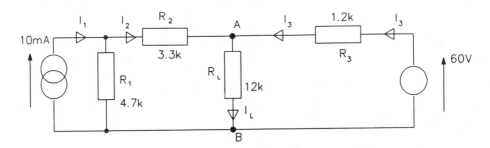

Fig. 3.30 — Network for worked example 3.4.

and draw the Norton equivalent circuit, indicating on the diagram the important parameter values.

A. We have to determine R_{N} and I_{N} in order to obtain the Norton equivalent circuit and subsequently calculate I_{L}. We remove the resistor of interest R_{L} and produce a short-circuit between terminals A and B, Fig. 3.31:

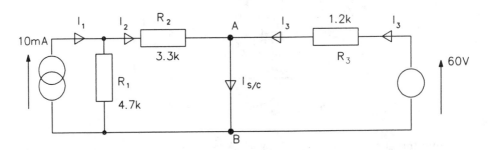

Fig. 3.31 — Short-circuit network.

The short-circuit current $I_{s/c}$ will be equal to the Norton current I_{N}, and from the diagram by the application of Kirchhoff's current summation law,

$$I_{s/c} = I_2 + I_3.$$

Also, by similar reasoning,

$$I_1 = I_2 + I_{R1},$$

The resistors R_1 and R_2 form a current divider with the current source, therefore we can say that,

$$\begin{aligned} I_2 &= I_1 \times \frac{R_1}{R_1 + R_2} \\ &= 0.01 \times \frac{4.7}{4.7 + 3.3} \\ &= 5.875 \text{ mA.} \end{aligned}$$

No component of the current I_2 will flow down the R_3 limb because of the zero resistance effect of the short-circuit.

The volt-drop across a short-circuit is zero, and if the R_3 limb did not have its own emf source, no current would flow: $I_3 = 0$. However, because it has its own emf and because the current through R_3 has no contribution from I_2, then from Ohm's law:

$$\begin{aligned} I_3 &= 60/R_3 \\ &= 60/1200 = 50 \text{ mA,} \end{aligned}$$

therefore

$$\begin{aligned} I_{s/c} &= 5.875 + 50 \text{ mA} \\ &= 55.875 \text{ mA} \\ &= I_N \end{aligned}$$

We have calculated I_N by deductive reasoning to save time. The answer could have been obtained by using loop equations which would have been somewhat lengthy. The type of reasoning we employed is embodied in a further circuit theorem known as the superposition theorem which we shall discuss in the next chapter. In the particular example we are working through the application of the properties of short and open circuits coupled with Kirchhoff's laws helped us to short-cut the loop style of analysis. You may find it a useful exercise to obtain I_N by loop/mesh analysis.

The next step in our problem-solving exercise is to calculate the Norton resistance R_N. Remember that we do this by replacing all current sources with their equivalent parallel resistances, and all voltage sources with their source resistances in series. In the example we have chosen neither the current source nor voltage source internal resistance has been included in the circuit since, in the majority of cases, they can be assumed to have little effect. However, you should note that this will not always be the case. Thus we have to calculate the Norton resistance of the remaining circuit as shown in Fig. 3.32.

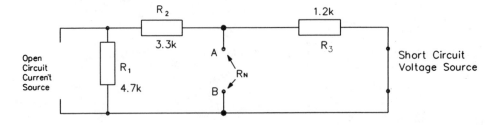

Fig. 3.32 — Circuit for calculation of R_N.

We can see that the R_2 and R_1 resistors form a series combination in parallel with resistor R_3, and therefore the total, that is, Norton resistance, is:

$$R_N = R_3 \| (R_2 + R_1)$$
$$= 1200 \| (3300 + 4700)$$
$$= 1.043 \text{ k}\Omega$$

Thus we have the parameter values required to produce the Norton equivalent circuit diagram, Fig. 3.33, and to determine the load current I_L, flowing through the

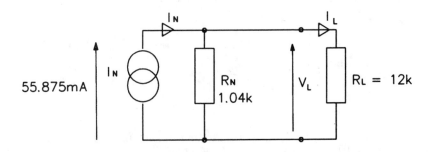

Fig. 3.33 — Norton equivalent circuit.

12 kΩ load resistor. The load current can be found by using the current divider method:

$$I_L = I_N \times \frac{R_N}{R_N + R_L}$$

$$= 55.875 \times [1043/(1043 + 12000)]$$
$$= 4.468 \text{ mA}$$

Aide memoire
When Nortonizing a resistive network the following procedure is worth adopting:

(a) Calculate the short-circuit current at the terminals of the network.
(b) Form an equivalent circuit by replacing each current source with an open-circuit in parallel with a resistor representing the value of its internal resistance, and by replacing each emf source by a short-circuit in series with a resistor representing the value of its internal resistance.
(c) Calculate the resistance of the equivalent circuit formed by the procedure just outlined as seen from the output terminals.

3.11   CHOICE BETWEEN THÉVÉNIN'S AND NORTON'S METHODS

Earlier, we gave a hint as to which of the two methods to use when confronted with a circuit problem. We said that if we were looking at a circuit containing a number of emfs, Thévénin's method was likely to be the better choice, wheres if current sources were involved, Norton's method should be used. Of course, there are circuits which contain both emfs and current sources, and indeed we have analyzed such circuits in our worked examples. In this case the choice between Thévénin and Norton may not be so obvious, and we have seen that both methods can be applied with equal accuracy. However, experience has shown that if the resistor of interest is part of a limb of components that are in series, Thévénin's theorem is the better choice, the reason being that when the open-circuit voltage $V_{o/c}$ is determined these components do not enter into the calculations, thus a reduction of work has been achieved. See Fig. 3.34.

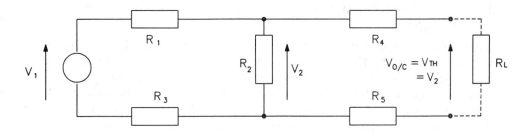

Fig. 3.34 — Thévénin's exclusion of series components.

If the resistor of interest is alone in its limb and is thus in parallel with the other limbs, then use Norton's theorem. This will mean that when the short-circuit, $I_{s/c}$, is determined, these components will be short-circuited and removed from our calculations, thus causing a reduction in work. Briefly, therefore, Thévénin's theorem allows a resistor to be removed whereas Norton's theorem allows a resistor to be short-circuited. See Fig. 3.35.

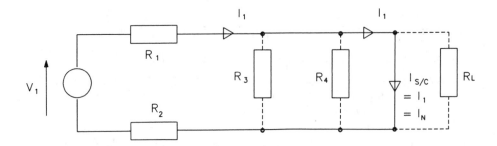

Fig. 3.35 — Norton's exlusion of parallel components.

Before we complete this chapter with some worked examples and review questions and problems, we must make it quite clear that:

(a) An equivalent circuit does not physically exist, but it does account exactly for the effect of all the circuit components that are actually there.
(b) Thévénin's and Norton's theorems both involved terminal pairs. The actual circuit to be analyzed may not contain terminals, but a pair of terminals can be introduced into the circuit, analytically, by breaking the circuit at any point or points that are convenient.
(c) The choice of the Thévénin or Norton approach when analyzing a circuit is quite arbitrary, and a matter of personal selection, but experience has suggested that there are certain situations in which there is a preferred method.

3.12   THE COMMON FACTORS IN THE THÉVÉNIN AND NORTONS THEOREMS

From the work given in the immediately preceding section it must be dawning upon most students that the Thévenin and Norton theorems are applicable to any circuit, thus if they both give compatible equivalents of our circuit under analysis, then the models generated are themselves compatible and thus there must be some common factors. We have already found by example that $R_{Th} = R_N$. The following deductions should confirm this, and also show the more dynamic effects of this compatibility of analytical models.

If the circuits in Fig. 3.36 are truely compatible, anything that is done to both circuits should produce the same result. Thus if we apply the open-circuit and short-circuit tests to both models, the results obtained must be the same.

For Thévénin model   For Norton model

$$V_{o/c} = V_{Th} \qquad\qquad V_{o/c} = I_N \cdot R_N$$

$$I_{s/c} = \frac{V_{Th}}{R_{Th}} \qquad\qquad I_{s/c} = I_N$$

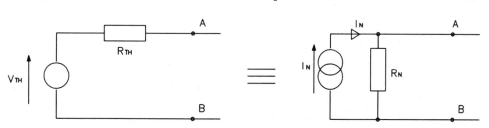

Fig. 3.36 — Thévénin and Nortons models compared.

Both tests suggest that:

$$V_{Th} = I_N \cdot R_N \text{ and } R_{Th} = R_N.$$

The advantages of this result are that we can now combine the methods for determining the model parameters and use whatever results we achieve to generate the model we prefer to work with. For most people the Thévénin model provides the preferred final step to solving an analysis, and very often forces this style onto a circuit that is patently easier to model as a Norton equivalent circuit. Now that we know the full compatibility of these two models we can apply whichever development we chose, and even apply whichever final model we choose. A worked example follows to show the use of this final set of deductions, and then there are some more general worked examples before you are invited to attempt the tutorial review questions at the end of the chapter.

WORKED EXAMPLES

Example 3.5
Q. Determine the current I_x in Fig. 3.37.

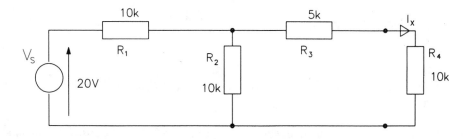

Fig. 3.37 — Network for worked example 3.5.

A. Use Thévénin's theorem, since open-circuiting R_4 will remove R_3 from calculations of V_{Th} (series limb).

Fig. 3.37 shows how V_{Th} is to determined as $V_{o/c}$.

$$V_{Th} = V_{o/c} = 20 \times \frac{10k\ \Omega}{10k\ \Omega + 10\ k\Omega} = 10\ V$$

If V_s is short-circuited it is easy to see that R_{Th} is determined as follows.

$$R_{Th} = R_3 + R_2 \| R_1 = 5\ k\Omega + 10k \| 10\ k\Omega = 10\ k\Omega$$

I_x can now be calculated from the final Thévénin model given in Fig. 3.38.

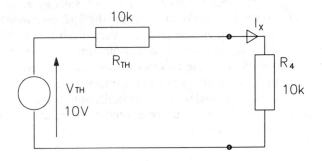

Fig. 3.38 — Thévénin model.

$$I_x = \frac{V_{Th}}{R_4 + R_{Th}} = \frac{10}{10\ k\Omega + 10\ k\Omega} = 0.5\ mA.$$

Example 3.6

Q. Determine the voltage, V_x, across resistor R_3 in Fig. 3.39 using Norton's theorem.

A. Point A is at $+10$ V above earth. Point B is at $+5$ V above earth. This means that R_4 has $+5$ V across it at a steady and fixed value. If either R_1, R_2, or R_3 are changed, then since V_1 and V_2 are fixed potential sources they cannot affect the voltage across R_4 in any way. This means that R_4 could be considered to be an ineffectual limb as far as V_x is concerned since it does not provide or divert current through R_3. We could therefore rewrite our network as shown on the right of the figure.

If we apply Norton's short-circuit rule to R_3 as shown on the left of Fig. 3.40 we can now possibly see more clearly that R_4 does not affect the current for R_3.

Now

$$I_N = I_{s/c} = I_1 + I_2 = 1 + 1 = 2 \text{ mA}$$

and

$$R_N = R_1 \| R_2 = 10 \| 5 = 3.333 \text{ k}\Omega.$$

Note that R_2 plays no part. It is short-circuited by the V_1 and V_2 exclusion rules. We can deduce $V_{Th} = I_N \cdot R_N = 6.666$ V.

The final model for our network could be either Thévénin or Norton. The choice is the student's. Both are shown in Fig. 3.41.

Using Thévénin:

$$V_x = \frac{V_{Th} \times R_3}{R_{Th} + R_3} = \frac{6.666 \times 2.7 \text{ k}\Omega}{3.3 \text{ k}\Omega + 2.7 \text{ k}\Omega}$$
$$V_x = 2.984 \text{ V}$$

Using Norton:

$$V_x = I_N \times R_P \ (R_P = R_{Th} \| R_3)$$
$$= 2 \text{ mA} \times 1.4917 \text{ k}\Omega$$
$$= 2.984 \text{ V}.$$

Example 3.7
Q. Determine the current flowing through R_L, in Fig. 3.42, using Norton's theorem.

A. A great deal of effort could be wasted in trying Thévénin's theorem to solve this problem to no real advantage, since open-circuiting the load R_L does not significantly reduce the network complexity.

Since we are asked for the current through R_L we can lump R_L together with R_5 into a single load of $R_L = 4$ kΩ and find the current through this combination to no disadvantage and to the considerable simplification of the network.

If we use Norton's theorem, as Fig. 3.42 indicates, the short-circuit across R_L (A to B) eliminates R_1, and **R_3** from the determination of I_N. The calculation of I_N is also seen to be significantly simplified.

$$I_N = I_1 + I_3 + V_2/R_2 + V_4/R_4$$
$$= 30 + 20 + 10 + 5$$
$$= 65 \text{ mA}.$$

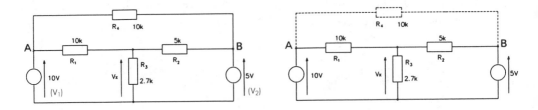

Fig. 3.39 — Network for worked example 3.6.

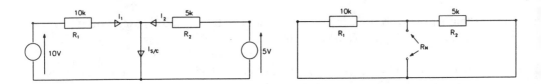

Fig. 3.40 — Derivation of Norton model.

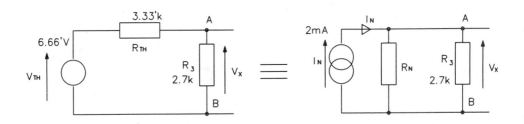

Fig. 3.41 — Thévénin and Norton models.

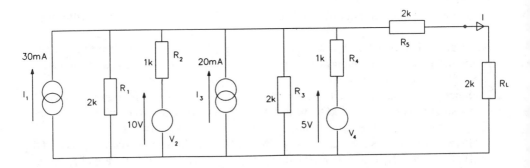

Fig. 3.42 — Network for worked example 3.7.

The determination of R_N is illustrated in Fig. 3.43, and it is important to note the

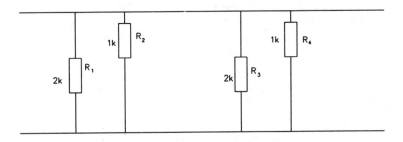

Fig. 3.43 — Determination of Norton Resistance.

elimination of voltage and current generators from the analysis.
  Replace all 'V' sources as short-circuits.
  Replace all 'I' sources as open-circuits.

$$R_N = R_1 \| R_2 \| R_3 \| R_4 = 0.333 \text{ k}\Omega \text{ (Thus } V_{th} = 21.66 \text{ V)}$$

We can deduce that $I_x = \dfrac{V_{Th}}{R_{Th} + R_L} = \dfrac{21.666}{4.3333 \text{ k}\Omega} = 5 \text{ mA}$.

REVIEW QUESTIONS AND TUTORIAL PROBLEMS

(3.1) In your own words state Thévénin's theorem and outline a procedure for Thévénizing a circuit.

(3.2) Compare the Norton equivalent circuit to the Thévénin equivalent circuit, and state how I_N relates to V_{Th}.

(3.3) Explain two methods for determining the short-circuit current in a Thévénin circuit.

(3.4) The Thévénin resistance is calculated by removing the …? and reducing all …? to zero.*

(3.5) When emf sources are reduced to zero in a Thévénin equivalent circuit they are replaced by …? circuits*

(3.6) Open-circuits are used to replace …? in a Thévénin equivalent circuit.*

*Complete the sentences by inserting the appropriate words.

(3.7) Consider the circuit shown in Fig. 3.44 and answer the following questions:

(a) What is the value of the Thévénin source? (4.67 V).
(b) What is the Norton current? (2.33 mA).
(c) What is the value of the Thévénin resistance? (2 kΩ).
(d) In the Norton equivalent circuit of Fig. 3.44 what would be the value of the resistance connected in parallel with the Norton current source? (2 kΩ).
(e) What is the value of I_2? (0.333 mA).

(3.8) Determine the current flows I_1, I_2, and I_3 indicated on the network diagram shown in Fig. 3.45 (2.39 A, −1.09 A, −1.3 A).

(3.9) Use (a) Thévévin's theorem (b) Norton's theorem to determine the current flowing the 5 Ω resistor in the circuit given in Fig. 3.46 (2.14 A)

(3.10) A potential divider has a tapping point a fraction x along its length. If the total resistance of the divider is R_T and an emf, $E = 400$ V, is applied to it, show that the volt-drop across the resistor R_β which is connected across the output of the divider is given by the expression:

$$V_\beta = \frac{xER_\beta}{x(1-x)R_T + R_\beta}.$$

(3.11) A maintenance engineer was working on a two-terminal network which had a number of interconnected battery emf sources and resistors. As part of the maintenance schedule he had to know the current flowing through a 20 Ω resistor when it was connected to the network's terminals. He was trying to solve a large set of loop equations when a colleague offered to help. The colleague first of all measured the open-circuit voltage across the terminals which was found to be 100 V, and then it was found that the current from the terminals with them short-circuited was 0.5 A. The colleague then performed a few calculations and quickly told the engineer the current flowing through the 20 Ω device., The engineer wanted to know how quick measurements could give him the information he wanted. What did his colleague tell him?

(3.12) Two electrochemical batteries are connected in parallel. The emf and internal resistance of one battery are 120 V and 10 Ω respectively, and the corresponding values for the other battery are 150 V and 20 Ω. A resistor of 50 Ω is connected across the battery terminals. Calculate the current flowing through the 50 Ω resistor, using Kirchoff's laws directly or a suitable circuit theorem. (2.295 A).
(3.13) In the Wheatstone bridge network shown in Fig. 3.47 determine the current flow through each resistor.

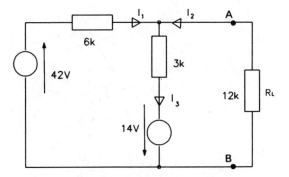

Fig. 3.44 — Circuit for problem 3.7.

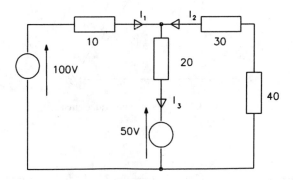

Fig. 3.45 — Network diagram for problem 3.8.

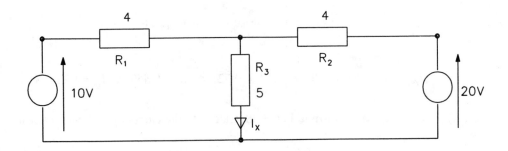

Fig. 3.46 — Circuit for problem 3.9.

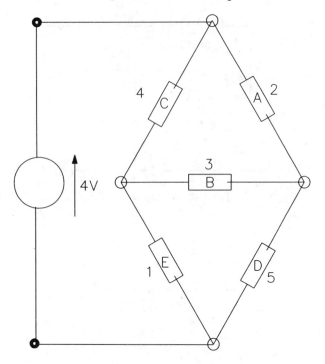

Fig. 3.47 — Wheatstone bridge circuit.

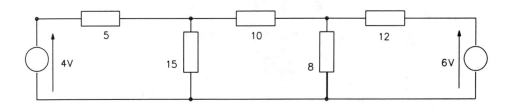

Fig. 3.48 — Network diagram for problem 3.14.

$(I_A = 0.852 \text{ A}; I_b = 0.392 \text{ A}; I_c = 0.721 \text{ A}; I_D = 0.459 \text{ A}; I_E = 1.114 \text{ A})$.

(3.14) For the network shown in Fig. 3.48. Calculate the current in the 8 Ω resistor by:

(a) Loop equations (0.32 A).
(b) Thévénin's theorem.

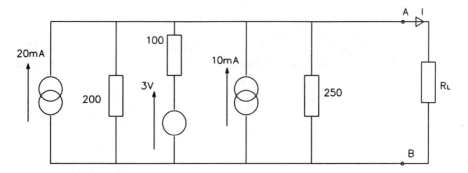

Fig. 3.49 — Circuit for problem 3.15.

(3.15) For the circuit shown in Fig. 3.49 determine:

(a) The Thévénin source voltage (3.16 V).
(b) The Norton current (60 mA).
(c) The Norton resistance (52.63 Ω).
(d) The Thévénin resistance (52.63 Ω).

(3.16) Using Norton's theorem, calculate the volt-drop across the resistor R_4 in the circuit shown in Fig. 3.50 (3.043 Volts).

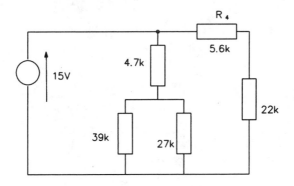

Fig. 3.50 — Circuit for problem 3.16.

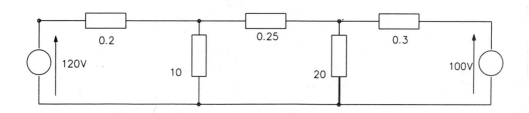

Fig. 3.51 — Circuit diagram for problem 3.17.

(3.17) Consider the circuit shown in Fig. 3.51, and calculate:

(a) The power dissipated in the 10 Ω resistor (1.27 kW).

(b) The energy dissipated in the 10 Ω resistor during 20 minutes (1.53×10^6 J).

(c) The total charge which passes through the 10 Ω resistor in 1/3 hours (13.5 kC).

4

Further network theorems and transformations

4.1 MAXIMUM POWER TRANSFER THEOREM

In Chapter 3 we concentrated on circuit networks and some of the theorems which we can use in the analysis of such networks. We shall now study other theorems and circuit transformations which help the analytical process, but before we do we will turn out attention to the main use of the type of circuits we have already analysed — the generation of power.

When a component is situated in a fixed electrical circuit where no additional power imput can be provided, the resistance of the component has an optimum value at which it receives maximum power from the rest of the circuit. If the component in question is the circuit load, we would wish to be able to optimize the power output of the device or the power dissipated in the device, if it was for example an electrical heater. To determine the conditions for the production of maximum power for each circuit we would have to analyze each circuit in detail, so we shall make use of the Thévénin circuit model in this study to simplify our deliberations. Thus consider Fig. 4.1 which illustrates a power producing electrical circuit and its Thévénin equivalent.

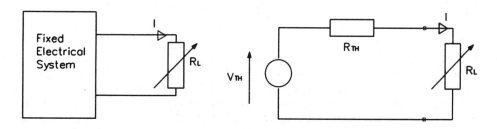

Fig. 4.1 — Power circuit and Thévénin's model.

We wish to know the value of R_L that achieves the maximum power output from the effective Thévénin source. It helps if we are clear about what we are calling the power output from the effective source. This is the power developed in the load resistor R_L, which you will recall is:

Power developed in R_L;

$$P = I_L{}^2 \cdot R_L$$

The load current will depend upon the circuit concerned, especially its resistance. If the circuit is fixed in terms of the components it contains and their relevant values, then the only variable factor is the load resistance R_L. Thus I_L will be affected by R_L.

Thus, although it could be implied from a cursory examination of the above power equation that to increase the power output merely requires the load resistor to be made larger in terms of resistance, this is not so, because the dominant term of the equation, $I_L{}^2$, alters as R_L changes. What we need to find out is how I_L changes with variations in R_L. Let us consider the Thévénin equivalent circuit shown in Fig. 4.2.

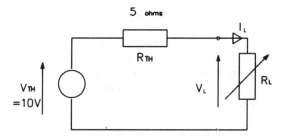

Fig. 4.2 — A Thévénin circuit with a variable load.

The parameter values for the circuit are:

$$I_L = \frac{V_{Th}}{R_{Th} + R_L}$$

$$V_L = I_L \times R_L$$

$$P_L = I_L{}^2 R_L \text{ or } V_L I_L$$

If we plot the values of I_L, V_L, and P_L for various value of R_L, we obtain the graph shown in Fig. 4.3. We can see that I_L decreases as R_L increases, and that P_L initially increases, reaches a peak value when $R_L = 5.0\,\Omega$, and then begins to decrease. The output current I_L is greatest when the load resistance R_L is a very low value, whereas V_L is very large when R_L is also large. The implication is that P_L has a maximum value for a particular combination of I_L and V_L, and for this particular example the maximum value occurs when $R_L = R_{Th}$.

We now need to determine if this is generally true or just a property of the

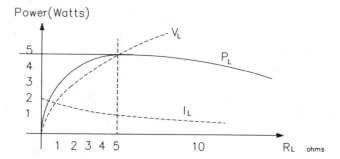

Fig. 4.3 — Variation of circuit parameter values with R_L.

particular circuit we have chosen. Let us return to our Thévénin circuit equations and use differential calculus to help us.

$$P_L = I_L^2 R_L; \quad \text{and} \quad I_L = \frac{V_{Th}}{R_{Th} + R_L}.$$

We want to know how the power output varies with load, and from differential calculus we know that the maximum value of P_L for a given range of values of R_L will occur when

$$\frac{dP_L}{dR_L} = 0.$$

To be able to carry out the differentiation we need an expression which relates P_L and R_L and in which the only two variables are P_L and R_L. If we substitute for I_L in the equation $P_L = I_L^2 . R_L$, we can obtain such an expression, namely

$$P_L = \left\{ \frac{V_{Th}}{(R_{Th} + R_L)} \right\}^2 . R_L,$$

and if we differentiate this equation with respect to R_L,

$$[R_{Th} + R_L]^{-2} V_{Th}^2 - 2R_L V_{Th}^2 [R_{Th} + R_L]^{-3} = 0$$
$$V_{Th}^2 [R_{Th} + R_L] - 2R_L V_{Th}^2 = 0,$$

and finally,

$$R_{Th} + R_L = 2R_L$$

i.e. $\quad\quad\quad R_L = R_{Th}$ when P_L is a maximum†

---

† More mathematical proof than we've supplied would be needed to confirm that the condition we have found is a maximum, but to save time we ask you to accept the conjecture — you can prove it if you wish.

This means that the load will draw maximum power from the effective source when it is equal to the effective source resistance R_{Th}. This, then, is a general result, and to further show its validity we provide a further numerical example, Fig. 4.4, where

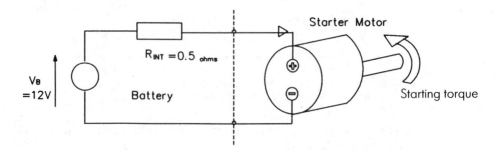

Fig. 4.4 — Further illustration of maximum power concept.

once again the maximum power is obtained when the load resistance is equal to the Thévénin resistance i.e., the starter motor resistance is designed to match battery internal resistance.

We used a Thévénin circuit to look at the maximum power concept, but we could have used a simple circuit containing a single emf with an internal resistance, r, and a single load resistor R_L, in which case we would have found that the maximum power would have been achieved when $r = R_L$. We chose the Thévénin approach because it implicitly covers all types of dc resistive circuits. Thus we have a general theorem called the maximum power transfer theorem, for which a formal definition is:

> Maximum output power is obtained from a network or source when the load resistance is equal to the output resistance of the network or source as seen from the source.

A further aspect worth noting is that at the point of maximum power the value of the terminal or load voltage V_L is half the Thévénin source voltage; that is,

at $P_{Lmax}, \ R_{Th} = R_L,$

and therefore

$$V_L = \frac{V_{Th}}{R_L + R_L} \times R_L = \tfrac{1}{2}V_{Th}.$$

Furthermore, it shold be acknowledged that the load current flowing through the output resistor is also flowing through the rest of the equivalent circuit which, at the point of maximum power transfer, has the same resistance as the load resistor. In other words, at the point of maximum power transfer only 50% of the total developed electrical power is dissipated through the load; the other 50% is dissipated in the remaining circuit. Thus the point of maximum power transfer may not be the point of most effective energy utilization. For example, consider the situation with the normal 12 V automobile battery. To start the engine the ignition circuit is closed and the maximum power is used to turn and fire the engine; that is, we are working at the point of maximum power transfer.

The terminal voltage is rapidly reduced from 12 V to about 6 V. The power transferred out of the system to start the engine is only about half the total power drained from the battery. This means that the remaining half of the power developed is lost as internal power drain. If the engine does not fire at the first turn of the ignition key, we can see why the battery power is soon depleted with subsequent attempts.

The need to have to use the maximum power transfer point for engine starting is an inefficient use of the available energy, but without this level of power the engine either would not start or a larger battery system would be required.

The point to this little aside is that you should always remember that although we may look analytically at circuits in isolation we must always realize that they will form part of a system, and what may be good for the circuit/network will not necessarily be so for the system.

4.2 MEASUREMENT OF RESISTANCE — THE WHEATSTONE BRIDGE

In our study of resistive circuits, especially in the last two chapters, when we have been considering circuit theorems we have stated that a particular value of resistance could be calculated or measured. Invariably we have proceeded to calculate resistance values. However, in practice they could be measured by using an instrument called, perhaps not too surprisingly, an ohmmeter. Another more accurate resistance measurement device is the Wheatstone† bridge. We have already encountered the circuit which constitutes a Wheatstone bridge in our problem-solving, and for completeness, before we continue with the more advanced circuit theorems, we will examine the Wheatstone circuit more closely. This is not purely a side issue, for as you will see it is an important circuit in dc network analysis, and we shall also use it when we consider ac network analysis. The Wheatstone bridge circuit is shown in Fig. 4.5(a) and (b). We have presented the version shown in Fig. 4.5(b) since until very recently that was the traditional way of depicting the circuit.

In the Wheatstone bridge circuit the only new item to us is the galvanometer in the centre of the bridge. This is a current measuring instrument, and it indicates when current flows from one side of the bridge to the other. The instrument normally has a very small internal resistance so that it does not significantly inhibit the free flow of current. The resistor R_x is the unknown resistor which is the target of our analysis. Resistor R_v has a variable resistance, and we can adjust its value until the galvanometer indicates that no current is flowing across the bridge. When this circuit condition has been achieved then the volt-drop V_1 equals V_2 and the bridge is said to

† Sir Charles Wheatstone (1802–1875) is perhaps one of the unsung heroes of electrical engineering. His inventions are endless from telegraph machines to self-excited generators, electric motors, linear motors, magnetic machines, rheostats, etc., etc. He worked with all the great men of the science: Faraday, Henry, Daniell, and so on. It is then somewhat ironic that his name should be associated with a device he attributed to S. H. Christie and which he called a 'differential resistance measurer'.

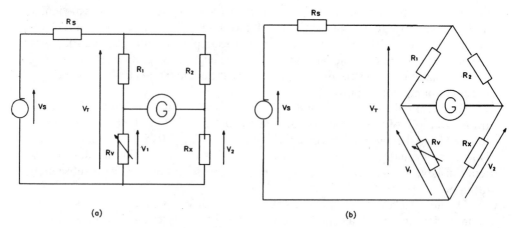

Fig. 4.5 (a) and (b) — Wheatstone bridge circuit.

be balanced. We can also say that since the galvanometer is registering no current flow, we can treat the galvanometer as being an open circuit.

The achievement of the balanced condition and the effective open circuit allows us to simplify the circuit representation to that shown in Fig. 4.6. The circuit is in

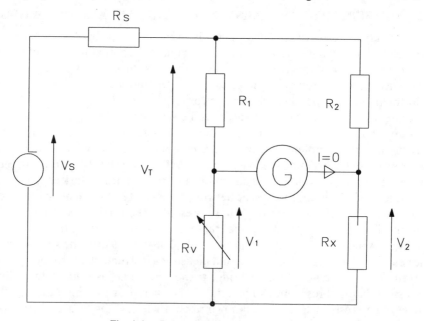

Fig. 4.6 — Balanced Wheatstone bridge.

balance when $V_1 = V_2$, and:

$$V_1 = V_T \cdot \frac{R_v}{R_v + R_1} \quad \text{and} \quad V_2 = V_T \cdot \frac{R_x}{R_x + R_2},$$

thus

$$\frac{R_v}{R_v + R_1} = \frac{R_x}{R_x + R_2} \quad \text{or} \quad R_v \cdot R_2 = R_x \cdot R_1,$$

giving

$$R_x = R_v \cdot \frac{R_1}{R_2}.$$

If the precise values of R_v, R_2, and R_1 are known, then R_x can be accurately calculated. Resistors R_1 and R_2 are normally called the ratio arms, the reason being that it is the ratio of their values which is used, as indicated by the above solution. The importance of our deduced result is what is missing from the final equation. If we consider the derived expression we will note that the calculation of R_x is independent of supply voltage V_s, source resistance R_s, and galvanometer resistance R_g, and the galvanometer need detect only the absence of current which is infinitely easier than the measurement of the current's actual value.

The Wheatstone bridge is a member of a measurement instrument class called null detectors. The null detectors all have this advantage of not requiring the accurate quantitative measurement of current and voltage, since they rely only upon the measurement of an absence of current or voltage.

We will now return to out study of circuit theorems. It is worth remembering that we use network or circuit theorems to simplify our analysis of complex circuits. Direct application of Kirchhoff's laws using loop/mesh equations can be laborious, as we have seen, but Thévenin's theorem permits complex circuits to be reduced to a single voltage source in series with a resistance. Thus simplified, the effect on load currents and load voltages of varying load resistances can be readily determined.

Norton's theorem is as useful as, and is as powerful an analytical tool as, Thévenin's theorem, but in this case the complex network is reduced to a single current source and a parallel resistance.

The maximum power transfer theorem enables the prediction of optimum load conditions to be readily established for complex networks.

The superposition theorem which we have mentioned previously enables complex circuits containing several emfs and/or current sources to be analyzed as several separate circuits each having only one source of emf or current. This very useful theorem will be our next subject for study.

Thus we can see that circuit theorems are to the analyst his 'tools of the trade'.

4.3   THE SUPERPOSITION THEOREM

The superposition theorem can be considered to be an extension of Kirchhoff's laws. If we have a complex circuit with more than one voltage (or current) supply, the current flowing through any given component is a summation of the individual currents provided from all of the supplies. If any one of these supplies were to be removed, the current flowing through our chosen component would be changed by some amount directly proportional to the size of the supply removed. This means that the total current flowing through our component can be considered to be a summation of the individual currents provided from the various sources. Thus, for example, if we had a load resistor connected to a very complex electrical black box, we could say that the load current was a summation of the various currents in the black box, as in Fig. 4.7. That is,

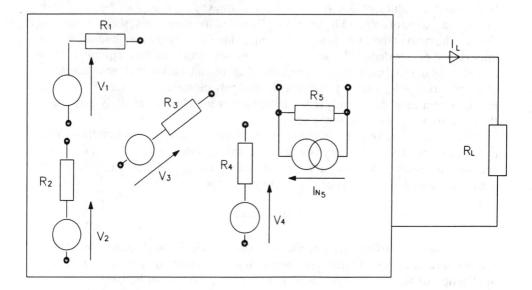

Fig. 4.7 — Superposition theorem generalized concept.

$$I_L = \Sigma \{I_1, I_2, I_3, I_4, I_5, I_n, \ldots \text{etc.}\}$$

where

I_1 = element of current due to supply (1)

I_2 = element of current due to supply (2), and so on.

An example will help show how the theorem is applied. Consider the circuit shown in Fig. 4.8. To calculate the current through the load component shown in the circuit diagram could entail a lengthy loop analysis or a slightly shorter but complicated use of Thévenin's theorem. A simpler technique would be the one embodied in the superposition theorem. We will consider the current flowing through our load component in two steps, since there are two sources. Firstly, we will calculate the load current due to source (1). We do this by removing the second source from the diagram to leave ourselves with the circuit of Fig. 4.9.

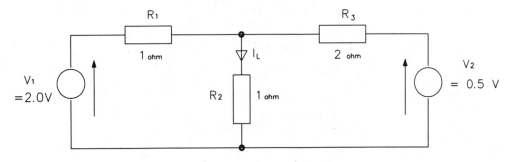

Fig. 4.8 — Circuit for analysis by superposition theorem.

We have drawn the equivalent circuit by replacing the parallel resistor limb with a single resistor equal to $R_2 \| R_3$ which is in series with resistor R_1, such that:

$$I_1 = \frac{V_1}{R_t}$$

where,

$$R_t = R_1 + R_2 \| R_3$$
$$= 1.0 + 0.666' = 1.666 \ \Omega,$$

therefore,

$$I_1 = \frac{2.0}{1.666'} = 1.2 \ \text{A},$$

and recalling our current divider work and the concept of conductance,

$$I_{L1} = I_1 \cdot \frac{G_2}{G_2 + G_3} = 1.2 \cdot \frac{1.0}{1.0 + 0.5} = 0.8 \ \text{A}.$$

We now repeat the process to determine the current contribution of the second source. This time we remove source (1) from the circuit as in Fig. 4.10. In this circuit the equivalent resistor representing the total circuit resistance is formed by a parallel combination of R_1 and R_2 in series with R_3 such that

$$I_2 = \frac{V_2}{R_{T2}} \qquad \text{where} \qquad R_T = R_3 + R_2 \| R_1,$$

$$= 2.0 + 0.5 = 2.5 \ \text{ohms}$$

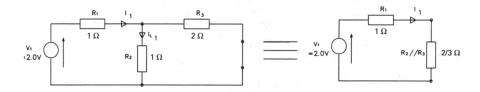

Fig. 4.9 — Circuit with source (1) only.

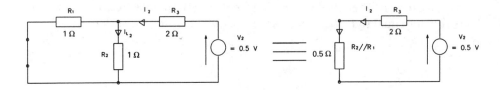

Fig. 4.10 — Circuit for analysis — source (2) only.

thus,

$$I_2 = \frac{0.5}{2.5} = 0.2\,\text{A},$$

and we can use current divider theory again and conductances to give;

$$I_{L2} = I_2 \cdot \frac{G_2}{G_2 + G_1} = 0.2 \cdot \frac{1.0}{1.0 + 1.0} = 0.1\,\text{A},$$

and from the superposition theorem:

$$I_L = I_{L1} + I_{L2} = 0.9\,\text{A}.$$

Norton's theorem should get you this result quite rapidly. The example is simple to illustrate the validity. The superposition theorem can be used to serious advantage when the quantity of supplies becomes overpowering. It is also used during the employment of other theorems where the deductions can be simplified if considered separately. See Worked Examples in Section 3.13 where the superposition theorem is clearly being employed.

4.4 PASSIVE CIRCUIT TRANSFORMATION THEOREMS

We have looked at a number of theorems which have been devised to simplify networks for the purpose of circuit analysis by reducing the effective number of circulating currents, thereby avoiding a large amount of algebraic manipulation. The theorems studied so far are generally applicable to circuits, or parts of circuits, containing emfs and/or currrent sources. We have not considered, as yet, circuits which contain no emfs (called passive networks). In such circuit or parts of circuits we often encounter particular configurations of resistive elements which are not easy to analyze. By using the theorems of Kennelly and Rosen we can transform particular types of circuit configuration into a different form more suitable for analysis. These theorems are called transformation theorems or simply transformations.

The two theorems we shall look at are (a) the star–delta or wye(Y)–delta transformation and (b) the delta–star or delta–wye transformation. The star–delta and delta–star theorems are both due to Kennelly, but are rarely referred to as Kennelly's theorems.

4.5 STAR (WYE) AND DELTA TRANSFORMATION

Examples of what is meant by a star and a delta network are shown in Fig. 4.11. Such

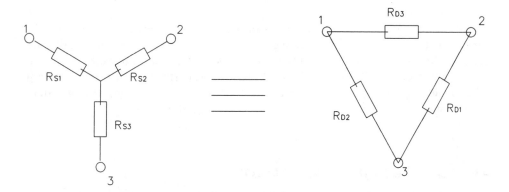

Fig. 4.11 — Star and delta networks.

networks are found in a great many circuits, and they can present a difficult analytical problem.

Let us consider the bridge circuit shown in Fig. 4.12. This circuit cannot be reduced to a single equivalent resistor between terminals A and B because there are no obviously simple parallel or series combinations to aid reduction. However, experience has shown that, depending upon the circuit and the analytical needs, it is sometimes convenient to convert a delta network into a star network, and at other times to convert a star network to a delta network. In the bridge circuit shown the bottom half of the circuit forms a delta network. If we could transform this part of the bridge into a star network, the circuit would be easier to analyze. See Fig. 4.13.

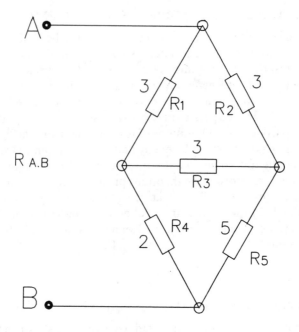

Fig. 4.12 — Bridge circuit with star and delta networks.

We require a technique that converts the delta network resistors R_3, R_4, and R_5 into their star equivalents shown in Fig. 4.13, so that we can more readily calculate R_{AB}. In the figure we have actually calculated the transformed values. Now we will discuss how we arrived at those values; that is, how we performed the transformation of a delta network into its star equivalent. When we have done this we shall investigate the converse circuit transformation from a star to a delta network.

4.6 DELTA TO STAR TRANSFORMATION

Any three-sided mesh or delta circuit may be replaced by an equivalent star circuit without affecting the circuits in the other parts of the network. However, if the delta circuit is to be replaced by a star circuit, and if two circuits are to be equivalent to each other, they must present the same resistance between any two terminals of interest. That is, the two networks must have exactly the same effect on the rest of the circuit.

Consider the transformation networks shown in Fig. 4.14. Note how we have labelled the terminals and how the labelling of the resistors is allied to the terminal designations.

Terminals 1–2

$$R_{1-2} = R_{d3} \| (R_{d2} + R_{d1}) \quad \dots \text{Delta}$$

$$R_{1-2} = R_{s1} + R_{s2} \dots \quad \dots \text{Star},$$

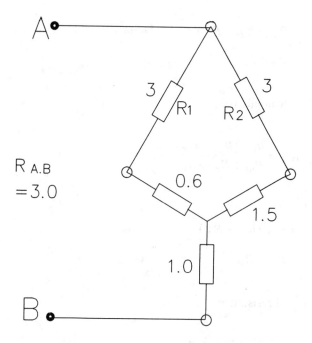

Fig. 4.13 — Transformation of bridge circuit.

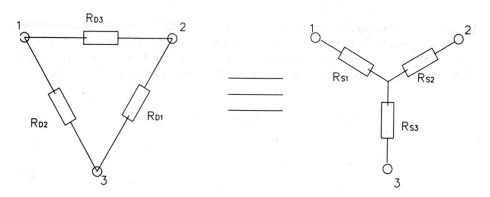

Fig. 4.14 — (a) Delta network. (b) Star network.

therefore if the resistance between terminals is to be the same,

$$R_{s1} + R_{s2} = \frac{R_{d3} \cdot (R_{d2} + R_{d1})}{R_{d3} + R_{d2} + R_{d1}} \quad \cdots \qquad \cdots \ (1\text{--}2)$$

Terminals 2–3

$$R_{2-3} = R_{d1} \| (R_{d3} + R_{d2}) \quad \dots \text{ Delta}$$

$$R_{2-3} = R_{s2} + R_{s3} \dots \quad \dots \text{ Star },$$

therefore as for terminals 1–2,

$$R_{s2} + R_{s3} = \frac{R_{d1} \cdot (R_{d3} + R_{d2})}{R_{d3} + R_{d2} + R_{d1}} \dots \qquad \dots (2\text{–}3)$$

Terminals 3–1

$$R_{3-1} = R_{d2} | (R_{d3} + R_{d1}) \quad \dots \text{ Delta}$$

$$R_{3-1} = R_{s3} + R_{s1} \dots \quad \dots \text{ Star },$$

therefore for equal resistance,

$$R_{s3} + R_{s1} = \frac{R_{d2} \cdot (R_{d3} + R_{d1})}{R_{d3} + R_{d2} + R_{d1}} \dots \qquad \dots (3\text{–}1)$$

We must now manipulate equations (1–2) to (3–1) so that we can obtain expressions for R_{s1}, R_{s2}, and R_{s3} in terms of the delta circuit resistors, R_{d1}, R_{d2}, and R_{d3}. We have, in fact, three simultaneous equations, and we can solve these by the normal elimination technique. Subtracting equation (3–1) from equation (2–3) gives:

$$R_{s1} - R_{s3} = \frac{R_{d3}(R_{d2} + R_{d1}) - R_{d1}(R_{d3} + R_{d2})}{R_{d3} + R_{d2} + R_{d1}}$$

$$= \frac{(R_{d3} \cdot R_{d2} - R_{d1} \cdot R_{d2})}{R_{d3} + R_{d2} + R_{d1}} \dots \qquad \dots (A)$$

Adding equation (3–1) to equation (A) gives:

$$2R_{s1} = \frac{(R_{d3} \cdot R_{d2} - R_{d1} \cdot R_{d2})}{R_{d3} + R_{d2} + R_{d1}} + \frac{R_{d2} \cdot R_{d3} + R_{d2} \cdot R_{d1}}{R_{d3} + R_{d2} + R_{d1}}$$

$$= \frac{2 \cdot R_{d3} \cdot R_{d2}}{R_{d3} + R_{d2} + R_{d1}},$$

and finally;

$$R_{s1} = \frac{R_{d3} \cdot R_{d2}}{R_{d3} + R_{d2} + R_{d1}} \cdots \qquad \cdots (R_{s1})$$

by back substitution in our equation set, and by further algebraic manipulation we find that:

$$R_{s2} = \frac{R_{d3} \cdot R_{d1}}{R_{d3} + R_{d2} + R_{d1}} \cdots \qquad \cdots (R_{s2})$$

and

$$R_{s3} = \frac{R_{d1} \cdot R_{d2}}{R_{d3} + R_{d2} + R_{d1}} \cdots \qquad \cdots (R_{s3})$$

If we look at the equations for R_{s1} to R_{s3} carefully we can see that there is a very clear pattern to the results, and it is not as difficult as it may seem to remember the formulae for delta to star conversion. We can summarize the expressions given in the above equation set as follows.

Aide memoire

To obtain the star network resistor R_{s1} connected to terminal 1, the two delta network resistors connected to terminal 1 must be multiplied together and then divided by the sum of the three delta resistors. This procedure must be repeated for terminals 2 and 3.

You may now wish to go back to Figs 4.12 and 4.13 to confirm the suggested transformation.

4.7 STAR TO DELTA TRANSFORMATIONS

It is sometimes necessary or more convenient to convert a star network to a delta network. In this case experience has shown that the required transformation expressions are more conveniently obtained if conductances rather than resistances are used in the formulations. Consider, then, Fig. 4.15 which shows a star and delta network illustrated in terms of conductances.

We shall find that the final results follow a similar format to that already obtained for the resistances of the previous transformation. However, rather than simply quote these results we will consider how they are obtained.

Once again we will use terminal pairs to set up our network equations, defining the terminal conductances as follows.

Let $G_{1-2} = G_{1-2}$ with terminals 2 and 3 short-circuited

and $G_{2-3} = G_{2-3}$ with terminals 3 and 1 short-circuited

and $G_{3-1} = G_{3-1}$ with terminals 1 and 2 short-circuited

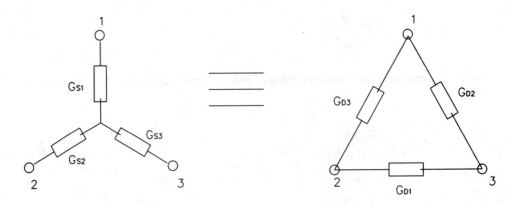

Fig. 4.15 — Star and delta network conductances.

This is an acceptable ploy so long as we remember to apply it to both circuits when we make our formulae deductions.

Terminals 1–2

Consider Fig. 4.16,

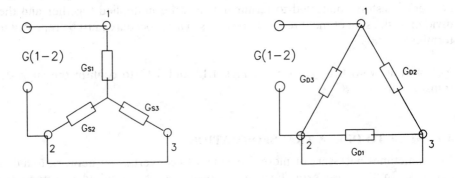

Fig. 4.16 — Star and delta circuits for G_{1-2}.

This employment of the product over sum rule is valid when considering conductances in series.

$$G_{1-2} = \frac{G_{s1} \cdot (G_{s2} + G_{s3})}{G_{s1} + G_{s2} + G_{s3}} \quad \dots \text{Star}$$

$$G_{1-2} = G_{d3} + G_{d2} \dots \quad \dots \text{Delta},$$

and equating the two expressions:

$$G_{d3} + G_{d2} = \frac{G_{s1} \cdot (G_{s2} + G_{s3})}{G_{s1} + G_{s2} + G_{s3}} \quad \ldots \qquad \ldots (1\text{--}2)$$

Terminals 2–3

Consider Fig. 4.17.

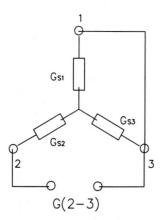
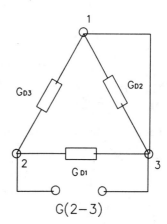

Fig. 4.17 — Star and delta circuits for $G_{2\text{--}3}$.

$$G_{2-3} = \frac{G_{s2} \cdot (G_{s1} + G_{s3})}{G_{s1} + G_{s2} + G_{s3}} \quad \ldots \text{ Star}$$

and

$$G_{2-3} = G_{d1} + G_{d3} \quad \ldots \qquad \ldots \text{ Delta}$$

and equating the two expressions:

$$G_{d1} + G_{d3} = \frac{G_{s2} \cdot (G_{s1} + G_{s3})}{G_{s1} + G_{s2} + G_{s3}} \quad \ldots \qquad \ldots (2\text{--}3)$$

Terminals 3–1

Consider Fig. 4.18.

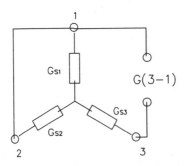
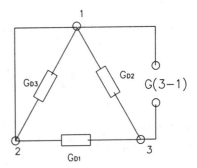

Fig. 4.18 — Star and delta circuits for G_{3-1}.

$$G_{3-1} = \frac{G_{s3} \cdot (G_{s2} + G_{s1})}{G_{s1} + G_{s2} + G_{s3}} \quad \dots \text{ Star}$$

$$G_{3-1} = G_{d1} + G_{d2} \dots \quad \dots \text{ Delta}$$

and equating the two expressions,

$$G_{d1} + G_{d2} = \frac{G_{s3} \cdot (G_{s2} + G_{s1})}{G_{s1} + G_{s2} + G_{s3}} \dots \qquad \dots (3\text{--}1)$$

We can now start to manipulate the equation set (1–2) to (3–1) to obtain expressions for the individual star conductances.

Subtracting equation (1–2) from equation (2–3) gives:

$$G_{d1} - G_{d2} = \frac{G_{s2}(G_{s3} + G_{s1}) - G_{s1}(G_{s3} + G_{s2})}{G_{s3} + G_{s2} + G_{s1}}$$

$$= \frac{(G_{s3} \cdot G_{s2} - G_{s1} \cdot G_{s3})}{G_{s3} + G_{s2} + G_{s1}} \dots \qquad \dots \text{(A)}$$

Adding equation (A) to equation (3–1) yields:

$$2 \cdot G_{d1} = \frac{(G_{s3} \cdot G_{s2} - G_{s1} \cdot G_{s3})}{G_{s3} + G_{s2} + G_{s1}} + \frac{G_{s2} \cdot G_{s3} + G_{s3} \cdot G_{s1}}{G_{s3} + G_{s2} + G_{s1}}$$

$$= \frac{2 \cdot G_{s3} \cdot G_{s2}}{G_{s3} + G_{s2} + G_{s1}},$$

therefore,

$$G_{d1} = \frac{G_{s3} \cdot G_{s2}}{G_{s3} + G_{s2} + G_{s1}}. \qquad \qquad \dots (G_{d1})$$

Similar equation reductions produce the following:

$$G_{d2} = \frac{G_{s3} \cdot G_{s1}}{G_{s3} + G_{s2} + G_{s1}}. \qquad \qquad \dots (G_{d2})$$

$$G_{d3} = \frac{G_{s1} \cdot G_{s2}}{G_{s3} + G_{s2} + G_{s1}}. \qquad \qquad \dots (G_{d3})$$

Once again there is a very clear pattern to the results which makes it easier to remember the formulae for star to delta conversion than it would appear from a cursory look at the equation set (G_{d1}) to (G_{d3}). Note also the very close resemblance in equation format to the delta to star transformation. The formulae are in fact the same except that one is in terms of resistance whilst the other is in terms of conductance.

Aide memoire

To obtain the delta network conductance G_{d1} connected to terminal 1, the two star network conductances not connected to terminal 1 must be multiplied together and the product divided by the sum of the three star network conductances. The procedure can then be repeated for the remaining terminals of interest.

WORKED EXAMPLES

Example 4.1
Q.   Determine the equivalent resistance between the terminals A and C of the network shown in Fig 4.19(a).
A. R_4, R_5, and R_6 must be delta to star transformed, therefore use resistor values.

$$R_D = R_B = R_C = \frac{1\,k\Omega \times 1\,k\Omega}{3\,k\Omega} = 0.333'\,k\Omega$$

Now our circuit can be redrawn as Figs 4.19(c) to (e) below.
Fig. 4.19(c) shows the step that combines R_1 with R_B and R_3 with R_D.
Fig. 4.19(d) shows R_{D3} combining in parallel with R_{B1}.
Fig. 4.19(e) shows the final circuit where R_C can be successfully deduced:

$$R_C = R_2 \| (R_C + R_{D3} \| R_{B1}) = 0.5\,k\Omega$$

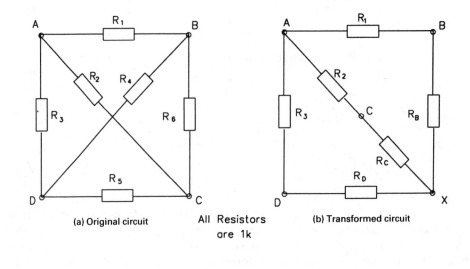

(a) Original circuit   All Resistors   (b) Transformed circuit
                                are 1k

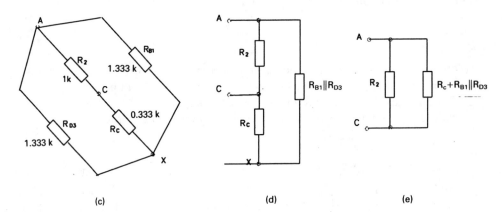

(c)   (d)   (e)

Fig. 4.19 (a) and (b) — Network for Example 4.1. (c) to (e) — Circuit transformation steps for determining R_{AC}.

Example 4.2

Q.   Convert the delta network shown in Fig. 4.20 to a star network.

A.   The conversion process simply requires substitution of the resistance values given in the diagram into the equation set developed in section 4.6 for the delta–star transformation.

Replacing the subscripts $_1$, $_2$, and $_3$ with $_a$, $_b$, and $_c$ respectively for the circuit as shown in Fig. 4.20 we can write for the star resistors R_a, R_b, and R_c:

$$R_a = R_{ab}R_{ac}/(R_{ab} + R_{ac} + R_{bc}) = 500 \times 400/(500 + 400 + 300) \ \Omega$$
$$= 166.7 \ \Omega$$

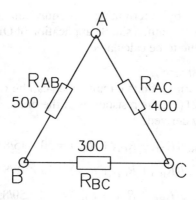

Fig. 4.20 — Delta network.

$$R_b = R_{ab}R_{bc}/(R_{ab} + R_{ac} + R_{bc}) = 500 \times 300/(1200) \; \Omega$$
$$= 125 \; \Omega$$
$$R_c = R_{ac}R_{bc}/(R_{ab} + R_{ac} + R_{bc}) = 400 \times 300/(1200) \; \Omega$$
$$= 100 \; \Omega$$

Example 4.3

Q.   Determine the currents in all branches of the network shown in Fig. 4.21. An

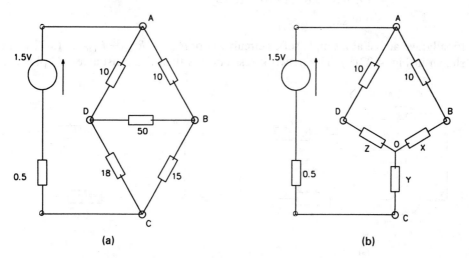

Fig. 4.21 — Wheatstone bridge circuit.

emf source of 1.5 V is connected across A and C, and the source has an internal resistance of 0.5 Ω.

To calculate the current in all parts of the circuit we must first calculate the supply current. We can do this by determining the equivalent resistance of the bridge network. Since we know the emf, a simple application of Ohm's law will then enable the required current value to be calculated.

Network equivalent resistance
The bridge limb BCD forms a delta circuit which can be replaced by an equivalent star as shown in Fig. 4.21 (b), the resistances of the branches being calculated from the equation set already derived.

$$R_{OB} = R_{BD}R_{BC}/(R_{BD} + R_{CD} + R_{BC}) = 50 \times 15/83 = 9.04\,\Omega$$

$$R_{OC} = R_{BC}R_{CD}/(R_{BD} + R_{CD} + R_{BC}) = 15 \times 18/83 = 3.25\,\Omega$$

$$R_{OD} = R_{CD}R_{BD}/(R_{BD} + R_{CD} + R_{BC}) = 18 \times 50/83 = 10.85\,\Omega$$

We thus have a series–parallel network as shown in Fig. 4.22 (a), where;

$$R_{ABO} = R_{AB} + R_{OB} = 10 + 9.04 = 19.04\,\Omega$$

$$R_{ADO} = R_{AD} + R_{OD} = 10 + 10.85 = 20.85\,\Omega$$

Resistances R_{ABO} and R_{ADO} form a parallel circuit whose equivalent resistance is:

$$R_{AO} = \frac{R_{ABO} \times R_{ADO}}{R_{ADO} + R_{ABO}}$$

$$= 19.04 \times 20.85/(19.04 + 20.85)$$

$$= 9.95\,\Omega.$$

Finally, we arrive at a simple series circuit where $R_{AC} = R_{AO} + R_{OC} = 13.21\,\Omega$, as shown in Fig. 4.22 (b). The network resistance is then the resistance AC plus the

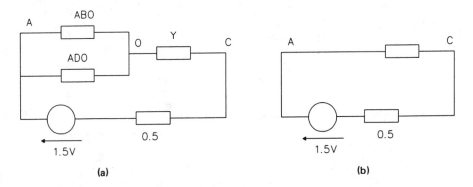

Fig. 4.22 — Transformed Wheatstone bridge circuit.

internal resistance of the emf source which is a series resistance such that

$$R_{NET} = 13.21 + 0.5 = 13.71\,\Omega$$

Supply current
The current supplied by the cell is therefore

$$I_S = \text{emf}/R_{\text{NET}} = 1.5/13.71 = 0.1095\,\text{A}$$

Branch currents

AB
We can determined the current in branch AB by using the current divider technique such that:

$$I_{\text{AB}} = I_S \times R_{\text{ADO}}/(R_{\text{ADO}} + R_{\text{ABO}})$$
$$= 0.1095 \times 20.85/39.89 = 0.0572\,\text{A}.$$

AD
The current in branch AD is determined in a similar manner to that in branch AB:

$$I_{\text{AD}} = I_S \times R_{\text{ABO}}/(R_{\text{ADO}} + R_{\text{ABO}})$$
$$= 0.1095 \times 19.04/39.89 = 0.0522\,\text{A}.$$

BD
The current in branch BD is determined by using the potential divider theorem coupled with Ohm's law:

$$I_{\text{BD}} = (V_{\text{AB}} - V_{\text{AD}})/R_{\text{BD}}$$
$$= [(0.0572 \times 10) - (0.0522 \times 10)]/50$$
$$= 1\,\text{mA (flowing from B to D)}$$

BC
The current flowing through BD can be calculated by using Kirchhoff's current summation law,

$$I_{\text{BC}} = I_{\text{AB}} + I_{\text{BD}} = 0.0572 + 0.001 = 0.0582\,\text{A}$$

DC
The current flowing through DC is calcuated by the same technique as for BC:

$$I_{\text{DC}} = I_{\text{AD}} - I_{\text{BD}} = 0.0522 + 0.001 = 0.0512\,\text{A}$$

These results can be checked by calculating the voltages around the circuit and confirming that they satisfy Kirchhoff's laws.

Example 4.4
Q. Use the superposition theorem to calculate the current flowing through the resistor R_3 in the circuit shown in Fig. 4.23.
A.   To use the superposition theorem we need to remove in turn the emf sources and analyze the remaining circuits. Thus the diagrams in Fig. 4.24 (a) and (b) are for;

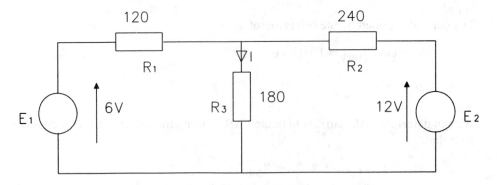

Fig. 4.23 — Circuit for Example 4.4.

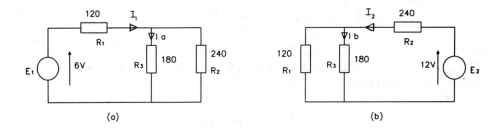

Fig. 4.24 (a) and (b) — Superposition diagrams.

(a) The circuit with V_2 removed and represented by its internal resistance R_2,
(b) The circuit with V_1 removed and represented by its internal resistance R_1.

The current we wish to know the value of, I_{R3}, is made up of the two components indicated in Fig. 4.24(a) and (b): i_a and i_b, such that

$$I_{R3} = i_a + i_b.$$

To determine I_{R3}, therefore, we must calculate i_a and i_b.

Calculation of current i_a
Let us consider Fig. 4.24(a). The current I_1 is divided between the current i_a and the current flowing through I_{R2}, that is,

$$I_1 = i_a + I_{R2},$$

but by current divider theory,

$$i_a = I_1 \times \frac{R_2}{R_3 + R_2},$$

the only unknown of the right-hand side of the equation being, I_1. However, this can be determined from;

$$I_1 = V_1/R_{\text{equivalent}}$$

The equivalent resistance of this circuit is R_1 in series with a parallel combination of R_2 and R_3:

$$\begin{aligned}
R_{\text{equiv}} &= R_1 + R_2 \| R_3 \\
&= 120 + 240 \| 180 \\
&= 222.86\,\Omega.
\end{aligned}$$

Therefore,

$$\begin{aligned}
I_1 &= 6/222.86 \\
&= 26.92\,mA
\end{aligned}$$

and,

$$\begin{aligned}
i_a &= 0.02692 \times [240/\{180 + 240\}] \\
&= 15.38\,\text{mA}
\end{aligned}$$

We determine i_b by similar reasoning, using Fig. 4.24(b).

$$i_b = I_2 \times \frac{R_1}{R_1 + R_3}$$

$$I_2 = V_2/R_{\text{eqiv2}}$$

$$\begin{aligned}
R_{\text{equiv2}} &= R_2 + R_1 \| R_3 \\
&= 240 + 120 \| 180 \\
&= 312\,\Omega.
\end{aligned}$$

Therefore,

$$\begin{aligned}
I_2 &= 12/312 \\
&= 38.46\,\text{mA}
\end{aligned}$$

and

$$i_b = 0.03846 \times [120/\{120 + 180\}]$$
$$= 15.38 \, \text{mA}.$$

Finally,

$$I_{R3} = i_a + i_b$$
$$= 15.38 + 15.38 \, \text{mA}$$
$$= 30.76 \, \text{mA}.$$

The fact that in this example $i_a = i_b$ is a pure coincidence.

This result can be checked by using Norton's theorem.

Example 4.5

Q. The circuit shown in Fig. 4.25 contains only parallel voltage and current

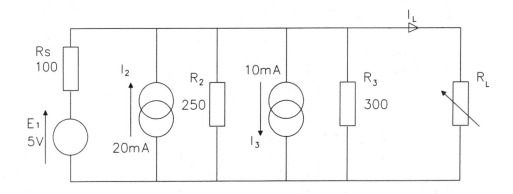

Fig. 4.25 — Complex network with parallel sources.

sources. Obtain the equivalent current generator circuit and the equivalent voltage generator circuit by applying the Thévenin and Norton theorems. Furthermore, determine the maximum power transfer in the load resistor.

A. The first point to note is that there is an emf source as well as constant current sources in the circuit, therefore this emf source will have to be converted to a current source before we can apply Norton's theorem. We can apply this theorem because all the sources are parallel.

(a) Conversion of emf source to current source

You will recall that an emf source with a series resistor can be replaced by a current source with a parallel resistor by making the current source $I_1 = E_1/R_S$ and $R_1 = R_S$; that is, as in

$$I_1 = I_c = 5/100 = 50 \, \text{mA}$$

$R_1 = R_S = 100\,\Omega$.

We can now redraw our circuit diagram, see Fig. 4.26.

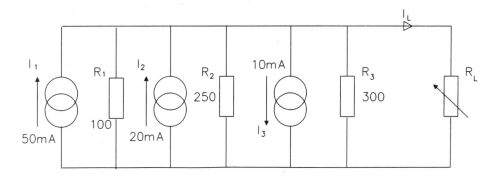

Fig. 4.26 — Redrawn circuit for worked Example 4.5.

(b)   Calculate of equivalent circuit parameter values
To determine the single source current we add together all the source currents:

$$I_S = I_1 + I_2 + I_3,$$

and we note the directions of the current flows to give

$$I_N = 0.05 + 0.02 - 0.01\,\text{A}$$
$$= 60\,\text{mA}.$$

To determine the single equivalent resistor we simply analyze the parallel resistive circuit,

$$I_N = R_1 \| R_2 \| R_3$$
$$= 100 \| 250 \| 300$$
$$= 57.69\,\Omega,$$

thus we have an equivalent current source circuit, which you should recognise as a Norton circuit, Fig. 4.27.

The equivalent voltage generator circuit, that is the Thévénin circuit, is shown in Fig. 4.28, where:

$$V_{Th} = I_S R_S = 0.06 \times 57.69 = 3.462\,\text{V}$$

and,

$$R_{Th} = R_S = R_N = 57.69\,\Omega.$$

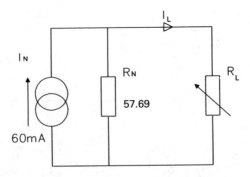

Fig. 4.27 — Norton equivalent circuit.

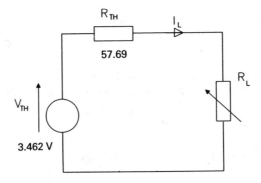

Fig. 4.28 — Thévénin circuit.

(c)   Maximum power transfer

We are not given the resistance value of the load, but we do not need it to complete our calculations because we know that at the point of maximum power transfer $R_L = R_{Th}$, and that $V_L = 0.5 V_{Th}$.

$$\text{Power} = V_L I_L = V_L^2 / R_L = 0.25 V_{Th}^2 / 57.69$$
$$= 51.94 \, \text{mW}.$$

We have now completed our study of circuit theorems as applied to dc linear circuits. There are other theorems, for example nodal analysis, which we shall not discuss. The theorems presented will equip the analyst more than sufficiently. One final point which needs to be stressed again before we pass on to circuit transformations is that the circuit models we have looked at so far cannot cope with non-linearities and transients. It should also be noted that because a circuit contains only resistors does not mean that it is necessarily linear, and if a circuit contains non-resistive elements it is not necessarily non-linear.

REVIEW QUESTIONS AND TUTORIAL EXAMPLES

(4.1)　State the superposition theorem and outline the steps to be taken in applying it to the analysis of a resistive network.

(4.2)　State Thévénin's theorem and list the procedural steps for its application to circuit analysis.

(4.3)　State the formulae which relate Thévénin's model components to Norton's model components.

(4.4)　What does the maximum power transfer theorem say about the value of the load resistance?

(4.5)　The Wheatstone bridge type of instrument is called a . . . detector. (Insert the word that completes the sentence.)

(4.6)　Derive the equations for the conversion of a star network to a delta network.

(4.7)　Derive the equations for the conversion of a delta network to a star network.

(4.8)　Use either a star ≡ delta or a delta ≡ star transformation to determine the total resistance connected across the supply voltage in Fig. 4.29 (17.143 kΩ).

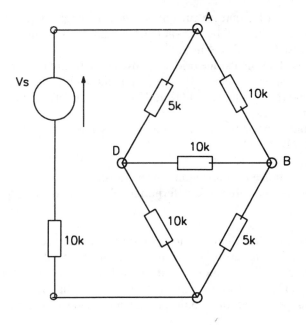

Fig. 4.29 — Circuit for problem 4.8.

(4.9)　In the circuit shown in Fig. 4.30, what alteration must be made in the value of

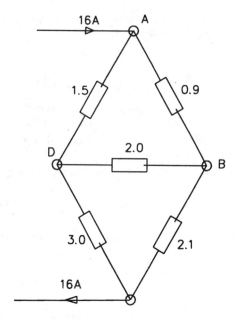

Fig. 4.30 — Circuit for problem 4.9.

the 3Ω resistor in order that no current will flow through the 2Ω resistor? If this alteration is made, what will be the value of the current flowing through the 1.5Ω resistor? (Increase by 0.5Ω; $6\,A$).

(4.10) The arms of a Wheatstone bridge are used to measure the terminal resistance of an inductor, as shown in Fig. 4.31. The system has a null when $R_V = 98\,\Omega$ and the ratio arms R_1 and R_2 are equal to $1\,k\Omega$ and $10\,k\Omega$ respectively. What is the resistance of the inductor? ($9.8\,\Omega$).

(4.11) A certain generator has an open circuit voltage of $12\,V$ and an internal resistance of $40\,\Omega$. Calculate:

(a) The load resistance for maximum power transfer.
(b) The corresponding values of the terminal voltage and of the power supplied to the load.

If the load resistance were increased to twice the value for maximum power transfer, what would be the power absorbed by the load? ($40\,\Omega$; $6\,V$; $0.9\,W$; $0.8\,W$).

(4.12) To achieve maximum power transfer will the $12\,k\Omega$ resistor in the circuit shown in Fig. 4.32 have to be changed, and if so to what value? Determine the maximum load power at the point of maximum power transfer. (Yes; $2\,k\Omega$; $2.73\,mW$).

(4.13) For the circuit shown in Fig. 4.33, use Norton's theorem to obtain a single current generator and then determine the load current when $R_L = 3300\,\Omega$ and when $R_L = 4.7\,k\Omega$. Plot a graph of appropriate circuit parameter values against R_L to demonstrate the maximum power transfer theorem. ($2.37\,mA$; $1.674\,mA$).

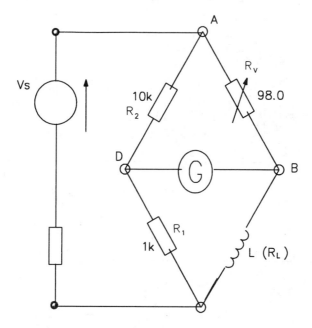

Fig. 4.31 — Circuit for problem 4.10.

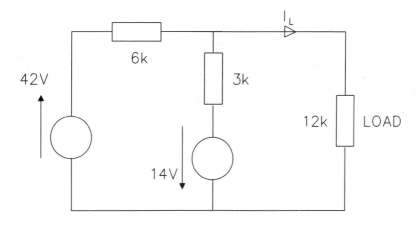

Fig. 4.32 — Circuit for problem 4.12.

(4.14) Use the superposition theorem to determine the current flowing through the 6.8 kΩ resistor shown in the circuit in Fig. 4.34. You may wish to compare your solution with that obtained by a direct application of Kirchhoff's laws. (0.536 mA).
(4.15) Determine the current from V_1 in the circuit shown in Fig. 4.35 by applying a star–delta transformation to resistors R_1, R_2, and R_3. (2.38 mA).
(4.16) The circuit shown in Fig. 4.36 contains both emfs and a constant current

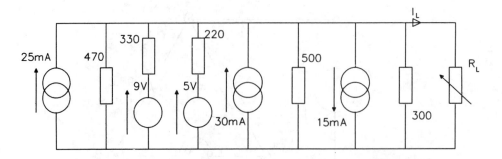

Fig. 4.33 — Circuit for problem 4.13.

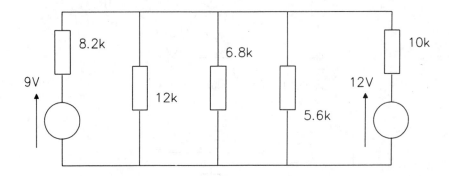

Fig. 4.34 — Circuit for problem 4.14.

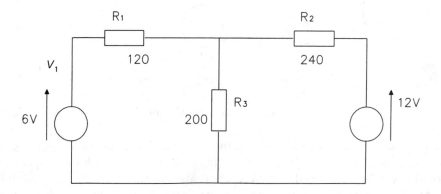

Fig. 4.35 — Circuit for problem 4.15.

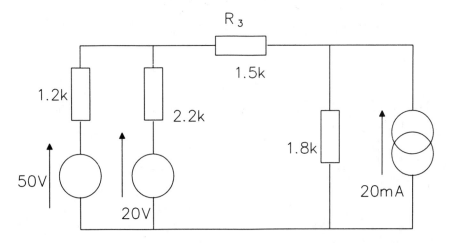

Fig. 4.36 — Circuit for problem 4.16.

generator. Using the superposition theorem, determine the current flowing through resistor R_3. (0.8366 mA).

(4.17) Use the superposition theorem to calculate the current in the 20 Ω resistor shown in Fig. 4.37 as R_2. (3 A).

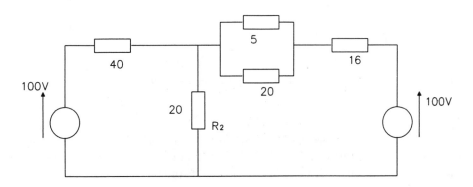

Fig. 4.37 — Circuit for problem 4.17.

(4.18) Analyze the circuit shown in Fig. 4.38 by means of the superposition theorem, and determine the current flow through the resistor R_2. (2.23 A).

(4.19) A power transfer circuit shown in Fig. 4.39. Determine the current flowing through the variable load resistor R_L when it is set at resistance values of 10, 15, and 100 Ω. Furthermore, determine the maximum power transfer possible and the value of the load resistance at this condition. (0.48 A, 0.453 A, 0.2308 A; 5.45 W; 73.334 Ω).

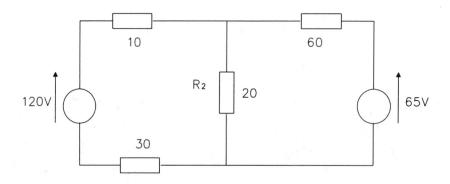

Fig. 4.38 — Circuit for problem 4.18.

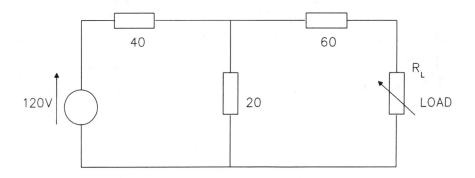

Fig. 4.39 — Circuit for problem 4.19.

Note: Thévénin's and Norton's theorem can be used to get simpler solutions to most of the examples in this section. Use these two theorems to 'check' your results but avoid the temptation to use them to circumvent the practice needed to master the less popular theorems.

Part 2
Transient analysis

5

Reactive circuit elements

5.1 MAGNETISM AND ELECTRIC CURRENT

Most people are familiar with the toy-sized permanent magnet which can be used to pick up small iron objects such as paper clips. In using the magnet they will have seen that the effects of the magnet can be felt some distance away from the magnet. The space within which the effect can be felt or detected is known as the magnet's magnetic field.

In engineering systems we are interested primarily in those magnetic fields which are generated by electric currents rather than those associated with permanent magnets. When a current flows through an electrical conductor a magnetic field is created around the conductor. The magnetic field so created depends upon the size of the current flowing through the conductor. The fundamental principles which govern the relationships between electric and magnetic fields were first investigated and highlighted by Oersted† in 1820. They formed the basis for the concept of electromagnetism. The operation of many types of electrical equipment depends upon these principles.

If a magnetic field is produced, by whatever means, and if this field moves relative to a conductor located in the area of the field, an emf will be induced in the conductor. Thus we have two important reactions between electricity and magnetism:

(a) A changing electric current produces a changing magnetic field.
(b) A changing magnetic field produces an induced emf.

These interactions are shown diagrammatically in Figs 5.1(a) and (b).

It is not difficult to imagine that the two cross-field effects suggested above will also have an interaction between themselves, and we shall investigate this relation-

† Hans Christian Oersted (1777–1851) was Professor of Physics at Copenhagen University. He discovered that when a current flows through a wire it could deflect a compass needle.

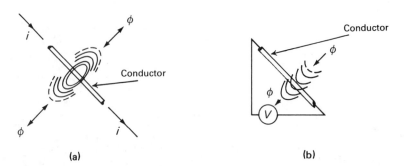

Fig. 5.1 — (a) Changing current produces changing magnetic field. (b) Changing magnetic field
produces induced emf.

ship in a later chapter. Before we can do this we must develop an understanding of
the unidirectional cross-field effects, and we must first consider some of the
fundamental properties of magnetic fields. The main properties we shall consider are
magnetic flux and magnetic flux density.

5.1.1 Magnetic flux
Consider Fig. 5.2, which shows the lines of magnetic flux (symbol Φ) assumed to exist

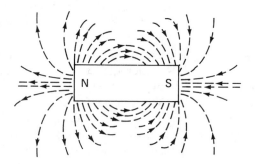

Fig. 5.2 — Magnetic field around a permanent bar magnet.

in the magnetic field around a permanent magnet. By convention the direction of a
magnetic field is taken to be away from the north pole and toward a south pole,
hence, direction arrows may be inserted as shown in the diagram. It must be
emphasized that the actual form that a magnetic field takes is not as a collection of
discrete lines of magnetic effect as suggested in the diagram, but as a continuous
homogeneous field of magnetic environment better compared to say a light beam.
However, a continuous medium is neither mathematically nor conceptually easy to
study, and it is more convenient to treat all simple magnetic fields as being discrete
collections of lines of magnetic effect which are called lines of magnetic flux.

   These lines of flux, or lines of force as they were once called, therefore indicate
the conventionally accepted direction of the magnetic field, and the closeness with

which they are packed within the field indicates the strength or pulling power of the field. The size of a magnetic field is expressed in the SI unit the weber (Wb)†. The 'size' is a measure of the number of magnetic flux lines contained within a specified cross-sectional area of the magnetic field. It must be clearly understood that the weber is a measure of magnetic line quantity and not magnetic line concentration or density. This is best illustrated by a diagram. Fig. 5.3 shows three areas of magnetic field where the flux or size of the field is, say, 10 Wb.

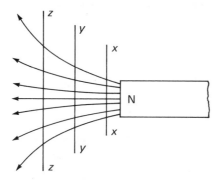

Fig. 5.3 — The concept of flux.

5.1.2 Magnetic flux density

The concentration of a magnetic field at any point in the field is defined by the density of the flux at that point which is measured in webers‡ per square metre of cross-sectional area. It is important that this flux density (B) is not associated with material density, which is mass per unit volume and thus contains a metre cubic term. The SI unit called the tesla (T)§ is also used in the measurement and description of magnetic flux density. The concept of magnetic flux density is shown in Fig. 5.4.

Flux density = flux at the point/cross-sectional area, or in the symbol form:

$$B = \Phi/A \text{ (webers per square metre) .}$$

Thus for the three locations under consideration:

$$B_x = \Phi/A_x, B_y = \Phi/A_y, \text{ and } B_z = \Phi/A_z ,$$

and note that $B_x > B_y > B_z$.

To allow us to appreciate the use of the expressions, two worked examples are given later in the chapter. (Examples 5.1 and 5.2).

† Pronounced Vay-ber.
‡ William Eduard Weber (1804–1891) invented the electrodynamometer in 1841 for the measurement of electric current.
§ Nicola Tesla (1856–1943) was born in modern-day Yugoslavia and emigrated to the USA in 1884. He discovered how to produce a rotating magnetic field in 1888, and is best known for his invention of the 'Tesla coil' ('shocking' coil).

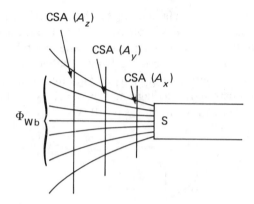

Fig. 5.4 — Flux density in a magnetic field. CSA is cross-sectional area.

5.2 ELECTROMAGNETIC INDUCTION

As previously stated, our main concern in this book when considering magnetism is the relationship between electric and magnetic effects, especially in an electromagnetic coil. We shall first of all consider these relationships from a non-mathematical point of view.

5.2.1 Magnetic fields and current-carrying conductors

The reaction in a single straight conductor or a coil conductor to the passage of a current flowing through it involves the interaction of two field systems: the electric and magnetic fields. Two of the more commonly known electromagnetic field patterns are produced by these interactions, and are shown in Fig. 5.5.

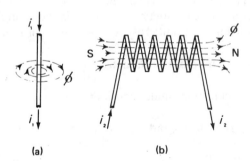

(a)   (b)

Fig. 5.5 — (a) Single current-carrying conductor. (b) Current-carrying coil conductor.

The size of the flux produced in each of the two cases can be experimentally shown to be proportional to the amount of current flowing through the conductors. The flux in the second case is also proportional to the number of turns present, usually referred to as the number of windings or coils (N). Thus the relationships between flux, current, and in the latter case the number of windings, can be expressed mathematically as:

(a) $\Phi_1 \propto I_1$

(b) $\phi_2 \propto N . I_2$

These experimental results indicate that the translation from electric field to magnetic field is done via current (I), in amperes, producing flux (Φ), in webers. This generalized deduction is of major importance, and must be appreciated if further study into electomagnetic effects are to be undertaken. A simple translation diagram. Fig. 5.6, will help to build up the necessary understanding.

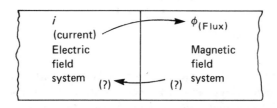

Fig. 5.6 — Field translation.

Current (i) in an electric field system creates flux (ϕ) in a magnetic field system. As yet we have not discussed the reverse mechanism from magnetic to electric translation.

5.2.2 Electrical effect generation from motion in magnetic fields
Consider Fig. 5.7 where a conductor is shown moving at right angles to the flux lines

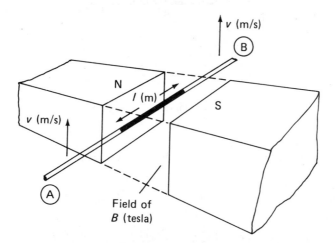

Fig. 5.7 — Conductor moving in a magnetic field.

in a magnetic field. The atoms of the conductor will experience a disturbing force that causes the electrons to move out of electrical balance with the main body of the atom. This atomic reaction manifests itself at the ends of the conductor (A and B) as an electromotive force or emf (volts). If the ends of the conductors were connected to an electrical circuit via a switch, a current would flow in a direct Ohm's law relationship to the generated emf. Experimentally, it can be shown that the size of this produced emf (in volts) is directly proportional to three separate factors:

(1) emf (volts) $\propto$ flux density B (tesla)
(2) emf (volts) $\propto$ conductor length l (metres)
(3) emf (volts) $\propto$ velocity υ (metres per second) of conductor perpendicular to the lines of flux.

This combination of factors yields an equation as follows if SI units are used.

emf $= B \cdot l \cdot \upsilon$ volts.

The velocity of the conductor with respect to the field could also have been stated in terms of the velocity of the field with respect to the conductor. In other words, we could have moved the magnetic field and held the conductor fixed to produce exactly the same result. This procedure is in fact the most commonly found method of electrical power generation. Let us take this concept a little further by looking at the sectional view of Fig. 5.7 as shown in Fig. 5.8.

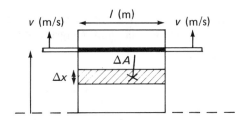

Fig. 5.8 — Sectional view of magnetic field.

A different expression for the generated or induced emf can be developed:

emf $= B \cdot l \cdot \upsilon$

and the velocity υ can also be stated as $\upsilon = \delta x / \delta t$.
    Combining these results gives us:

$$\text{emf} = \frac{\Phi}{A} \cdot l \cdot \frac{\delta x}{\delta t} \quad \text{. (Note } \delta x = \Delta x, \ \delta A = \Delta A, \text{ etc.)}$$

But $l . \delta x$ is the area cut by the conductor in δt seconds, and we could call it δA.

If we assume that the field is evenly formed, we can also state the flux density as being $\delta\Phi/\delta A$ as shown in Fig. 5.9. Thus the equation for emf can be restated as

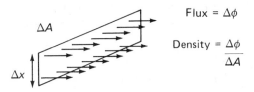

$$\Delta A$$

Flux $= \Delta\phi$

Density $= \dfrac{\Delta\phi}{\Delta A}$

$$\Delta x$$

Fig. 5.9 — Flux density in the region of interest.

follows:

$$emf = \frac{\delta\Phi}{\delta A} \times \frac{\delta A}{\delta t}$$

or	$emf = \delta\Phi/\delta t$.

That is, the induced emf is equal to the rate at which the flux is cut. In full differential form this equation can be written:

$$emf = \frac{d\Phi}{dt}$$

This result is very important for further understanding of electromagnetic systems. Once again we shall use a translation diagram to re-enforce the point.

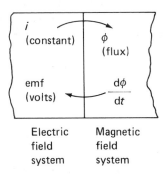

i
(constant)

ϕ
(flux)

emf
(volts)

$\dfrac{d\phi}{dt}$

Electric
field
system

Magnetic
field
system

Fig. 5.10 — Translation diagram for magnetic to electric fields.

The single conductor electromagnetic effect can be enhanced, as we have already seen, by the use of a coil of conductors and in this case the induced emf can be stated as:

$$\text{emf} = N \cdot \frac{d\Phi}{dt}$$

where N = number of coil winding turns.

The thread of this section is further re-enforced by worked Example 5.3, which the student is advised to consider before progressing further.

5.3 SELF-INDUCTANCE

We have, so far, considered the cross-field effects, i.e. the interaction between electric and magnetic fields, when a current is flowing through a conductor whether it be a single straight wire or a coil of wire. We said that these interactions form the basis for the science of electromagnetics. Our next step is to introduce the concept of self-inductance (symbol L). Consider the simple circuit shown in Fig. 5.11, in which

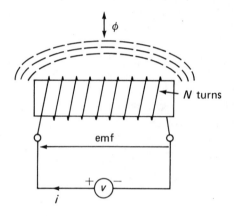

Fig. 5.11 — Single coil supplied from an electrical source.

neither the applied current nor the coil emf has a constant value. The electrical source parameters are also not constant, thus we have not put any values on the diagram. We are going to consider the interaction between the applied current (i) and the resultant emf in a situation where these two parameters could vary with time.

The magnetic flux (Φ) created by the current (i) will vary in direct response to this current, as suggested by the equation $\Phi \propto N \cdot i$. Thus

$$\frac{d\Phi}{dt} \propto N \cdot \frac{di}{dt}$$

The emf present at the terminals of the coil must also satisfy the equation relating emf to flux change. Thus

$$\text{emf} \propto N \cdot \frac{d\Phi}{dt} \propto N \cdot N \cdot \frac{di}{dt}$$

or

$$\text{emf} \propto N^2 \cdot \frac{di}{dt} \ .$$

Since it has been shown above that the induced emf is directly proportional to the rate of change of current, then mathematically we can write:

$$\text{emf} = k \cdot N^2 \cdot \frac{di}{dt} \ .$$

The mathematical constant of proportionality k and the coil windings factor can be combined into a generalized constant for the coil construction. This constant is called the coil's self-inductance (L). Thus we can write the last equation as:

$$\text{emf} = L \cdot \frac{di}{dt} \ ,$$

which is a mathematical statement of Lenz's law. The SI unit for the coil's self-inductance is the Henry† (H).

The constant of proportionality k for a simple coil can be experimentally shown to be dependent on the length of the coil, the cross-sectional area of the coil, and a factor called the permeability of the core material. This latter factor is a measure of the core material's ability to sustain a magnetic field; it is given the Greek symbol 'μ' and is pronounced 'mew'. Thus for a simple coil arrangement as shown in Fig. 5.12

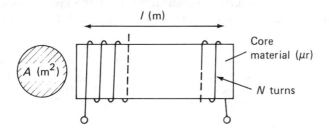

Fig. 5.12 — Simple coil and its self-inductance factors.

the self-inductance, L, would be:

$$L = \mu \frac{A}{l} N^2 \ , \qquad\qquad \text{where } \mu = \mu_o \cdot \mu_r$$

μ_o = permeability of free space ($4\pi/10^7$ H/m), μ_r = material relative permeability.

† Joseph Henry (1979–1878), an American, was probably the first person to appreciate that electromagnetism could be used for the production of mechanical power.

Thus the value of a coil's self-inductance is apparently dependent upon factors of constant value that are related to the physical dimensions and material nature of the coil.

In the real world of coil design and analysis the inductance of a coil is also found to be dependent upon working conditions such as the magnitude of the current passing through it and whether this current has any dc component. Our equation does not involve any consideration of these effects, and this must always be remembered.

This disruption of our simple solution is mainly due to the assumption that μ is constant for all working conditions. We must appreciate that a material's magnetic effect is nonlinear, and for a more formal analysis we must develop a more exhaustive formula that takes this effect into consideration.

For our present introduction to the whole area of electromagnetic effects it is easiest to begin without the burden of in-depth appreciation, whilst remembering our simplistic foundation. The study of the physical construction and design of coils does not form part of this book, and we shall not need to investigate the magnetic properties of materials. This means we do not require, as yet, an in-depth appreciation of permeability. The current-to-voltage relationship stated earlier in equation form is Lenz's law is all we require as we proceed on the on to the remaining parts of our studies when we are considering current-to-voltage relationships for situations involving a coil.

Lenz's law tell us that if we try to force a changing current through a coil, the coil will react against this change by producing an emf at the coil terminals. Thus this emf is usually referred to as a 'back emf', and often a negative sign is placed in front of the right-hand-side of Lenz's law to indicate this.

We have already considered the circuit element called the resistor. The coil arrangement we have just considered forms the circuit element which we call an inductor. Lenz's law for inductors is comparable to Ohm's law for resistors (see Fig. 5.13). However, we must never forget that when inductive circuits are being

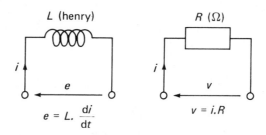

Fig. 5.13 — Lenz's law and Ohm's law compared.

considered, we are dealing with changing currents, and that Lenz's law reflects the conditions existing for this situation only.

5.4 MUTUAL INDUCTANCE

We have introduced the concept of self-inductance, and to complete this section we now look at mutual inductance.

Consider the two coils shown in Fig. 5.14. For convenience we shall call the coil

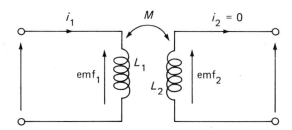

Fig. 5.14 — Mutual inductance between two coils.

shown on the left-hand-side the primary coil and the coil shown on the right-hand-side the secondary coil. If a varying current flows through the primary coil, a varying magnetic field will be set up around this coil. If the adjacent secondary coil is affected by this varying field, an emf will be induced in it. This experimental phenomenon is known as a mutually induced emf, and we say that the two coils have mutual inductance (M). The equations for both the primary and secondary emf's are given below.

$$\text{emf}_1 = L_1 \cdot \frac{\text{d}i_1}{\text{d}t} \quad \text{and} \quad \text{emf}_2 = M \cdot \frac{\text{d}i_1}{\text{d}t}$$

5.5 INDUCTORS

So far we have looked at the relationship between magnetic fields and electrical current, and have established some basic and important concepts. These have been used to introduce the phenomenon of inductance as associated with coils and the use of the term inductor to identify the coil as an electrical circuit element. As we have seen in an electrical circuit, elements can be connected in either series or parallel. Thus we now need to consider the series and parallel combination of inductors.

5.5.1 Inductors in series

For a circuit containing inductors we are interested not only in the currents and voltages present but also the inductances. We have already developed equations for inductive effects, and in the previous chapter we studied Kirchhoff's circuit laws and theorems. Armed with these analytical tools we can look at circuits which contain inductors in series.

In Fig. 5.15 we have four individual inductors each with its own value of inductance. We wish to know what is the total inductance of the circuit, L(total). We know from Kirchhoff's second law that the algebraic sum of the voltages must be zero.

$$V_{\text{total}} = \text{emf}_1 + \text{emf}_2 + \text{emf}_3 + \text{emf}_4$$

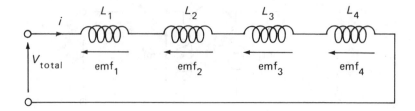

Fig. 5.15 — Inductors in series.

We also know from Lenz's law that

$$\text{emf} = L \, di/dt \ ,$$

and also that the changing current flowing through each inductor is the same. That is,

$$\frac{di_1}{dt} = \frac{di_2}{dt} = \frac{di_3}{dt} = \frac{di_4}{dt} = \frac{di}{dt} \ , \text{ thus:}$$

$$L_{\text{total}} \cdot \frac{di}{dt} = L_1 \cdot \frac{di}{dt} + L_2 \cdot \frac{di}{dt} + L_3 \cdot \frac{di}{dt} + L_4 \cdot \frac{di}{dt} \ ,$$

finally giving us:

$$L_{\text{total}} = L_1 + L_2 + L_3 + L_4 \ ,$$

which is a similar type of result to that found when resistors in series were considered.

5.5.2 Inductors in parallel
Consider the circuit shown in Fig. 5.16.

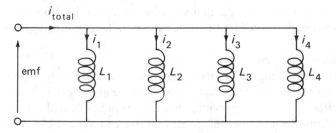

Fig. 5.16 — Inductors in parallel.

In this circuit we know that

$$\text{emf}_{\text{total}} = \text{emf}_1 = \text{emf}_2 = \text{emf}_3 = \text{emf}_4 \ .$$

Furthermore, for a parallel circuit, from Kirchhoff's first law,

$$i_{\text{total}} = i_1 + i_2 + i_3 + i_4 \ ,$$

therefore:

$$\frac{di_{\text{total}}}{dt} = \frac{di_1}{dt} + \frac{di_2}{dt} + \frac{di_3}{dt} + \frac{di_4}{dt} \ .$$

But $\text{emf} = L \cdot di/dt$, therefore:

$$\frac{\text{emf}}{L_{\text{total}}} = \frac{\text{emf}}{L_1} + \frac{\text{emf}}{L_2} + \frac{\text{emf}}{L_3} + \frac{\text{emf}}{L_4} \ ,$$

thus,

$$\frac{1}{L_{\text{total}}} = \frac{1}{L_1} + \frac{1}{L_2} + \frac{1}{L_3} + \frac{1}{L_4}$$

The concept of inductance and the analysis of circuits containing inductors will be readdressed in worked examples.

5.6 ELECTROSTATICS AND CAPACITANCE

When developing the concept of inductance and introducing the circuit element called the inductor we considered the relationship between electrical current and magnetism; that is, electromagnetism. In a similar manner we now consider electrostatics, so that the concept of capacitance can be understood, and also so that the circuit element called the capacitor can be introduced.

Electrostatics was the earliest branch of electricity to be studied. In fact it was from these studies that the name electricity emerged. Electrostatics in it's crudest form is electrification by friction. All school children know that if a pen or pencil is rubbed on a coat sleeve or if a hair comb is vigorously passed through the hair, then the pen, pencil, or comb gains the power to attract lightweight bodies such as small pieces of paper or hair.

It is impossible to say how long this practice has been known, but we do know that 500 years ago the Queen of England's physician, William Gilbert, experimented with this effect, using rods of amber. The greek word for amber is elektron, and Gilbert used a derivative of this word when describing his experiments; he said the amber rod was 'electrified'. Gilbert was not the only one to show an interest in the phenomenon, and over the next 150 years these types of experiment were often repeated, and it was found that if two glass rods were rubbed separately with silk then brought together they would repel each other, and if rods made of a material called ebonite† were rubbed on fur these ebonite rods would similarly repel each other. However, if an 'electrified' glass rod was put together with an 'electrified' ebonite rod, then the two rods experienced a force of attraction mimicking the type of movement associated with magnets of dissimilar poles.

Benjamin Franklin (1706–1790), one of the founding fathers of the United States of America, experimented with such phenomena and suggested that some form of fluid was being passed from the silk to the glass rod, and that the glass then contained a 'positive' amount of electricity; but in the case of the ebonite rod he suggested that a 'negative' 'electric fluid' was being passed from the fur to the ebonite, thus giving the ebonite rod a 'negative' amount of 'electricity'. The fluid idea that Franklin was talking about is today recognized as 'electron flow'.

5.6.1 Electrostatic fields

If a glass and ebonite rods are held close to each other and restrained from actually moving toward each other, we can consider the area between the two rods and investigate what has been created.

The glass rod can be considered to be 'electrified' or 'charged' with an excessive attachment of positive ions, and the ebonite rod can be considered to be 'charged' with an excessive amount of negative ions. The overall result is that we have a positively charged body and a negatively charged body in close proximity to each other, as shown in Fig. 5.17. The electrostatic field shown in the figure can be deduced if we imagine the path taken by any electron injected into the immediate area around the two rods. For example an electron entering at point X would move toward the glass rod end under the attractive force of the positive charge. The path it would take would not be direct, since the lines of electrostatic force act upon each other in a way similar to that found in magnetic fields. Thus the electron would follow the curved trajectory shown in Fig. 5.18.

This experimental observation allows us to deduce that there is a field of electrostatic force between two charged bodies, and that the form of this force field is

---

† Black vulcanized rubber.

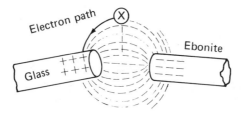

Fig. 5.17 — Electrostatic field between glass and ebonite rods.

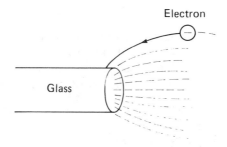

Fig. 5.18 — Electron path in electrostatic field.

in many ways similar to that of a magnetic or an electromagnetic field. There are a great many engineering systems that employ electrostatic fields, and the study of electrostatic fields is a large and interesting area. We are interested in obtaining only an appreciation of the electrostatic conditions necessary to help in our understanding of capacitance and capacitors. We will therefore not be delving too deeply into the more complex studies of electrostatic systems.

5.6.2 Capacitance
In Chapter 1 we looked at charge (in coulombs) and its relationship to current (in amperes). Let us now recall the expressions we used:

$$I = \frac{\delta Q}{\delta t} \quad \text{or} \quad i = \frac{dq}{dt}$$

Consider now two electrically charged spheres as shown in Fig. 5.19. We are going to determine how to define the system's ability to maintain an electrostatic charge, and which factors govern the size of the charge.

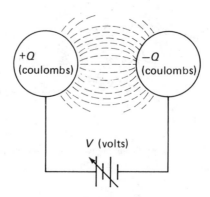

Fig. 5.19 — Two charged spheres in air.

The capacitance of a system is a direct measure of its capacity to contain electrostatic charge (Q). What we need to know is how the size of a charge (Q) is related to the voltage (V) needed to maintain the two spheres in their charged state. It has been experimentally shown that the size of charge (Q) is directly proportional to the size of the voltage (V). That is,

Charge (Q) $\propto$ applied voltage (V)

or $Q \propto V$

giving (Q) $\propto k . V$.

The constant of proportionality, k, which relates Q to V is called the systems capacitance (C), and it represents the proportional relationship between a system's stored charge and the applied voltage. The capacitance of a system is given units of farads (F), and the most common subdivision of this unit are microfarads (μF) down to picofarads (pF).† Thus

$Q = V . C$ for static or settled states

or $q = v . C$ for variable or transient states ,

where in the second equation the parameters relate to instantaneous conditions.

5.7 CAPACITORS

An electrostatic system can be, and usually is, specifically designed to produce capacitance. Such a system or creation is called a capacitor.‡ It is important to realize

† A capacitor with a capacitance of one farad would be an enormous structure.
‡ The long-obsolete term 'condenser' is still sometimes used. It should be avoided.

that capacitance exists in any system where an electrostatic field is generated, and an electrostatic field is generated where charge exists. Thus we will have to become used to seeing capacitance quoted or mentioned in systems where charge is present but there is no identifiable circuit element called a capacitor, as well as in the limited consideration of circuits containing purpose-built capacitors.

All electrical systems thus contain capacitance to various quantitative degrees, but we for the moment are interested only in the condition of purpose-built capacitors.

5.7.1   An example of a purpose-built capacitor

Fig 5.20 shows a very simple form of capacitor where two plates of metal are held

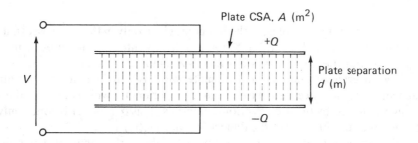

Fig. 5.20 — A parallel plate capacitor.

apart by an insulating material which is called a dielectric when used in the construction of a capacitor. A voltage (V) is applied to the conductors connected to the plates, and charge (Q) gathers on the plate material. The presence of the charge could be evidences by testing for an electrostatic field, but we will presume a successful charging of the plates.

Since $Q = V . C$ we can deduce what is happening to the system capacitance by imagining what will happen to Q for various physical changes when the voltage is maintained constant.

If we enlarge the area of the plates (A) it is a simple matter to deduce that more charge could be accepted, therefore we must have increased the capacitors capacitance. That is,

$$C \propto A .$$

If we increase the separation (d) between the plates, the charge will be more difficult to maintain, therefore we must have decreased the capacitor's capacitance. That is

$$C \propto 1/d \text{ (also experimentally proven) },$$

It has also been found that changing the material between the plates can dramatically alter the ability of the plates to sustain charge. We must therefore allow for a material factor when calculating the capacitor's capacitance.

If the plates were held in a vacuum with no material between them, a capacitive effect would still be present. This indicates that a constant 'material' factor for vacuum exists. This constant is a common standard, and is known universally as the permittivity of free space (ε_0). This is a measure of a vacuum's ability to sustain electrostatic fields. It is the base constant to which all other materials are referred. It has a value:

$$\varepsilon 3_0 = 8.85 * 10^{-12} \text{ farads/metre.}$$

The number quoted above is, at the moment, given only in the same way that we can say $\pi = 3.145 \ldots$, and we will not look too deeply into its many uses or its original discovery. For the present we will use it as a standard constant.

If we insert a selection of different materials between the plates we can affect the capacitor's capacitance, thus we need another parameter which indicates the scale of change achieved by the use of various materials. This parameter is commonly called the relativce permittivity of the dielectric material (ε_r).

We can now finally deduce a formula for the capacitance of a parallel plate capacitor as being:

$$C = \frac{\varepsilon_0 \varepsilon_r A}{d} \text{ farads .}$$

Note 1
ε_r for air $= 1.0$ and ε_r for polystyrene $= 2.5$.

Note 2
ε_0 is a genuine constant and has applications far beyond our current simple considerations. ε_r, however, is similar to μ_r for magnetic fields in that it is variable with respect to operating conditions such as applied voltage (V). Once again we will acknowledge the fact but do little with it, since for our simple considerations we can treat ε_r as being relatively constant.

5.7.2 Current and voltage relationship for capacitors
If we wish to look at the relationship between current and voltage for capacitors (Fig. 5.21) we can do so only for transient or changing conditions. There is no mystery to this; it is simply because current is a measure of change in charge with time, thus current (i) cannot exist unless charge (q) is changing. This simple fact should never be forgotten, since it is often of value in simplifying the analysis of electrical circuits containing capacitors, particularly when trying to deduce static conditions where the realization that certain currents cannot exist is of significant value.

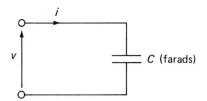

Fig. 5.21 — Current and voltage applied to a capacitor.

We already know the following fundamental equations:

$$q = v \cdot C$$

$$i = \frac{dq}{dt}$$

$$\text{thus } i = \frac{d(vC)}{dt}$$

$$\text{giving } i = C\frac{dv}{dt} \ .$$

This equation is very similar in form to Lenz's law for inductors, and we will be using it later to model the relationship between the voltage applied to a capacitor and the resultant current through that capacitor. This equation is a satisfactory mathematical model for most capacitors, but we must not forget that it really represents the ideal relationship and does not contain allowances for the resistance and inductance found in practical capacitors.

5.7.3 Capacitors in parallel
Fig. 5.22 shows four capacitors connected in parallel. From Kirchhoff's first law we

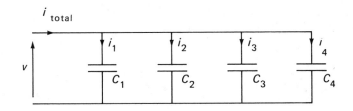

Fig. 5.22 — Capacitors in parallel.

can write:

$$i_{\text{total}} = i_1 + i_2 + i_3 + i_4 \ .$$

By using the capacitor mathematical model, the above expression can be written:

$$C_{\text{total}} \cdot \frac{dv}{dt} = C_1 \cdot \frac{dv}{dt} + C_2 \cdot \frac{dv}{dt} + C_3 \cdot \frac{dv}{dt} + C_4 \cdot \frac{dv}{dt} \ .$$

The voltage change across each capacitor is the same, thus we can conclude that:

$$C_{\text{total}} = C_1 + C_2 + C_3 + C_4 \ .$$

5.7.4 Capacitors in series

Fig. 5.23 shows four capacitors connected in series. From Kirchhoff's second law we

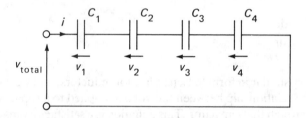

Fig. 5.23 — Capacitors in series.

can write:

$$v_{\text{total}} = v_1 + v_2 + v_3 + v_4 \ .$$

This equation can be differentiated to produce:

$$\frac{d \cdot v_{\text{total}}}{dt} = \frac{d \cdot v_1}{dt} + \frac{d \cdot v_2}{dt} + \frac{d \cdot v_3}{dt} + \frac{d \cdot v_4}{dt} \ .$$

A transposition of the capacitor equation gives us:

$$\frac{dv}{dt} = \frac{i}{C} \ ,$$

And if we substitute for this equation in each of the above cases for $\frac{dv}{dt}$ we get:

$$\frac{i}{C_{total}} = \frac{i}{C_1} + \frac{i}{C_2} + \frac{i}{C_3} + \frac{i}{C_4}$$

The current, i, is common, since we have a series circuit. Thus:

$$\frac{1}{C_{total}} = \frac{1}{C_1} + \frac{1}{C_2} + \frac{1}{C_3} + \frac{1}{C_4}$$

This is the end of the chapter. We have introduced in a cursory manner the concepts of magnetism, electromagnetism, and electrostatics. This has enabled us to study two more fundamental circuit components, the inductor and the capacitor. We have developed some simple mathematical models which allow us to analyze circuits containing these elements, and which we will use in our studies of the concept of transient response. You should now carefully examine the worked examples that follow, and attempt the tutorial problems given after the worked examples.

WORKED EXAMPLES
Example 5.1 Magnetic flux.
Q. The magnetic flux per pole in a dc machine is 6 mWb. If the dimensions of the pole face are 0.15 m by 0.2 m, calculate the average flux density at the pole face.

A. We shall use the flux density equation to carry out the required calculation. Remember that flux density B is measured in teslas or webers per square metre. Thus it is important to use the correct units. Recalling $B = \Phi/A$, the flux, $\Phi = 5$ mWb, that is, 0.005 Wb, and the cross-sectional area is

$$A = 0.15 \text{ m} \times 0.2 \text{ m} = 0.03 \text{ m}^2 \ ,$$

therefore

$$B = 0.006/0.003 \text{ T or Wb/m}^2; \text{ that is}$$

$$B = 2.0 \text{ T} \ .$$

Example 5.2 Magnetic flux
Q. An electromagnet uses circular pole faces of 50 mm radius. What is the magnetic flux produced per pole face if the average flux density is 2 T?

A. Once again the flux density equation will be used, but this time in transposed form, since Φ rather than B has to be calculated.

$$B = \Phi/A \ ; \quad \text{that is,}$$

$$\Phi = B \times A$$

$A = \pi \times r^2$ m^2; that is,

$A = \pi(0.05)^2$ m^2, giving

$A = 0.007855$ m^2.

Now $B = 2$ T , thus

$\Phi = 0.007855 \times 2$ Wb, giving

$\Phi = 0.01571$ Wb, or

$\Phi = 15.71$ mWb.

In these very simple examples it has been presumed that the magnetic flux is spread evenly throughout the chosen cross-sectional area. This is not the case in practical magnetic systems, thus we must accept that differences will appear between theoretical calculations and practical results. These differences can be kept to acceptable levels by either improving the theoretical model or the practical system design.

Example 5.3 Electromagnetic induction
Q. An aircraft flying over the magnetic North Pole at 500 mph will experience an induced emf in its wings. Estimate the size of this induced emf if we consider the overall wing span to be 50 m and the effective flux density of the earth's magnetic field to be 9×10^{-7} Tesla in the vertical plane at the pole.

A. The equation of interest is $e = Blv$.

$$v = 500 \text{ mph} = \frac{1.60934 \times 10^3 \times 500}{60 \times 60} \text{ m/s}$$

$$= 223.52 \text{ m/s} .$$

$$\therefore \text{ emf} = 9 \times 10^{-7} \times 50 \times 223.52$$

$$= 10 \text{ mV} .$$

Example 5.4
Q. Determine the self inductance of a coil if a current changing from 20 A to 0 A in 3 seconds induces a back emf of 300 mV.

A. The equation of interest is Lenz's law.

$$e = L\frac{di}{dt} .$$

$$\therefore L = \frac{e}{\frac{di}{dt}} = \frac{300 \times 10^{-3}}{\frac{20}{3}} = 45 \text{ mH}$$

Example 5.5

Q. The induced emf in an unconnected coil is measured and found to be 237 mV every time a current of 50 A is disconnected from another coil in close proximity. If the current takes 20 mS to drop to 1 A during the disconnection. Estimate the mutual inductance between the two coils.

$$e_2 = M \frac{di}{dt} .$$

$$\therefore M = \frac{e_2}{\frac{di}{dt}} = \frac{237 \times 10^{-3}}{\frac{49}{20 \times 10^{-3}}}$$

$$\therefore M = 9.673 \times 10^{-5} \text{ H}$$
$$= 0.9673 \ \mu\text{H}$$

Example 5.6

Q. A coil of construction similar to Fig. 5.11 is required to have an inductance of 5 mH. How many turns will be required if it has a length of 10 cm and a cross-section area of 5 cm^2 and is wound on an non-ferous former. $\left(\mu_o = \frac{4\pi}{10^7} \right)$

A. The equation of interest is

$$L = \frac{\mu_o \mu_r A N^2}{e}$$

$$\therefore N^2 = \frac{L \times l}{\mu_o A} \ (\mu_r = 1)$$

$$\therefore N^2 = \frac{5 \times 10^{-3} \times 10 \times 10^{-2}}{4\pi \times 10^{-7} \times 5 \times 10^{-4}}$$

$$\therefore N = 892 \text{ turns.}$$

Example 5.7

Q. Three capacitors are charged up in series from a 100 V dc supply. The supply is then disconnected to leave the capacitors fully charged. The capacitors are then separated and connected in parallel. What is the parallel voltage across them after this action. ($C_1 = 10 \ \mu\text{F}$, $C_2 = 15 \ \mu\text{F}$, $C_3 = 20 \ \mu\text{F}$).

A. In the series case we need to know the charge stored on each capacitor. Since charge is directly related to current we can deduce that for a series combination of capacitors they all receive the same charge.

$$\therefore Q_T = Q_1 = Q_2 = Q_3 = V_T C_T$$

and $\dfrac{1}{C_T} = \dfrac{1}{C_1} + \dfrac{1}{C_2} + \dfrac{1}{C_3} = \dfrac{10^6}{10} + \dfrac{10^6}{15} + \dfrac{10^6}{20}$

$$\therefore C_T = 4.615 \ \mu F$$
$$\therefore Q_T = 461 \ \mu C$$

When these capacitors are connected in parallel, Kirchhoff's laws suggest that the voltage must be the same on each capacitor. The charge will remain constant at 461 μC on each capacitor but it will be redistributed to satisfy the common voltage requirement.

$$V_{total} = V_1 = V_2 = V_3$$

and $V = \dfrac{Q}{C}$

$$\therefore V = \dfrac{Q_{total}}{C_{total}} = \dfrac{Q_1}{C_1} = \dfrac{Q_2}{C_2} = \dfrac{Q_3}{C_3}$$
$$Q_{total} = 3 \times 461 \ \mu C = 1384.6 \ \mu C$$
$$C_{total} = 45 \ \mu F \ \text{(parallel combination)}$$

$$\therefore \dfrac{Q_{total}}{C_{total}} = 30.77 \ \text{volts} = V_T .$$

We could go on to calculate the individual charges on each capacitor.

REVIEW QUESTIONS AND TUTORIAL EXAMPLES

(5.1) An inductive circuit is carrying a current of 4 amps. If its inductance is 0.15 H find the value of the self-induced emf when the current is reduced to zero in 0.01 seconds. (60 V).

(5.2) The coils of an electromagnet have an inductance of 0.2 H and are carrying a current of 8 A. What will be the value of the induced emf if the current is reversed in 0.02 secs? (160 V).

(5.3) Calculate the inductance of a circuit in which 30 V are induced when the current varies at a rate of 200 A/s. (0.15 H).

(5.4) At what rate is the current varying in a circuit having an inductance of 50 mH when the induced emf is 8.0 V? (160 A/s).

(5.5) Two coils are connected in series and the back emf to a 100 A/s change in current is 10 V. When the coils are connected in parallel the back emf is 2.4 V for the same applied change in current, 100 A/s. Determine the self inductance of the two coils. (40 mH, 60 mH).

(5.6) What is the value of the emf induced in a circuit having an inductance of 700

μH when the current varies at a rate of 5000 A/s? (3.5 V).

(5.7) Explain the meaning of the terms 'self-inductance' and 'mutual inductance' and define the SI units in which they are measured. Calculate the inductance of an 120 turn iron ring having a mean circumference of 750 mm and a cross-sectional area of 500 mm^2. μ_R for iron $= 2000$. (24.13 mH).

(5.8) The total flux emitted from the pole of a bar magnet is 2×10^{-4} Wb. If the magnet has a cross-sectional area of 1 cm^2, determine the flux density within the metal. If the flux spreads out so that a certain distance from a pole it has distributed itself over an area of 2 cm by 2 cm, find the flux density at that point. (2 T), (0.5 T).

(5.9) The flux density in an air gap between two N and S poles is 2.5 T. The poles have a circular cross-section with a diameter of 5.6 cm. Calculate the total flux that crosses the gap. $(6.16 \times 10^{-3}$ Wb).

(5.10) The cross-sectional area of a solenoid is 15 cm^2, and the flux density within it is 30×10^{-3} T. Calculate the total flux. $(4.5 \times 10^{-5}$ Wb).

(5.11) Determine the emf induced in a conductor of length 1 metre when it is passed through a magnetic field of density 2.5 T at a speed of 3 m/s. (7.5 V).

(5.12) The cable in the wing of an aircraft is 30 m long. What will be the emf induced in this cable as the aircraft passes through the Earth's magnetic field at the speed of sound? The speed of sound is 343 m/s and the Earth's magnetic field density is 1 μT at the aircraft's position. (10.3 mV).

(5.13) A 50 μF capacitor is connected across a 220 V supply. What charge in coulombs does it acquire. What charge would it acquire if the supply voltage was increased to 400 V? (11 000 μC, 20 000 μC).

(5.14) Three capacitors of 5, 10 and 15 μF are connected in series across a 100 V supply. Find the total charge stored on each capacitor and also the voltage across each capacitor. (273 μC, 54.5 V, 27.3 V, and 18.2 V).

(5.15) In (5.14) the series capacitors are disconnected whilst charged and connected together in parallel with plates of similar polarity connected together. Determine the total charge of the combination once the system has settled to a common voltage. Determine how the charge is distributed on each capacitor. Determine the voltage across the parallel combination. (818.2 μC, 136.4 μC, 272.7 μC, 409.1 μC, and 27.3 V).

(5.16) Three capacitors are connected in series across a 120 V supply, the voltages across them are measured as being 30, 40, and 50 V and the charge on each of them is 4500 μC. What is the value of each capacitor and the capacitance of the total series combination? (150 μF, 112.5 μF, 90 μF, and 37.5μF).

(5.17) Four capacitors are connected in parallel across a 250 V supply. The charges taken by them are 750, 1000, 1500, and 2000 μC. What is the capacitance value of the total parallel combination? (21 μF).

(5.18) Three capacitors A(10 μF), B(15 μF), and C(25 μF) are charged as follows; $V_A = 100$ V, $V_B = 150$ V, and $V_C = 200$ V. They are then connected in parallel with like, polarities together. Find the voltage across the combination. (165 V).

(5.19) The three capacitors in Example 5.18 are charged as per their initial condition and are now connected, again in parallel, across a fourth capacitor of unknown value. The resulting voltage of this parallel combination is found to be 100 V. What is the value of this fourth capacitor? (32.5 μF).

(5.20) Two capacitors A and B are connected in series across a 200 V dc supply, and the voltage across A is measured as being 120 V. If B has a 3 μF capacitor connected in parallel with it, then the voltage across A is increased to 140 V. Determine the values of C_A and C_B. (3.6 μF and 5.4 μF).

(5.21) A capacitor consists of two metal plates, each having an area of 900 cm^2 spaced 3 mm apart. The whole of the space between the plates is filled with a dielectric having a relative permitivity of 6. A voltage of 500 V is maintained across the two plates. Calculate the capacitance of the system and determine the charge stored in the system. (1593 pF, 0.796 μC).

(5.22) Calculate the capacitance in μFarads of a capacitor having 11 parallel plates separated by mica sheets of 0.2 mm thickness. The area of each plate is 1000 mm^2 and the relative permitivity of mica is 5. (2212 pF).

(5.23) A parallel plate capacitor has a capacitance of 300 pF. It has 9 plates each 40 mm $\times$ 30 mm and each separated by mica which has a dielectric constant (μ_R) of 5. Calculate the thickness of the mica separators (1.416 mm).

6

Transient response

6.1 INTRODUCTION TO TRANSIENT RESPONSE ANALYSIS

6.1.1 Summary of required reactive circuit theory

In Chapter 5 the concepts of inductance and capacitance were introduced and their relationship with circuit currents and voltages were established for the circuit elements called inductors and capacitors with which these effects are associated. Earlier, we studied the effects of resistance and the circuit element called the resistor, and its current-voltage relationship. Let us quickly summarize the major results of our studies so far.

Property	Circuit CCT element	Symbol	Unit	I/V relationship
Resistance	Resistor	R	Ω (ohm)	$v = i . R$
Inductance	Inductor	L	H(henry's)	$v = L . (di/dt)$
Capacitance	Capacitor	C	F(farads)	$i = C . (dv/dt)$

This is the ideal place to introduce a theorem that is often quoted in these studies. We refer to the totally ubiquitous 'Murphy's' theorem and states that '. . . if a law or equation is known or deduced for an inductor, then an equivalent law or equation is probably in existence for the capacitor. This projected capacitor law or equation will also be a direct inversion of the source inductor law where we operate the following replacement procedure.'

I becomes V

V becomes I

L is replaced with C

This theorem has proved to be an invaluable, if unsupportable, aid in the our understanding of inductive and capacitive circuits. A look at the I/V relationships given in the above table illustrates the use of the theorem quite will, for we can see that the application of it to Lenz's law readily produces the capacitor law. Note also how the series & parallel combination laws for inductors are the inverse of those used for capacitors. 'Murphy's' theorem will be referred to throughout the following sections, and this should help to build up a simple appreciation of how inductors and capacitors behave in electrical circuits.

6.1.2　The concept of transient response

In this section we are going to introduce the study of reactive circuits (i.e. circuits containing R, L and/or C.), and their transient response. We must explain, therefore, what is to be meant by transient response within the limits of our course. Consider Fig. 6.1 where the movement of a robot arm is shown.

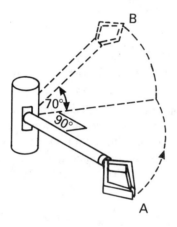

Fig. 6.1 — Robot arm movement as a transient response.

The robot arm has moved from position A to position B in response to a control signal to the electric motors in its 'muscle source'. This movement involved two responses of a transient nature. Our control signal demanded an immediate circular movement of 90° and an arm inclination of approximately 70°. Both these actions will be complete only after a measurable passage of time. If we look at a graph of angular movement and arm inclination in response to the control signal demand, the nature of transients may become easier to appreciate (see Fig. 6.2).

The nature of transients should now be much clearer, since we can see the obvious delay between the call for action and the completion of that action. It is also apparent that there is a clear discontinuity between the situation before the demand and the situation during the response to the demand. We could then broadly define a transient response or a transient waveform as a discontinuous result of a transient demand for a change in system conditions. In general, this definition covers almost all waveforms which are irregular and non-periodic. There are periodic waveforms like square waves and triangular waves that are commonly considered to be

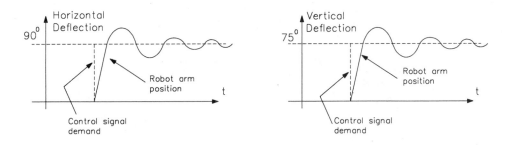

Fig. 6.2 — Robot arm movement in response to demand.

transients. In general we shall consider all waveforms to be transients if they are neither fixed dc nor pure sinusoidal ac. In our studies we will be principally concerned with the transient conditions inherent in the switching off and on of both dc and ac electrical circuits.

6.2   TRANSIENT RESPONSE IN AN ELECTRIC CIRCUIT

6.2.1   Introduction to practical circuit elements

Let us now consider electrical circuits where the applied voltage or input signal can be varied. Using our acquired knowledge of the basic properties of the circuit elements studied so far we will try to determine how a circuit will respond to different input signals. We will identify the response by calculating the currents and voltages associated with the circuit and how they change with time.

We have already said that in all electrical circuits, regardless of their composition, we must be prepared to consider the mutual existence of resistance, inductance, and capacitance. However, we will start our investigations by looking at the idealized resistor and inductor in a simple series circuit. Nevertheless, we must not forget, that these ideal elements exist only in our, and most engineers' imagination. Practical experimental results inevitably confirm that we can deduce only about 90% of the real situation by using the idealized approach, since all practical circuit elements contain inherent resistive, inductive, and capacitive components.

6.3   INDUCTANCE AND RESISTANCE IN SERIES

Consider Fig. 6.3. We shall analyze this simple circuit with respect to its transient response to two different input signals. The input supply voltage will be considered, first of all, to be simple step function, as shown in Fig. 6.4. We will then deal with the case when the input supply voltage is a square wave function as shown in Fig. 6.5.

6.3.1   Introduction to circuit and input signal conditions

Although only these two transient inputs will be considered here, they will allow the introduction of the type of mathematical and circuit analysis used in the deduction of most transient responses. The mathematical analysis which we will employ is called

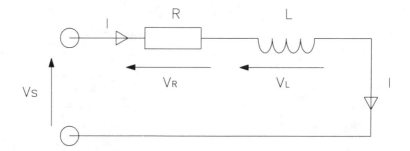

Fig. 6.3 — Inductor and resistor in series.

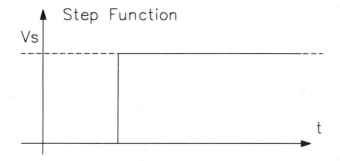

Fig. 6.4 — Step function.

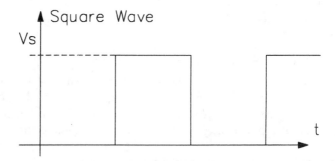

Fig. 6.5 — Square wave.

differential equation solution. To deal with the two input transients already introduced we shall use a mathematical technique known as 'the separation of variables'.
However, if more complex input waveforms were to be studied, it would be better to
employ a more sophisticated mathematical tool such as Laplace transforms. In this
course we will not need to use these transforms, but you should be aware of their
existence and of their use in transient analyses.

For the circuit shown in Fig. 6.3 we can use Kirchhoff's voltage summation law to
produce the following equation:

$$v_s = v_R + v_L \ .$$

Now let us consider the case where the input signal, a supplied voltage, is a step
function as shown in Fig. 6.4. We shall assume, for convenience, that the step from
an initial value of zero volts up to a dc level of V_s volts takes place at time $t_1 = 0.0$ secs
and in an instantaneous moment. From our earlier studies we know that the inductor
will react to the sudden attempt to force current through its coils by producing a back
emf. Our analysis will show how the circuit variables i, V_L, and V_R respond to this
sudden change in input signal.

6.3.2 Solution of the circuit to find the current response
Using Ohm's law and Lenz's law we can rewrite the voltage summation equation
thus:

$$v_s = i \cdot R + L \cdot \frac{di}{dt} \ .$$

The procedure we will adopt is as follows. We will analyze this mathematical
equation in such a way as to solve it for a single circuit variable i. We will then use this
solution to deduce what is happening to the other variables in the circuit. A
rearrangement of the above equation will give us the following

$$i = \frac{v_s}{R} - \frac{L}{R} \cdot \frac{di}{dt}$$

When the current flowing through our series circuit has finally settled down, that is,
when $d_i/dt = 0$, the back emf from the coil will be zero and the supply voltage will be
appearing totally across the resistor. This means that the settled or final current level
in the circuit, since $v_s = V_s$, will be given by:

$$I_{Final} = V_s/R \ .$$

We shall make use of this result in the remaining analysis.

Consider the voltage summation equation again. At time $t = 0$, $v_s = V_s$:

$$i = \frac{v_s}{R} - \frac{L}{R} \cdot \frac{di}{dt}, \text{ or, using } I_{\text{Final}},$$

$$i = I_{\text{Final}} - \frac{L \cdot di}{R \cdot dt} \ .$$

This equation now contains only i and t as a variables. This type of differential equation can be solved by the separation of variables technique as follows, where $I = I_{\text{Final}}$:

$$(I - i) = \frac{L \cdot di}{R \cdot dt} \ .$$

Further transposition produces:

$$\frac{R \cdot dt}{L} = \frac{di}{(I - i)} \ .$$

The solution of this differential equation is relatively simple. We integrate both sides with respect to their relative differential element. This means the left-hand-side is integrated with respect to 'dt' and the right-hand side is integrated with respect to 'di'. This is allowable since we previously separated our relevant variable 'i' and collected it next to 'di'. This form of solution, called the separation of variables technique, cannot be applied to all differential equations, but it is more than satisfactory for our present purposes.

Thus:

$$\frac{R \cdot dt}{L} = \frac{di}{(I - i)} \ , \tag{1}$$

which yields the following result:

$$\frac{R \cdot t}{L} = -\ln(I - i) + A \ ,$$

where A is the constant of integration.
We now need to deduce an expression for A. We do this by looking at known

conditions, often referred to as boundary conditions. We know that at time $t = 0$ the current $i = 0$, thus we can substitute for these values in our result so far:

$$\frac{R(0)}{L} = -\ln(I - 0) + A \ .$$

Transposition yields:

$A = \ln(I)$, therefore

$$\frac{R.t}{L} = -\ln(I - i) + \ln(I),$$

and recalling basic logarithmic maths we can transpose to get:

$$\frac{R.t}{L} = \ln\frac{(I)}{(I - i)}, \text{ which yields}$$

$$e^{t.R/L} = \frac{I}{(I - i)} \ ,$$

and finally

$$i = I(1 - e^{-t(R/L)})$$

This equation is a version of the well known Helmholtz's equation. We can use Helmholtz's equation to produce a graphical representation, Fig. 6.6, of the current

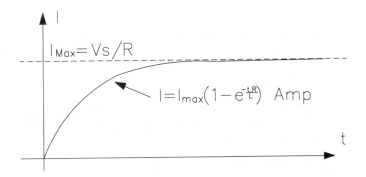

Fig. 6.6 — Current response to a step demand in V_S (R and L in series).

response in a series resistance and inductance circuit when the input voltage is stepped from zero to a fixed dc level of V_s volts. It is important to note that if the initial applied circuit voltage had not been zero there would have been an extra term in our derived equation. (We will deal with situation in a worked tutorial example.)

The next part of the analysis is the deduction of the response of the other variables in the circuit; that is, v_L and v_R to the step change in input voltage.

6.3.3 Solution of the circuit to find the resistor voltage response
Using the Helmholtz equation and Ohm's law we can determine the equation for the voltage across the resistor quite easily:

$$v_R = I \cdot R(1 - e^{-t(R/L)})$$

But $I \cdot R$ is equal to V_s, so that

$$v_R = V_s \cdot (1 - e^{-t(R/L)})$$

The graphical representation of the voltage variation across the resistor is shown in Fig. 6.7.

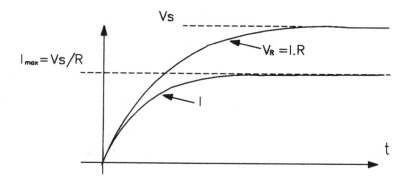

Fig. 6.7 — Resistor voltage response to a step in input voltage.

6.3.4 Solution of the circuit to find inductor voltage response
Once again we can transform the voltage summation equation to obtain an expression for the voltage variation across the inductor:

$$v_L = v_s - v_R, \text{ and therefore, since } v_s = V_s,$$
$$v_L = V_s - V_s \cdot (1 - e^{-t(R/L)}), \text{ and finally}$$

$$v_L = V_s \cdot e^{-t(R/L)}$$

This equation is shown graphically in Fig. 6.8 where we can also see that a simple graphical subtraction could have been used to deduce v_L.

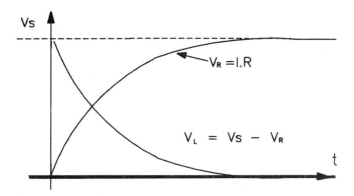

Fig. 6.8 — Inductor voltage response to a step in input voltage.

6.3.5 Deduction of the circuit time constant

We have so far deduced that the circuit responses to the step change in input signal from $v_s = 0$ to $v_s = V_s$ will all be exponential, i.e. they are dependent on the mathematical constant 'e'. From the graphs that have been produced the implication is that in theory the settled condition of $V_R = V_s$ is never really reached. In mathematical terms we would say that the curve as described by the equations is asymptotic to the straight line that describes the final value of the variable. This means that only at infinity is the final value reached.

In engineering systems, for all practical purposes a measurable final state is reached after a measurable time, since effective change eventually decreases to an insignificant level. As engineers we wish to know exactly when our acceptable final value is reached. We cannot make use of the mathematics developed in our analysis because of this problem with asymptotes, but we still require some method of distinguishing the response time in seconds, and a satisfactory parameter exists in a measure called the circuit time constant.

We will now develop a definition for this circuit time constant. Consider Fig. 6.9 which is a development of Fig. 6.6. If the current had continued to increase at the initial rate suggested by the tangent shown as X–X the final current value I, would have been reached in a significantly shorter time τ (tau) than it actually needed. We shall make use of this fact in our definition. The slope, m, of this tangent can be easily calculated:

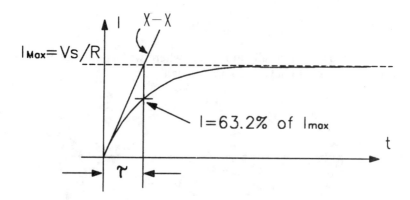

Fig. 6.9 — Current response to a step demand in V_S (R and L in series).

$$m = \frac{I-0}{\tau - 0} \text{ or } m = \frac{I}{\tau} \ ,$$

The slope of the tangent is also equal to the initial rate of current change at the beginning of the transient. Let us return to the equation from which we originally calculated the transient current form. With an instantaneous step change we noted that at time $t = 0$, the applied voltage was stepped up to V_s, thus:

$$V_s = i \cdot R + L \cdot \frac{di}{dt}$$

But at $t = 0$ we know that $i = 0$, so the above equation reduces to:

$$V_s = L \cdot \frac{di}{dt} \text{ or, } \frac{di}{dt} = \frac{V_s}{L} \ .$$

But V_s is the constant value of the supply voltage after $t = 0$, and has already been shown to be equal to $I \cdot R$, therefore: ($I = I_{max}$)

$$\frac{di}{dt} = I \cdot \frac{R}{L} \ ,$$

but, as we have seen,

$$\frac{di}{dt} = \frac{I}{\tau}$$

thus, we finally deduce that:

$$\tau = L/R \text{ secs.}$$

This means that we have a measure of the circuits delaying properties in terms of the circuits primary constants L and R. The Helmholtz equation can now be written in its more commonly quoted form:

$$i = I(1 - e^{-t/\tau}) \text{ amps.}$$

The previous development of an expression for τ might have appeared somewhat unnecessary since the equation appears to be little changed.

We will see in later analysis, however, that whatever the circuits being investigated, they will have time constants associated with the particular circuit elements. These constants can be directly inserted into the Helmholtz equation, and will have the correct units of time.

We shall now consider other standard parameters commonly associated with the circuit time constant. From Fig. 6.9 we can see that τ was originally introduced as the time taken to reach I if the initial rate of current growth had been maintained. It is of interest to know the actual value of current reached in time τ. If we use Helmholtz's equation and replace t with τ we can calculate the current level at time τ seconds into the transient:

$$i = I(1 - e^{-\tau/\tau}); \text{ that is,}$$

$$i = I(1 - e^{-1}, \text{ or}$$

$$i = I(1 - 0.368..) = 0.632 . I, \text{ or}$$

$$i = 63.2\% \text{ of } I \text{ (where } I \text{ is the final settled circuit current.)}$$

This is an important result, and it is used extensively in engineering practise. For many circuits the time constant and the value of the current reached at the end of the period defined by the time constant will be quoted.

6.3.6 Transient response to a square wave input signal

We can now repeat our style of circuit analysis for the case of an input signal which is a square wave. This means that the input voltage chops back and forth between two voltage levels as shown in Fig. 6.10. This kind of waveform is commonly found in digital circuits, and it occurs in modified form in analogue circuits where equipment switching is of a repeated nature. The major item to note with this form of input is that we are introducing another time factor into our transient analysis: the period T of our waveform.

Our analysis so far has shown that the particular composition of a circuit has a

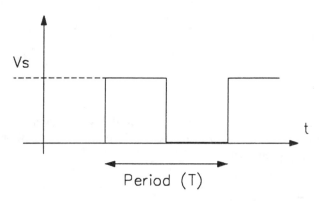

Fig. 6.10 — Square wave input voltage to our R and L series circuit.

particular inherent delaying effect upon the circuit and on its elements' ability to respond to sudden demands for change.

The employment of the switching waveform shown in Fig. 6.10 now superimposes this other time factor upon our circuit operation. The problem is simple to define if not necessarily simple to solve. Our input is demanding a change in circuit response every $T/2$ seconds, but our circuit can respond with only 63.2% of the demand in a time of τ seconds. We must therefore look at the relationship between the waveform period T and the circuit time constant τ. Experience has shown that if the period of the waveform is significantly larger than the circuit time constant, the analysis of the circuits transient response is relatively straightforward. Unfortunately, in real systems this it is not always the case. Therefore we will have to consider the waveform period effects.

We must also consider the response of the circuit current when the input signal is suddenly reduced from maximum to zero. We could repeat the mathematical analysis again, but using 'Murphys' law'. It is, perhaps, an obvious conclusion that the decay of the circuit current on removal of the supply will behave in an exponential manner similar to that already shown for the decaying coil emf when the supply signal is applied. Fig. 6.11 shows this reasoning diagramatically. A full mathematical analysis of this deduction will be given in a worked example (see worked example 6.3).

Fig. 6.11 shows how the current would decay on removal of supply current if sufficient settling time were allowed before the next input excursion toward a maximum. If we now look at the current response when the initial application of the square wave is too rapid, we can see that the current response never reaches a final condition but sweeps between the two extremes in an exponential manner. The waveform shown in Fig. 6.12 gives the current response immediately after the application of the input square wave. The mathematics to support the figures quoted on the diagram will be given in a worked example (see worked example 6.3).

For the moment it is important for us to note that the current is obviously approaching a settled set of extremeties, and this shows us that if we were to look at the current waveform on an oscilloscope or similar device we would see a saw-tooth-

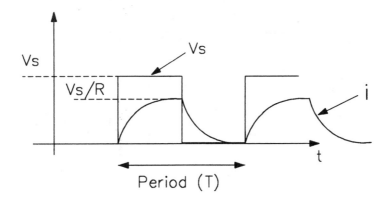

Fig. 6.11 — Deduction of current delay at removal of input. (Note that period T is $\geqslant$ time constant τ).

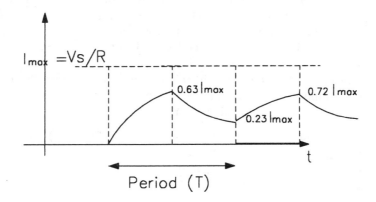

Fig. 6.12 — Current response for limited settling time. (Note that period $T = 2 \times$ (time constant τ)).

like pattern as the current attempts to respond to the input voltage's demand for it to switch from zero to a maximum and back again. We must never lose sight of the fact that the reason for this delayed response lies wholly with the inductive element which is objecting to the changes in current flowing through it.

We will now consider three more reactive circuits, using the mathematical and analytical techniques we have developed in our studies.

6.4 INDUCTANCE AND RESISTANCE IN PARALLEL

Consider the circuit shown in Fig. 6.13.

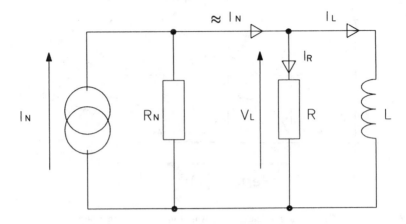

Fig. 6.13 — R and L in parallel fed by a Norton generator.

6.4.1 Introduction to input conditions

The parallel R and L circuit shown is fed from a constant current generator source where the Norton resistance (see section 3.8) R_N is very much larger than the circuit resistance R. Later we will consider the case where R_N is of the same order of magnitude as the circuit resistance, and we will find that a simple adjustment to the following analysis has to be made.

A Norton generator is used in this example to facilitate the use of simple mathematics and the type of equation development we have previously used in series circuit analysis. It is worth recalling that:

(a) If the circuit is predominantly series to the eyes of the supplies, then convert all sources to Thévénin.
(b) If the circuit is predominantly parallel to the eyes of the supplies, then convert all sources to Norton.

Our initial requirement that we presume $R_N \gg R$ also means we can presume that all of the Norton current (I_N) flows into the parallel circuit we are about to analyze.

6.4.2 Solution of circuit to find inductor current

Using Kirchhoff's first law we can write our circuit current summation law to develop our initial equation:

$$I_N = i_R + i_L \ .$$

We can also deduce that the voltage across the parallel combination of R and L, V_P, must satisfy the independent requirements of both R and L. That is,

$$V_P = i_R \cdot R \quad \text{(but also)} \quad V_P = L \cdot \frac{di_L}{dt} \ ,$$

thus

$$i_R \cdot R = L \cdot \frac{di_L}{dt} \quad,$$

and therefore we can write:

$$(R/L)dt = \frac{di_L}{i_R} \quad,$$

but

$$i_R = I_N - i_L \quad,$$

and if we substitute for I_R we obtain:

$$\frac{R}{L} dt = \frac{di_L}{(I_N - i_L)} \quad.$$

This form of differential equation was solved in the last section where the variable was circuit current, i. If we look at the first equation in 6.3.2 and its eventual solution, the Helmholtz equation, we can deduce that solution of the above differential equation is as follows:

$$i_L = I_N(1 - e^{-t/\tau}) \text{ amps} \quad.$$

where $\tau = L/R$ secs.

6.4.3   Inclusion of R_N in analysis

In our analysis so far it has been assumed that the resistance, R_N, of the signal source is very much greater than the circuit resistance, R. In some practical cases this will not be an acceptable assumption. Let us dwell for a moment on the implications of R_N being of a similar order of magnitude. If we look at the circuit given in Fig. 6.13 we can observe that R_N is in parallel with R, and as such we can declare a combination of them to be R_P, where R_P satisfies the following equation:

$$R_P = \frac{R_N \cdot R}{(R_N + R)} \quad,$$

Now if $R_N \gg R$, the denominator on the right-hand-side could be sensibly taken to R_N, and therefore

$$R_P = R_N \cdot \frac{R}{R_N}; \quad \text{that is,}$$

$$R_P = R \ .$$

We have built this result into our analysis. But in the situation where R_N is not much larger than R we will need the full expression for R_P as given above. This means that our analysis could have proceeded by using this conclusion, and everywhere we used R we could have used R_P. It is unnecessary for us to repeat the analysis since R appears quite independently in our result as part of the circuit time constant. To include R_N we need only re-calculate our time constant to account for the substitution of R by R_P:

$$\tau = L/R_P \quad \text{where} \quad R_P = R_N \cdot R/(R_N + R) \ .$$

Our overall result for the parallel R and L circuit is mathematicallyh unaffected since the inclusion of R_N simply occurs in the time constant. The Helmholtz equation is then a mathematical representation of what the inductor current does when a current source of I_N is suddenly applied to it. A graphical representation of the result is shown in Fig. 6.14.

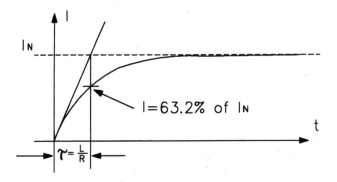

Fig. 6.14 — Inductor current response to a step input of I_N.

6.4.4 Solution of resistor current

The resistor current can be deduced by using the inductor current when it is remembered that they must both add up to give us a constant current I_N.

$$i_R = I_N - i_L \ .$$

Note: If $R_P = \dfrac{R_N R}{R_N + R}$ is being considered then the deduced current i_R is the total current flowing through both R_N & R. Simple current splitting deductions could be used to achieve the individual resistor currents.

This subtraction is illustrated in Fig. 6.15.

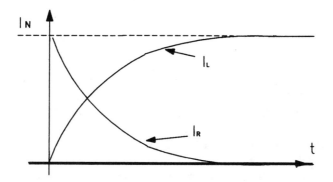

Fig. 6.15 — Resistor current response to a step input.

6.4.5 Solution of circuit to find parallel circuit voltage
The voltage V_P developed across the two parallel components can be obtained from Ohm's law:

$$V_L = V_R = i_R \cdot R \ .$$

(again be aware of $R_P = \dfrac{R_N \cdot R}{(R_N + R)}$ considerations)

This result is shown on Fig. 6.16.

6.4.6 Solution for Thévénin style input signal
In many electrical circuits the current generator supply does not have the simple input form of the Norton generator type. However, you will recall that the Norton and Thévénin generator models are interchangeable. So if we are given a practical circuit where the most suitable circuit model supply is a Thévénin type, we simply convert it to a Norton model and apply our already developed analysis.

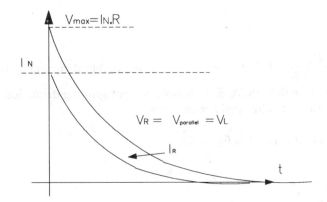

Fig. 6.16 — Parallel voltage response to a step input.

After applying the Norton generator type analysis it is relatively straightforward to convert back to the Thévénin model where appropriate. This technique will be covered as part of a worked example (see worked example 6.1).

6.4.7 Square wave response of R and L in parallel

The response of the circuit variables to a square wave input of I_N would be very similar to that already deduced for the series combination of R and L. The two extremes of response type are shown in Figs 6.17 and 6.18 for the inductor current and resistor current. The parallel voltage response can be obtained by multiplying the resistor current waveform by R. The negative excursion in I_R is due to the

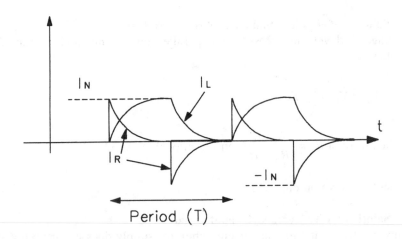

Fig. 6.17 — Response to square wave input when $T \gg \tau$.

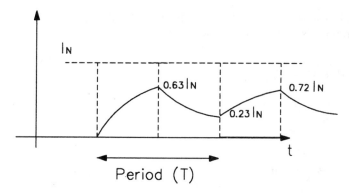

Fig. 6.18 — Response to square wave input when $T = 2\tau$.

inductor current flowing through R_N as it decays to zero. The current thus passes through R in the opposite direction to that supplied from the Norton generator.

6.5 TRANSIENT RESPONSE OF *C* AND *R* IN SERIES

We shall now look at C and R in *series*, thus our analysis will require a Thévénin model for the input signal.

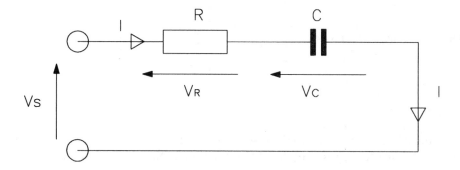

Fig. 6.19 — Series combination of R and C.

6.5.1 Considerations of source output impedance R_{Th}

In our analysis we will assume initially that R_{Th} is very much less than R, and thus V_S is sensibly equal to V_{Th}. This condition was not significantly emphasized in the series combination of R and L, and this was deliberate. The inclusion of R_{Th} in any analysis at the first stages invariably leads to complications, and we have seen in the parallel case that a simple technique exists for the inclusion of source impedance once a generalized result is obtained. We will use a similar ploy in the current analysis.

6.5.2   Solution of the circuit to find capacitor voltage

From Kirchhoff's voltage summation law,

$$V_S = V_R + V_C,$$

but

$$V_R = i.R \quad \text{and} \quad i = i_C = C.\frac{dV_C}{dt} .$$

We can therefore write:

$$V_S = i.R + V_C$$

and

$$V_S = CR.\frac{dV_C}{dt} + V_C$$

which on transposing gives:

$$\frac{dt}{CR} = \frac{dV_C}{V_S - V_C}$$

This equation is comparable to the result already obtained in section 6.3.2, thus we can once again use the result of that differential equation to predict the result of this differential equation. That is,

$$V_C = V_S(1 - e^{-t/CR}) \ V \ ,$$

or

$$V_S = V_S(1 - e^{-t/\tau}) \ V \ ,$$

where

$$\tau = CR \text{ secs (the circuit time constant)}$$

The simplistic method for arriving at this result is perfectly valid, and we have eliminated the need to introduce lengthy developments of mathematical equations. See Fig. 6.20 for the graphical result.

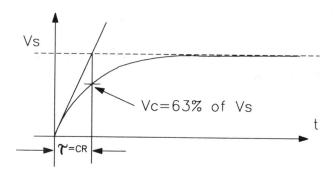

Fig. 6.20 — Capacitor voltage transient response.

6.5.3   Prediction of all other circuit variables response

We can now predict the transient response of the other circuit variables by employing once again nothing more complicated than subtraction and division. See Fig. 6.2.1.

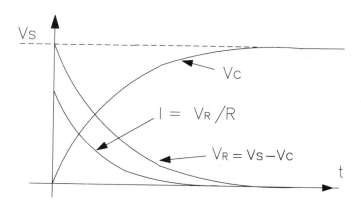

Fig. 6.21 — Resistor voltage and circuit current response to a step input.

6.5.4   Consideration of source impedance R_{Th} in results

If the source resistance R_{TH} is not very much less than the circuit resistance R, we can alter our transient response result to the following:

$$V_C = V_S(1 - e^{-t/\tau}) \text{ Volts}$$

where

$$\tau = C.(R_{Th} + R) \text{ seconds.}$$

If the reason for this result is not clear, you should consider the circuit shown in Fig. 6.22 and deduce an expression for the circuit resistance.

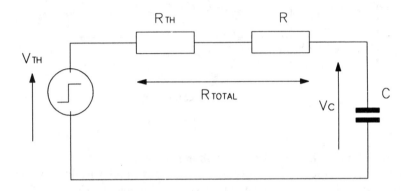

Fig. 6.22 — C and R in series with R_{Th} allowed for in analysis.

6.5.5 Square wave response of C and R in series

The square wave response for this type of circuit can be deduced by using our acquired knowledge about the step function response together with what we know about square wave response from our deductions in the previous two sections. The response of the circuit variables to a square wave input is shown in Figs 6.23 and 6.24 for the two extreme cases of the T and τ relationship. The capacitor voltage and the resistor voltage are shown and the circuit current could be deduced by using the methods outlined in the last section.

The negative excursions in V_R are due to the removal of V_S causing the decaying voltage V_C to be presented across R in a reversed form.

6.6 CAPACITOR AND RESISTOR IN PARALLEL

6.6.1 Introduction to the analysis

Once again we will use a current generator-based technique to begin our transient response analysis. We will also neglect R_N for the moment and assume that $R_N \gg R$, remembering that we can include R_N in a simple way when the analysis is complete. The initial equations are introduced below (see Figure 6.25).

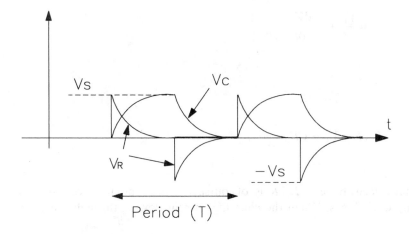

Fig. 6.23 — Square wave response of capacitor voltage ($T \gg \tau$).

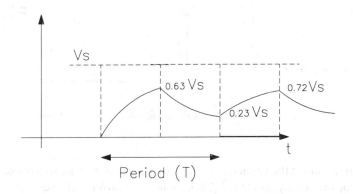

Fig. 6.24 — Square wave response of capacitor voltage ($T = 2\tau$).

$$I_N = i_R + i_C$$

but,

$$i_R = \frac{V_C}{R} \quad \text{and} \quad i_C = C \cdot \frac{\mathrm{d}V_C}{\mathrm{d}t} \; ,$$

thus,

$$I_N = \frac{V_C}{R} + C\,\frac{dV_C}{dt}$$

or

$$I_N \cdot R = V_C + CR \cdot \frac{dV_C}{dt} \ .$$

The term seen above as '$I_N \cdot R$' is, of course, a voltage, but it is a very special voltage, as Fig. 6.25 shows. When the charging current flowing through the capacitor has

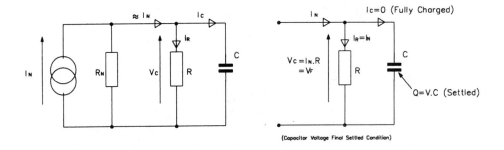

Fig. 6.25 — Settled condition when the capacitor is charged.

successfully raised the capacitor voltage to a maximum, we can assume that most, if not all, of the supply current, I_N, is now flowing through the resistor (R). Since the capacitor and the resistor are in parallel we can deduce that the voltage calculated as $I_N \cdot R$ is the fully charged voltage that the capacitor will reach. In other words,

$$V_{C(\text{final})} = I_N \cdot R = V_F,$$

therefore,

$$V_F = V_C + CR \cdot \frac{dV_C}{dt} \ ,$$

and transposition yields

$$V_F - V_C = CR \cdot \frac{dV_C}{dt} \ .$$

Thus,

$$\frac{dt}{RC} = \frac{dV_C}{(V_F - V_C)} \ .$$

This equation can be readily solved, using the results we have already obtained in our previous studies for the separation of variables method.

$$V_C = V_F(1 - e^{-t/\tau}) \text{ volts}$$

where $\tau = CR$ secs . . . the circuit time constant.
The response graphs can be deduced quite easily by using the methods and results already developed in the previous sections.

6.6.2   Transient response to a step input with C and R in parallel

Consider Figs 6.26 and 6.27 which show the transient response. The resistor current has been deduced by using Ohms law and the parallel voltage.

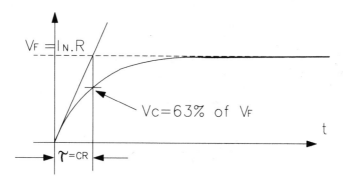

Fig. 6.26 — Voltage response to a step function.

The capacitor current (Fig. 6.28) is deduced by using simple subtraction since the resistor current and the capacitor current must at all times add up to the input current I_N.

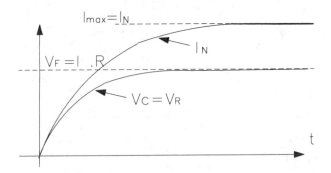

Fig. 6.27 — Resistor current response to a step function.

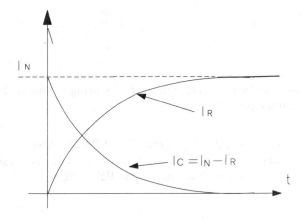

Fig. 6.28 — Capacitor current response to a step function.

6.6.3   Inclusion of R_N in the analysis

If R_N was not very much greater than R, as our initial analysis presumed, we can employ the technique originally introduced in section 6.4.3, that is:

$$\text{Let } \tau = C . R_P \quad \text{where } R_P = \frac{R_N . R}{(R_N + R)} \; .$$

The formula developed is still valid so long as we remember this amendment.

6.6.4   Changes if a Thévénin input is presumed

The simplest method for dealing with the next circuit (Fig. 6.29) is to convert the Thévénin source to a Norton source and use the analytical results already obtained. That is,

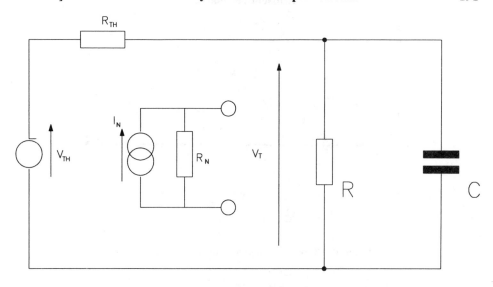

Fig. 6.29 — C and R in parallel with a Thévénin source.

$$I_N = V_{Th}/R_{Th} \quad \text{and} \quad R_N = R_{Th}$$

For those requiring a form of analysis that does not use this initial step, a worked example will be provided (see section 6.7.5).

6.6.5 Circuit response to a square wave input

The waveforms that would be found in the circuit if the input were a square wave is illustrated in Figs 6.30 and 6.31 for the two extreme conditions already covered in the previous sections. Fig. 6.30 shows the circuit responses if the circuit time constant is very much less than the period of the square wave input. Fig. 6.31 shows the circuit responses if the circuit time constant is equal to half the period of the square wave input. These results have been deduced from the results obtained in previous sections and the results found in the present section.

We have now developed sufficient analytical tools to enable us to attempt to solve a wide variety of problems associated with transient response and general circuit theory when the three main circuit elements are present.

6.7 CIRCUIT ANALYSIS OF MORE COMPLEX CIRCUITS, USING THE CIRCUIT TIME CONSTANT APPROACH

6.7.1 Introduction

It should be apparent from the preceding sections that our circuit constants of R, L, and C can be translated into circuit time constants of the form $\tau_L = L/R$ and $\tau_C = CR$. This gives us a constant that we can ally to our time variable 't', and the formulae developed can then be readily interpreted in terms of time or transient response. The

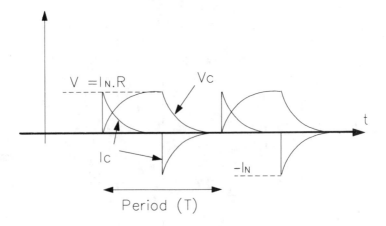

Fig. 6.30 — Circuit response to a square wave ($T \gg \tau$).

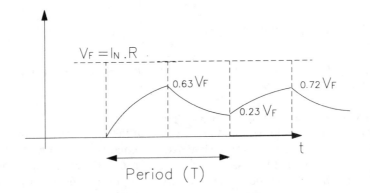

Fig. 6.31 — Circuit response to a square wave ($T = 2 . \tau$).

analysis of all linear circuits with respect to their transient response does lead to equations that are generally interpreted in the time domain, therefore this conversion of our circuit constants into circuit 'time' constants is of significant value. Thus it is not surprising to find that linear circuit transient response analysis develops equations riddled with time constants. For the less complex circuits there is a simple technique for determining the circuit time constants, and it has a remarkably simplifying effect upon the development of the transient response equations.

6.7.2 Deduction of time constant in an *RC* series network
Fig. 6.32(a) shows a circuit already analyzed in section 6.5. This circuit had a time constant result of:

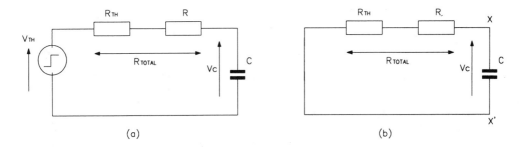

Fig. 6.32 — C and R in series with R_{Th} allowed for.

$$\tau_C = C \cdot (R + T_{\mathrm{Th}}) \text{ seconds.}$$

Fig. 6.32(b) shows the same circuit with the Thévénin voltage removed and the capacitor terminals labelled X–X'. If we now look at the effective resistance connected between terminals X–X', that is, across the capacitor, we can see that it is simply R and R_{Th} in series. That is,

$$R_{\mathrm{eff}} = R + R_{\mathrm{Th}}$$

and we can say $\tau_C = C \cdot R_{\mathrm{eff}} = C \cdot (R + R_{\mathrm{Th}})$ seconds.

In general, the time constant associated with a capacitor is deduced as follows. The capacitor value in farads is multiplied by the 'effective' resistance connected aross the component's terminals. This 'effective' resistance is deduced as suggested above. The important requirement is that the time constant is deduced with the supplies disconnected and replaced with their equivalent zero effects. That is,

Voltages at zero are 'short circuits'.

Currents at zero are 'open circuits'.

Source resistances R_{Th} and R_N (or R_s) are not to be removed, as they are involved in the operation of the circuit in normal use. The proving test of this idea is if it works for all combinations of C and R. We already have another result for a simple C and R combination, and this has been analyzed in section 6.6 where we looked at C and R in parallel.

6.7.3 Deduction of time constant in an *RC* parallel network
Fig. 6.33(a) shows a circuit already analyzed in section 6.6, with a time constant result of:

$$\tau_C = C \cdot R_P \text{ seconds,}$$

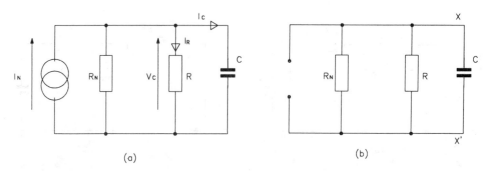

Fig. 6.33 — C and R in parallel with R_N allowed for.

where $R_P = R_N . R/(R_N + R) \; \Omega$.

Fig. 6.33(b) shows us the same circuit with the Norton generator removed and the capacitor terminals labelled X–X′. If we now look at the effective resistance connected between terminals X–X′, that is, across the capacitor, we can see that it is simply R and R_N in parallel, which is a confirmation of the result already known. This confirms the validity of the technique.

This means that when we look at capacitor networks with a single capacitor and any combination of resistors, we can deduce the circuit time constant and hence predict the transient response of the complete network without recourse to heavy mathematics. The following example illustrates the technique in full operation.

6.7.4 Worked example of the time constant technique
For the circuit shown in Fig. 6.34 we wish to know how the capacitor voltage

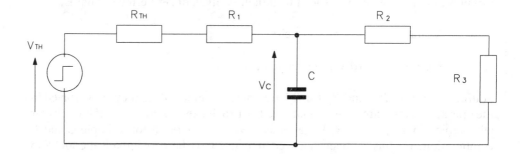

Fig. 6.34 — RC network for example analysis.

responds to a sudden application of a Thévénin voltage to its input. The full mathematical analysis is given later, but we will first of all use the suggested deduction technique.

Part (1) Before application of step demand in input
Before the application of the supply as suggested, the capacitor voltage must be zero since no current is in existence in the circuit.

$$V_C = 0 \text{ volts at } t = 0 \text{ seconds.}$$

Part (2) After the circuit response has settled down
Once the circuit has settled down to an unchanging state we can presume that the capacitor has achieved full charge and is thus drawing zero current, which means that we can redraw our circuit as in Fig. 6.35. Since the capacitor is drawing zero current

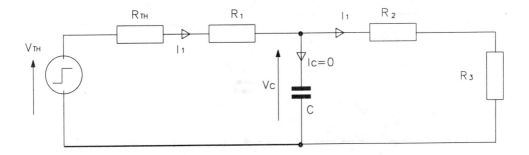

Fig. 6.35 — Example *RC* network at settled condition.

we can deduce the voltage across the capacitor by using the potential divider theorem, as shown below.

$$V_{C(settled)} = \frac{V_{Th} \cdot (R_2 + R_3)}{(R_{Th} + R_1 + R_2 + R_3)} = V_{Th} \frac{(R_B)}{(R_B + R_A)}.$$

where $R_A = (R_{Th} + R_1)$ and $R_B = (R_2 + R_3)$.

Part (3) What happens in between
The capacitor voltage starts at zero volts and ends up at a settled voltage level as determined above. It is not difficult to surmise that in between these extremes it behaves as all other capacitors do by rising to its final value in an 'exponential' manner. Now this change in capacitor voltage should be successfully represented by:

$$v_C = V_{step}(1 - e^{-t/\tau}) \text{ volts,}$$

where τ is the circuit time constant and V_{step} is the difference between the condition existing before application of the step function and the condition finally achieved as a settled state. That is,

$$V_{\text{step}} = V_{\text{C(settled)}} - \text{zero} = V_{\text{C(settled)}}$$

The circuit time constant is deduced by the method already introduced in this section, and the relevant circuit is shown in Fig. 6.36.

$$\tau = C.(R_A \| R_B)$$

where $R_A = R_{\text{Th}} + R_1$ and $R_B = R_2 + R_3$.

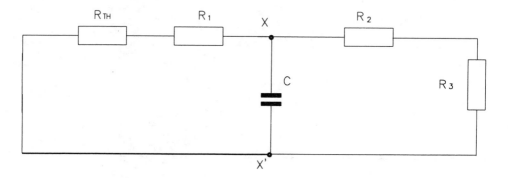

Fig. 6.36 — *RC* time constant deduction for the example.

It only remains to confirm this deduction by a full mathematical analysis. To do this we must return to the circuit given in Fig. 6.34.

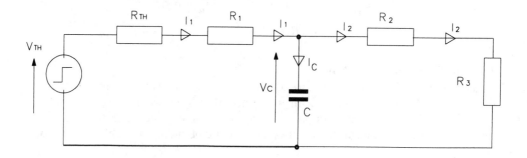

Fig. 6.34 — *RC* network for the example analysis.

$$i_C = i_1 - i_2$$

and

$$i_C = C \cdot \frac{d\upsilon_C}{dt} \quad i_1 = \frac{V_{Th} - \upsilon_C}{R_{Th} + R_1}, \quad i_2 = \frac{\upsilon_C}{R_2 + R_3},$$

thus

$$C \cdot \frac{d\upsilon_C}{dt} = \frac{V_{Th} - \upsilon_C}{(R_{Th} + R_{1)}} - \frac{\upsilon_C}{(R_2 + R_3)}$$

$$C \cdot \frac{d\upsilon_C}{dt} = \frac{V_{Th}}{(R_{Th} + R_1)} - \frac{\upsilon_C}{(R_{Th} + R_1)} - \frac{\upsilon_C}{(R_2 + R_3)},$$

$$C \cdot \frac{d\upsilon_C}{dt} = \frac{V_{Th}}{(R_A)} - \upsilon_C \left(\frac{1}{R_A} + \frac{1}{R_B} \right)$$

$$C \cdot \frac{d\upsilon_C}{dt} = \frac{V_{Th}}{(R_A)} - \upsilon_C \frac{(R_A + R_B)}{R_A \cdot R_B}$$

Multiplying through by R_A and R_B gives:

$$C \cdot R_A \cdot R_B \cdot \frac{d\upsilon_C}{dt} = R_B \cdot V_{Th} - \upsilon_C (R_A + R_B) \ .$$

Dividing through by $R_A + R_B$ gives:

$$\frac{CR_A \cdot R_B \cdot d\upsilon_C}{(R_A + R_B)dt} = \frac{R_B \cdot V_{Th}}{(R_A + R_B)} - \upsilon_C \ .$$

$$C \cdot (R_A \| \cdot R_B) \cdot \frac{d\upsilon_C}{dt} = \frac{(R_2 + R_3) \cdot V_{Th}}{(R_{Th} + R_1 + R_2 + R_3)} - \upsilon_C \ .$$

Now the simplified technique generated some of the terms that are beginning to appear here, and it is proposed that we use the earlier results to reduce the size of the equations given above.

The early work gave us:

$$V_{C(\text{settled})} = \frac{V_{\text{Th}} \cdot (R_2 + R_3)}{(R_{\text{Th}} + R_1 + R_1 + R_2 + R_3)}$$

and $\tau = C \cdot (R_A \| R_B)$
where $R_A = R_{\text{Th}} + R_1$ and $R_B = R_2 + R_3$

Thus our equation becomes:

$$\frac{\tau \cdot \mathrm{d}\upsilon_C}{\mathrm{d}t} = V_{C(\text{settled})} - \upsilon_C ,$$

which, on transposing, gives:

$$\frac{\mathrm{d}t}{\tau} = \frac{\mathrm{d}\upsilon_C}{(V_{C(\text{settled})} - \upsilon_C)} ,$$

which we know eventually yields:

$$\upsilon_C = V_{C(\text{settled})}(1 - e^{-t/\tau}) \text{ volts.}$$

If we compare this to the result obtained by using the simpler deduction technique we can see that the results are the same, and it is therefore recommended that the simpler technique be adopted where possible. It was also clear that the 'simple' technique generated results that allowed us to simplify our full mathematical analysis half way through. although this might seem a little bit of a cheat, it does highlight another aspect of the simple technique which is that it can guide us to some of the relevant gatherings of constants that will eventually appear in our final result. Thus we can use the simple technique to make us aware of potential parts of our result that will ease a full analysis if it proves necessary.

This use of the simple technique is also of value in the analysis of linear circuits where a quick deduction of a full result is not possible (for example, if we have more than one capacitor or inductor). However, the technique will allow us to generate an appreciation of, say, the time constants of our circuit and hence give us a guide as to what we should expect our full analysis to yield.

As a completion to this chapter we will look at another complicated circuit where we can use the simple technique to generate information about circuit time constants that in turn will allow us to simplify the full deduction.

6.7.5   A further worked example using time constant deductions
Consider the circuit shown in Fig. 6.35(a). Our deduction proceeds as follows.

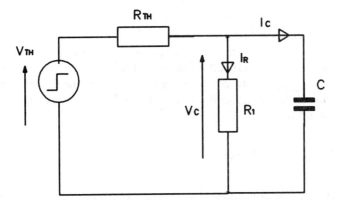

Fig. 6.35(a) — *CR* circuit for time constant deduction.

Part (1) Before application of step demand in input
Before the application of the supply the capacitor voltage must be zero since no current is in existence in the circuit.

$$V_C = 0 \text{ volts at } t = 0 \text{ seconds.}$$

Part (2) After the circuit response has settled down
Once the circuit has settled down to an unchanging state we can presume that the capacitor has achieved full charge and is thus drawing zero current, which means we can redraw our circuit as in Fig. 6.35(b).

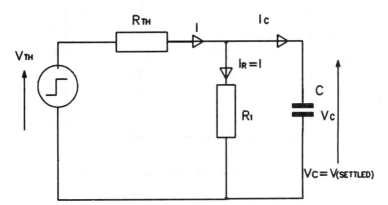

Fig. 6.35(b) — Example *RC* network at settled condition.

Since the capacitor is drawing zero current we can deduce the voltage across the capacitor to be:

$$V_{C(\text{settled})} = V_{R(1)} = \frac{V_{\text{Th}} \cdot R_1}{(R_{\text{Th}} + R_1)} \; .$$

Part (3) What happens in between

The capacitor voltage starts at zero volts and ends up at a settled voltage level as determined above. It is not difficult to surmise that in between these extremes it behaves as all other capacitors do by rising to its final value in an 'exponential' manner. Now this change in capacitor voltage should be successfully represented by the following equation:

$$v_C = V_{step}(1 - e^{-t/\tau}) \text{ volts,}$$

where τ is the circuit time constant and V_{step} is the difference between the condition existing before application of the step function and the condition finally achieved as a settled state. That is,

$$V_{step} = V_{C(settled)} - \text{zero} = V_{C(settled)}$$

The circuit time constant is deduced by the method already introduced in this section. The relevance circuit is shown in Fig. 6.36. Thus our final result will be:

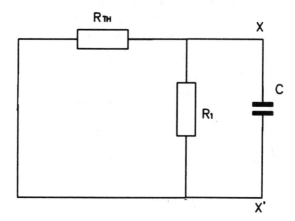

Fig. 6.36 — *RC* time constant deduction for the example.

$$v_C = V_{(settled)}(1 - e^{-t/\tau}) \text{ volts.}   (\tau = C \cdot R_{eff}) \ \& \ (R_{eff} = R_{th}/R_1)$$

If we hark back to the dc sections of the book we are hopefully aware of the two theorems substantially covered in these sections i.e. Thévénin & Norton. With these two theorems in the forefront of our minds we can review the practices outlined in the preceeding section 6.7 and hopefully see that we have been developing the Thévénin & Norton equivalent circuits that are effectively supplying our reactive elements (L & C). This allows us to suggest that this is always the case and it significantly simplifies the deduction of the transient response of the reactive elements. The only awareness we need to always carry is the following.

$$i_L = I_{STEP}(1 - e^{-t/\tau_L}) \text{ Amps}$$
$$\upsilon_C = V_{STEP}(1 - e^{-t/\tau_C}) \text{ Volts}$$

I_{STEP} is deduced from the overall effective Norton generator applied to our induction,

and $\quad \tau_L = \dfrac{L}{R_N}$.

V_{STEP} is deduced from the overall effective Thévénin generator applied to our capacitor,

and $\quad \tau_C = C R_{TH}$.

WORKED EXAMPLES

Example 6.1 *L–R* transient response

Q. Consider the *L–R* network shown as Fig. 6.37 and determine the terminal voltage V_T. 1ms after the circuit is energized.

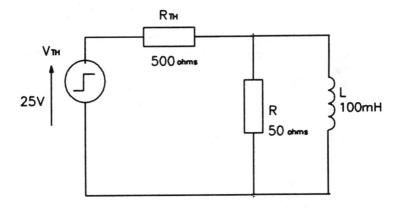

Fig. 6.37 — *L–R* network.

A. The circuit shown is predominantly parallel in form, therefore it would be convenient to convert the Thévénin generator shown to a Norton generator. To do this we must first calculate the Norton current and resistance,

$$I_N = V_{Th}/R_{Th} = 50 \text{ mA} \quad \text{and} \quad R_N = R_{Th} = 500 \,\Omega \ .$$

We can now redraw the circuit diagram (see Fig. 6.38):

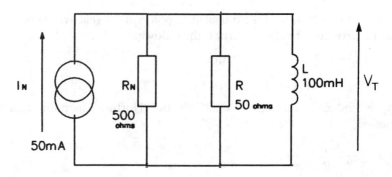

Fig. 6.38 — *L–R* network redrawn.

The Norton resistance will be in parallel with the resistor R. (You will often see this written $R_N//R$.) Thus the resistance R_P will be:

$$\frac{1}{R_P} = \frac{1}{R_N} + \frac{1}{R}$$
$$= \frac{1}{500} + \frac{1}{50}$$
$$\therefore R_P = 45.45\ \Omega$$

The determination of V_T could be approached in a variety of ways, but we shall tackle the problem initially by using the rules we developed in section 6.4. You will recall that in almost every case when problems were solved for circuits with inductors and resistors, one of the main parameters was the current flowing through the inductor. In this problem we need to calculate V_T. See Fig. 6.38.

$$V_T = i_{R_P} \cdot R_P$$

but $i_{R_P} = I_N - i_L$

where $i_L = I_N(1 - e^{-t/\tau})$ amps,

and $\tau = L/R_P$ secs.
           $= 2.2$ ms.

At $t = 1.0$ ms, $i_L = 50$ mA$(1 - e^{-0.4546}) = 18.26$ mA
Therefore $i_{R_P} = 31.74$ mA and $V_T = 1.443$ V.

We have solved the problem by using the approach discussed in our studies. Of course there are other methods by which the problem could have been attempted. Consider, for example, the following deduction. Let us first of all redraw the circuit (see Fig. 6.39).

V_T would eventually reach a static value when the coil reaction had ceased, and this would be zero volts since the coil is short-circuit to dc (ideally) see Fig. 6.39(b). At circuit turn-on the coil reaction would have been at a maximum, and, as shown on Fig. 6.39(a) the maximum voltage applied to the coil windings would have been:

$$V_{T(max)} = 25 \times 50/550 = 2.27 \text{ V}.$$

It is reasonable to presume that the coil voltage decreased thereafter in an exponential manner. That is,

$$V_L = V_{T(max)}(e^{-t/\tau}) \quad \tau = \text{same as before,}$$

thus $V_{L(t=1.0\,ms)} = 2.27(e^{-0.4546}) = 1.44 \text{ V}.$

Note: This method is hopefully seen as the conversion of the circuit external to the inductor into its Thérénin & Norton equivalent effects.

Example 6.2   *R–C* transient analysis
Q. Determine, for the network shown in Fig. 6.40, which contains capacitive and resistive circuit elements, the terminal voltage 1 ms after the circuit has been energized.
A. We will attempt this problem in the same manner as we did with the inductor–resistor circuit problem addressed in the last worked example. Since the circuit is predominantly a series circuit we must convert our Norton generator to a Thévénin equivalent.

$$V_{Th} = I_N \cdot R_N = 50 \text{ V and } R_N = R_{Th} = 5 \text{ k}\Omega$$

We can now redraw the circuit as in Fig. 6.41.
You will recall that for circuits of this type the voltage across the capacitor will almost always be used in the problem-solving process.
To find V_C at $t = 1.0$ ms,

$$V_C = V_{Th}(1 - e^{-t/\tau}) \text{ V}$$

where $\tau = C(R + R_{Th})$ s. $= 0.75$ ms.

$$V_C = 36.81 \text{ V,}$$

and $V_{R(Total)} = V_{Th} - V_C = 13.19 \text{ V,}$
and $V_R = 2/3(V_{R(Total)}) = 8.79 \text{ V.}$

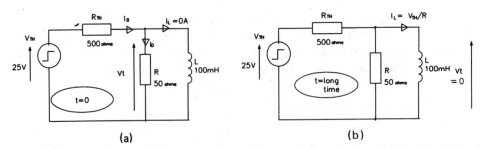

(a)   (b)

Fig. 6.39 — *L–R* network (remodelled).

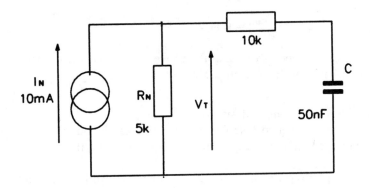

Fig. 6.40 — *R–C* network.

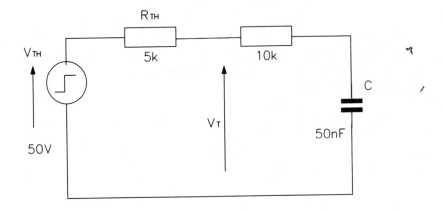

Fig. 6.41 — *R–C* network (remodelled).

Finally, $V_T = V_C + V_R = 45.6$ V.

Once again we shall try a different process, using deduction rather than the strict application of a set procedure.

If the capacitor can be assumed to be initially at zero volts, the initial current flow through the 10 kΩ resistor is given by:

$$i_{C(max)} = 50 \text{ V}/(5 + 10) \text{ k}\Omega = 3.33 \text{ mA}$$

This current will decay exponentially until the capacitor is fully charged and it will do so under the influence of the full circuit time constant:

$$i_C = i_{C(max)}(e^{-t/\tau}) \text{ A};$$

and after $t = 1.0$ ms;

$$i_C = i_{C(max)}(e^{-1/0.75}) = 0.8788 \text{ mA} \ .$$

Now the voltage across the capacitor at all times is given by:

$$v_C = V_{TH} - V_{R(TOTAL)}$$
$$\therefore v_C = 50 - 15 \text{ k}\Omega.(0.8788 \times 10^{-3}) \text{ mA}$$
$$= 36.81 \text{ volts.}$$
$$\therefore V_T = v_C + V_{R_{10k}} = 36.81 + 10 \text{ k} (0.8788 \times 10^{-3})$$
$$= 45.6 \text{ volts.}$$

Once again the problem is not necessarily solved more quickly by the second method, but it does show how we can logically approach the deductive solution of problems in circuits of this type.

Example 6.3   Square wave transient response R–C network.
Q. Consider the circuit shown in Fig. 6.42.

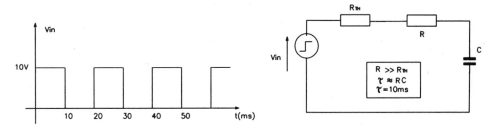

Fig. 6.42 — R–C network with a square wave input.

Draw a time response for the capacitor voltage V_C over 5 complete cycles of input signal, calculating its values at $t = 10$ ms, 20 ms, 30 ms and incremental intervals until a steady state condition emerges.

A. The selection of a circuit time constant of 10 ms is mathematically convenient, as the time steps under consideration have the same value: that is, $t = \tau$, and $t/\tau = 1$. Remember that the voltage across the capacitor will have two parts, an initial value existing at the time of the time step and an exponential part directly related to the decay or rise in the voltage over the time step under consideration.

(1) First cycle (exponential rise)

$$V_C = V_{Init} + V_{exp(rise)}$$

Initial conditions, $V_C = 0$ V, $V_{step} = 10$ V and $V_{C(10\,ms)} = V_{C(Initial)} + V_{step}(1 - e^{-1})$
Therefore $V_{C(10\,ms)} = 0 + 10(1 - e^{-1}) = 6.3$ V.

(2) Second cycle (exponential decay)
When the capacitor voltage reaches 6.3 V it is 'asked' to descend or decay back toward 0 V. The mathematics for the development of the equation to allow calculations during the decay cycles was covered for inductor current in section 6.10.4 where an expression for V_L during decay was found to be:

$$V_L = V_S(e^{-t \cdot R/L}) = V_S(e^{-t/\tau})$$

To develop an expression for capacitor voltage during its decay cycle we need only copy the above expression, taking into account the conditions present in our current analysis.

$$V_C = V_{step}(e^{-t/\tau}) \text{ where } \tau = CR \text{ s, and } V_{step} = V_{start} - V_{final}$$

Thus for our first occurrence of a decay in capacitor voltage we proceed as follows.
Initial conditions $V_C = 6.3$ V and

$$V_{step} = [V_{start} - V_{final}] = [6.3 - 0] = 6.3 \text{ V.}$$
$$V_{C(20\,ms)} = V_{step}(e^{-1}) = 2.318 \text{ V.}$$

(3) Third-cycle (exponential rise $V_C = V_{Init} + V_{exp(rise)}$)
Initial conditions $V_C = 2.318$ V and

$$V_{step} = V_{final} - V_{start} = 10 - 2.318 = 7.682 \text{ V}$$
$$V_{C(30\,ms)} = V_{C(initial)} + V_{step}(1 - e^{-1}) = 7.174 \text{ V.}$$

(4) Forth cycle (exponential decay $V_C = V_{exp(decay)}$)
Initial conditions $V_C = 7.174$ V and

$$V_{\text{step}} = [V_{\text{start}} - V_{\text{final}}] = [7.174 - 0] = 7.174 \text{ V}$$

$$V_{C(40\text{ ms})} = V_{\text{step}}(e^{-1}) = 2.64 \text{ V}$$

(5) Fifth cycle (exponential rise $V_C = V_{\text{init}} + V_{\text{exp(rise)}}$)
Initial conditions $V_C = 2.64$ V and

$$V_{\text{step}} = V_{\text{final}} - V_{\text{start}} = 10 - 2.64 = 7.36 \text{ V}.$$

$$V_{C(50\text{ ms})} = V_{C(\text{initial})} + V_{\text{step}}(1 - e^{-1}) = 7.29 \text{ V}.$$

(6) Sixth cycle (exponential decay $V_C = V_{\text{exp(decay)}}$)
Initial conditions $V_C = 7.29$ V and

$$V_{\text{step}} = [V_{\text{start}} - V_{\text{final}}] = [7.29 - 0] = 7.29 \text{ V}.$$

$$V_{C(60\text{ ms})} = V_{\text{step}}(e^{-1}) = 2.68 \text{ V}.$$

(7) Seventh cycle (exponential rise $V_C = V_{\text{init}} + V_{\text{exp(rise)}}$)
Initial conditions $V_C = 2.68$ V and

$$V_{\text{step}} = V_{\text{final}} - V_{\text{start}} = 10 - 2.68 = 7.32 \text{ V}.$$

$$V_{C(70\text{ ms})} = V_{C(\text{initial})} + V_{\text{step}}(1 - e^{-1}) = 7.30 \text{ V}.$$

It is now easy to see that a settled condition is emerging and the circuit response is settling down to an exponential sweep between approximately 2.68 V and 7.3 V. The waveform (Fig. 6.43) shows the above seven cycles in association with the demanding input waveform.

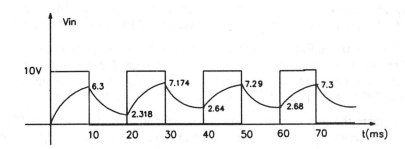

Fig. 6.43 — Square wave response timing diagram.

REVIEW QUESTIONS AND TUTORIAL EXAMPLES

(6.1) A Norton generator of 50 mA and 2 kΩ is driving a series circuit containing a 100 nF capacitor and a 5 kΩ resistor. Determine the voltage across the capacitor 1.4 ms after the generator is connected to the circuit. (86.46 V).

(6.2) A non-inductive resistor of $4\,\Omega$ is connected in series to a non-resistive inductor of 4 H via a switch across a 110 V dc supply. Calculate: (a) the circuit time constant, (b) the final value of the circuit current, and (c) the value of the current 1 s after the switch is closed. (1 s, 27.5 A, 17.4 A).

(6.3) A circuit comprises an 8 H inductance, a $50\,\Omega$ resistor, and a 100 V source of emf, all in series. Calculate:

(a) The circuit time constant.   (160 ms)
(b) The current after one time constant.   (1.264 A)

(6.4) A coil of resistance $10\,\Omega$ and inductance 0.2 H is switched suddenly on to a 100 V dc supply. Find:

(a) The circuit time constant.   (0.02 s).
(b) The rate of current increase at the time of closing the switch.   (500 A/s).
(c) The final steady value of current.   (10 A).

(6.5) An echo sounder with an inductance of 15 H and a resistance of $800\,\Omega$ operates with a 15 mA current. What time will elapse after a 20 V battery is switched across the sounder before the current reaches the operating value? (0.0172 s).

(6.6) The armature of a relay working on a 200 V circuit operates when the current reaches 0.24 A. It is required that the relay contacts shall close 0.004 seconds after the relay circuit is closed, this time corresponding to the time constant of the circuit. Find:

(a) The resistance and inductance of the relay circuit.
(b) The rate at which the current begins to increase the instant the switch is closed.

  $(526.6\,\Omega, 2.106\text{ H}, 94.97\text{ A/s})$.

(6.7) Determine an expression for the capacitor voltage response of the circuit given in Fig. 6.44 if the Input voltage V_{in} is a step voltage of 10 V. $(v_C = 5(1 - e^{-20t})\text{ V})$.

(6.8) Calculate the inductor current after 30 μs in the circuit given in Fig. 6.45. Do this after you have determined the general expression for the inductor current response of the circuit to a sudden application of a step function to the input of a voltage of 200 V. $(27.113\,\mu\text{s}, I_{L(max)} = 19.04\text{ m A}, I_{(30\,\mu\text{s})} = 12.74\text{ m A})$.

(6.9) Estimate the time constant of the series-wound dc motor shown in Fig. 6.46 and hence determine the supply current 0.5 ms after the application of the supply voltage and before the rotating machine begins to generate a back emf. $(\tau = 0.128\text{ ms}$ supply current $= 0.88\text{ A})$.

(6.10) Evaluate the circuit time constants for the two capacitors shown in Fig. 6.47. Use these values to estimate whether it would be reasonable to expect the output voltage to respond successfully to the application of a 1.0 kHz square wave input. To do this simply compare the circuit time constants with the applied signal change times; that is, 1.0 kHz is changing state every 0.5 ms. (Ok to 1 μF capacitor). (Not ok to 2 μF capacitor).

(6.11) A Thévénin generator of 50 V and 4 kΩ is connected across a 4 kΩ resistor. In parallel with the 4 kΩ resistor is a series combination of a 10 mH inductor and an 8 kΩ resistor. Determine the settled voltage condition across the 4 kΩ resistor and

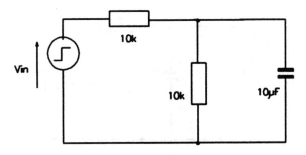

Fig. 6.44.

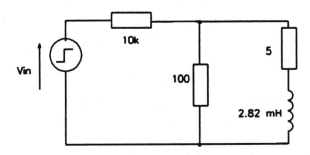

Fig. 6.45.

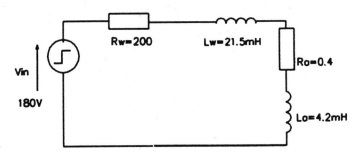

Fig. 6.46.

the value of the inductor current 2 μs after the application of the source. ($V_{4k} = 20.68$ Volts, $i_L = 2.162$ mA).

(6.12) A coil having an inductance of 1 H and a resistance of 30Ω is connected in series with a non-inductive resistor to a dc supply. The circuit has been designed so that 20 ms after turn-on the circuit current has reached 50% of its final value. Determine the resistance value of the non-inductive resistor necessary to achieve the design specification. (4.66 Ω).

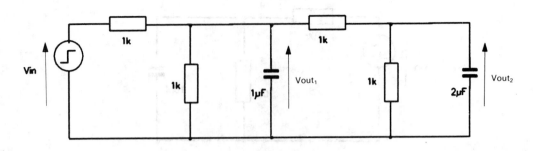

Fig. 6.47.

Part 3
AC circuit analysis

7

AC waveforms

7.1 INTRODUCTION

The currents and voltages in dc circuits are to all intents and purposes considered to be constant. In previous chapters we have looked at the effects of introducing inductive and capacitive elements into resistive circuits, and there is a very clear time response disturbance effect that we studied in the transient analysis section. The effects of inductance and capacitance were observed to be significant only during the time it took the systems to respond to the transient change in circuit conditions. The previous chapter also looked at the effect of supplying our systems with a repeated or periodic change in circuit conditions, although only square wave demands of a limited variation were considered.

An alternating current (ac) source is, in general, considered to be defined as: 'A source of current that reverses polarity with a distinct periodic nature'. This puts all periodic waveforms in the same basket, but the study of ac circuit analysis is now generally considered to be the study of sinusoidal ac sources and the resultant effects found in R, L and C circuit combinations.

7.2 TIME-VARYING WAVEFORMS

The four waveforms shown in Fig. 7.1 are examples of what are considered to be ac waveforms. At this stage it is of help to recognize some basic defining characteristics of ac waveforms. Each waveform can be seen to have a maximum value to which it moves in both directions. For example, the triangular waveform rises to 10 V and descends to -10 V. These maximums are commonly referred to as the peak values of the ac waveform.

Each waveform is obviously repetitive in nature, and the time taken for each cycle to repeat is called the period of the ac waveform. For example, the square wave has a period of 2 ms. These two basic characteristics of periodic waveforms are summarized for the four examples in the table given below:

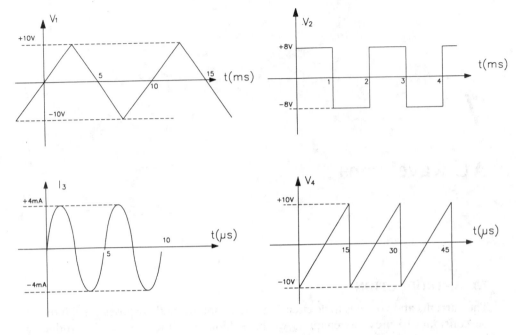

Fig. 7.1 — Typical ac waveforms.

AC waveform	Peak value	Period
Triangular	10 V	10 ms
Square wave	8 V	2 ms
Sinewave	4 mA	5 μs
Sawtooth	10 V	15 μs

Fig. 7.2 shows two waveforms that appear to exhibit all the characteristics of ac waveforms. However, they are not considered to be pure ac waveforms since, as the diagram shows, they can be broken down into a pure ac waveform plus a dc 'shifting' element. It is best to remember this qualification of what we will consider to be a pure ac waveform, since failure to distinguish the dc element is liable to cause confusion over the definitions of the terms used to describe the ac waveforms.

7.3   THE SINUSOIDAL WAVEFORM

Fig. 7.3 illustrates a typical sinewave voltage waveform. This is the most commonly found type of ac waveform throughout the electrical and electronic industrial world. The sinewave is a natural mathematical form and has its roots in all aspects of simple

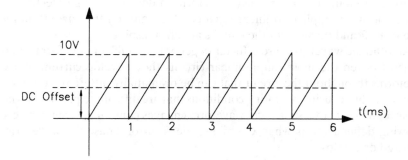

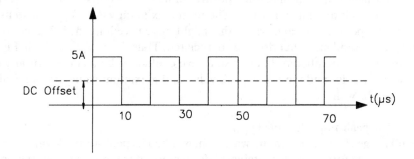

Fig. 7.2 — Non-ac waveforms.

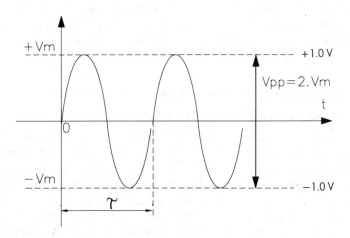

Fig. 7.3 — Sinewave with period T.

harmonic motion. It is a very easy waveform to develop in high electrical energy forms, and when applied to linear circuits (R, L, and C) the current and voltage waveforms found throughout the circuits are all sinusoidal.

All other ac waveforms are difficult to generate in high energy forms, and when applied to even the most simple linear circuits they develop current and voltage waveforms throughout the circuit that can be dramatially different from the source waveform, thus causing operating conditions that are difficult to predict and control.

Since the value of a sinusoidal waveform changes continually we must accept the following defined terms when describing the form of sinusoidal waveform being discussed or employed.

7.3.1 The peak value
The peak value, V_P, is the maximum positive or negative excursion in the waveform. In Fig. 7.3 this is a voltage of 1.0 V. The term maximum value (V_m) is also used to indicate the peak value, and whilst this might appear redundant it is a commonly found practice and must therefore be appreciated. Thus, $V_P = V_m = 1.0$ V in Fig. 7.3.

It must be remembered that our sinewave could also be a current or any other electrical variable, and the terms peak value and maximum value are applicable in these cases as well.

7.3.2 The peak-to-peak value (V_{pp})
The full range of excursion in the waveform is called its peak-to-peak value, and in a perfect ac waveform, which contains no dc element, it is the value from the positive peak to the negative peak, thus:

$$V_{PP} = 2 \times V_P = 2 \times V_m = 2.0 \text{ V in Fig. 7.3 .}$$

7.3.3 The effective or root mean square value (V_{rms})
The effective or 'rms' value of the ac sinusoidal waveform is related to the power-delivering capability of the ac waveform, this it will be better introduced after we have discussed the ac power waveforms. For the moment it is quoted as '$V_{rms} = V_P/\sqrt{2}$'.

7.4 THE GENERATION OF SINUSOIDAL AC WAVEFORMS
7.4.1 The development of the sinusoidal equation

Fig. 7.4 illustrates a simple ac sinusoidal generator and the resultant sinewave output. Practical ac sinusoidal generators are obviously not of such simple construction, but the diagram will help us grasp the necessary appreciations about the shape and form of the ac sinusoid. The 'Armature' is a single length of conductor material being rotated around the magnetic field in a continuous circular arc as described by moving from A to B to C, etc. The conductor may be considered to be of length l metres into the shown plane, and we can presume the magnetic field to have a density of B tesla. If the conductor is rotating at v metres/sec, we can write down a formula to represent the emf generated at the conductor ends.

$$\text{emf} = B.l.v. \qquad \text{V.}$$

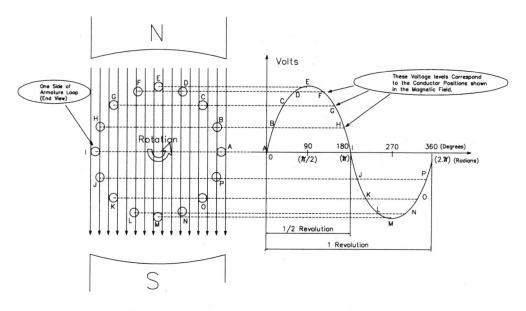

Fig. 7.4 — Cross sectional view of a sinusoidal ac generator.

Before we leap into the mathematics of the generator output let us first of all consider a few simple appreciations about what is happening.

At position 'A' the conductor is travelling upward parallel to the magnetic field. The conductor is not 'cutting' the lines of flux, hence no magnetic disturbance is taking place in the conductor atoms. This means that no emf is being induced. This is also true when the conductor is in position 'I'.

At position 'E' the conductor of travelling at right angles to the magnetic field, and the emf induced will be at a maximum and directly comparable to the emf induction discussed in section 5.2.2. (electrical effect generation from motion in magnetic fields). This yields a formula:

$$\text{emf}_{(\text{at E})} = B \cdot l \cdot v \ . \qquad \text{V.}$$

At position 'M' the effective velocity to magnetic field direction is reversed, hence we get a maximum induced emf in exactly the opposite direction. That is,

$$\text{emf}_{(\text{at M})} = -B \cdot l \cdot v \ . \qquad \text{V.}$$

This means that as the conductor rotates through the magnetic field there is a constantly changing emf generated throughout the circular or cyclic travel. It is also obvious that the emf is changing polarity between two common maximums, and this is a condition called alternating current (ac).

For us to make a serious attempt at describing the emf generated in time as the conductor rotates through a full cycle, we must look at the conductor position away from the obvious maxima and minima at, say, position 'C', as in Fig. 7.5.

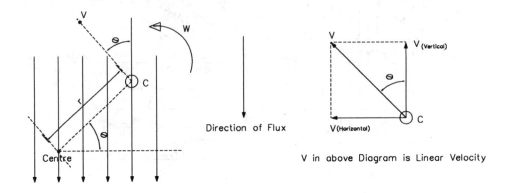

Fig. 7.5 — Exploded view of position 'C'.

It is normal to talk of rotating bodies as having 'angular velocity' ω (omega) with units of radians/sec when we develop the mathematics required. This minor problem can be forgotten when we accept that the 'linear velocity' υ metres/sec is related to the angular velocity ω rads/sec through the formula:

$$\upsilon = \omega . r \text{ metres/sec}$$

where r = radius of conductor path.

However, at position 'C' we can see that the velocity of the conductor can be resolved into a vertical component and a horizontal component. The vertical component is never going to contribute to the creation of 'emf', since it will never cut the magnetic field. It is the horizontal component that will solely contribute to the creation of 'emf', since it cuts across the magnetic field at right angles. The horizontal component of the conductor velocity can be stated as:

$$\upsilon_{(horiz)} = \upsilon . \sin (\theta) \qquad \text{(where } \theta \text{ is in radians)}$$

or

$$\upsilon_{(horiz)} = \omega . r . \sin (\omega . t) \qquad \text{(since } \omega . t = \theta \text{ radians)}$$

If we now put this into the equation for the induced emf given earlier, we can see clearly the sinusoidal nature of the generated emf.

$$\text{emf} = B \,.\, l \,.\, \omega \,.\, r \,.\, \sin(\omega \,.\, t) \qquad \text{V.}$$

The $B \,.\, l \,.\, \omega \,.\, r$ (or $B \,.\, l \,.\, \upsilon$) part of the equation can be treated as being effectively a constant for normal generator operation, and we know that it is equal to the maximum value of generated emf, so we can call it V_{max} or, as we have already decided we can call it, V_{peak} (V_{P}). Thus

$$\text{emf} = V_{\text{P}} \,.\, \sin(\omega \,.\, t) \qquad \text{V.}$$

It is wise to remember that the peak value of our generated emf is directly dependent upon the speed of rotation, and if the speed changes we must expect a change in peak voltage as well as the change in sinusoidal generation suggested in the $\omega \,.\, t$ part of the equation.

7.4.2   Sinusoidal waveforms to different X axes

In Fig. 7.4 the horizontal axis of the waveform is labelled in degrees and radians. This is a toally acceptable form of axis labelling if we are using the formula 'emf = $V_{\text{P}} \,.\, \sin(\theta)$, where θ is in radians or degrees. However, when an ac sinusoidal waveform is observed by practical means like an oscilloscope, we see a signal to an X axis of time (t). We must therefore get into the habit of talking about and analyzing our ac sinusoids to an X axis of time (t) in seconds, which means that we are using the formula emf = $V_{\text{P}} \,.\, \sin(\omega \,.\, t)$.

Fig. 7.6 now allows us to gather some practical defining observations about how we intend to describe and qualify the different qualities of an ac sinusoidal waveform. The three forms of the equation for a generated sinewave are:

$$\text{emf} = V_{\text{P}} \,.\, \sin(\theta) \qquad (\theta \text{ is in radians or degrees})$$

$$\text{emf} = V_{\text{P}} \,.\, \sin(\omega \,.\, t) \qquad (\omega \text{ is in rad/s})$$

$$\text{emf} = V_{\text{P}} \,.\, \sin(2 \,.\, \pi \,.\, f \,.\, t) \qquad (f \text{ is in cycles/s or hertz, and } \omega = 2 \,.\, \pi \,.\, f)$$

The main features of ac sinusoids are now highlighted in the following sections.

7.5   THE KEY POINTS ABOUT SINUSOIDAL WAVEFORMS

7.5.1   The period of a sinusoidal waveform

The period, T, of a sinusoidal waveform is the time, in seconds, required to generate one complete cycle of the waveform (see Fig. 7.6).

7.5.2   The cyclic frequency of a sinusoidal waveform

The cyclic frequency, f, of a sinusoidal waveform is the measure of how many cycles are completed in one second. It is, therefore, not surprisingly, related to the period T. Thus:

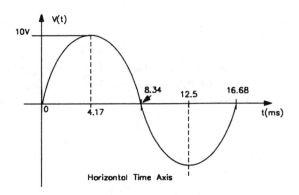

Horizontal Time Axis

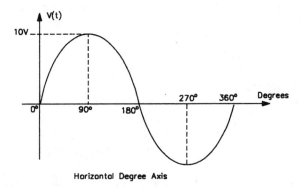

Horizontal Degree Axis

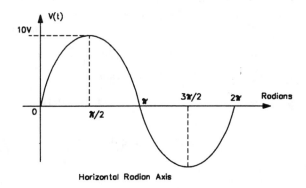

Horizontal Radian Axis

Fig. 7.6 — Generated emf to three different X axes.

$f = 1/T$ cycles/sec or hertz (Hz)

For example, a sinewave whose period is 10 ms has a frequency of 100 Hz, and a sinewave whose period is 21.123 μs has a frequency of 47.342 kHz.

7.5.3   The radian frequency of a sinusoidal waveform

Every time the generator conductor completes a cycle of generation it passes through 360° or 2π radians of angular displacement. The frequency with which it completes this movement has already been stated in cycles/sec (Hz). We can also talk about the conductor having a frequency of revolutions/ min or degrees/hour or any combination of displacement/time. Obviously, some commonly agreed units are in existence, and the normal complement to Hertz is radians/sec with the symbol ω (omega). Thus,

$$\omega = \text{radian frequency in rad/s}$$
$$f = \text{cyclic frequency in Hz .}$$

Note that one cycle is equivalent to 2π radians, which is equivalent to 360°, therefore

$$f = \text{cycles/sec}$$

and

$$\omega = 2 . \pi . f \text{ rad/sec;}$$

and, since

$$2\pi \text{ radians} = 360°$$
$$1 \text{ radian } = 360°/2 . \pi = 57.3° .$$

Worked examples 7.1 later in this chapter should bring each student up to a working familiarity with the necessary translations between the two main methods of describing the frequency of an ac sinusoidal waveform.

7.6   THE PHASE ANGLE OF A SINUSOIDAL WAVEFORM

In Fig. 7.7 we can see the effect of considering our generator as having been started up at the three positions 'A', 'M', and 'K'. All three waveforms have the same sinusoidal shape, and differ only in their effective start position. When waveforms are unsynchronized in the way suggested by these diagrams they are said to be out of phase. We must obviously be able to mathematically distinguish between waveforms that are not in phase, and this is done by the inclusion of a phase angle, term in the formula emf $= V_P . \sin(\theta)$.

In Fig. 7.7 the start-up position M, curve (b), was displaced by $-90°$ or $-\pi/2$ radians. We therefore write our formula in the following form to take this into account:

$$\text{emf} = V_P . \sin(\omega . t - \phi) \qquad \text{(where } \phi = \pi/2 \text{ rad)}$$

Thus the formula for Fig. 7.7 (curve (c)), where the start-up position, K, was dispaced by $-135°$ or $-3\pi/4$ rad, would be:

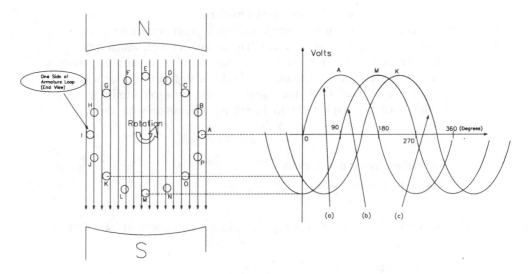

Fig. 7.7 — Sinewaves with differing phase angles.

$$\text{emf} = V_P \cdot \sin(\omega \cdot t - \phi) \qquad (\text{where } \phi = 3\pi/4 \text{ rad})$$

Not all ac waveforms that we will be encountering will be generated emfs, and we must now move to a general expression for any sinusoidal waveform.

The formulae given below are examples of the kinds of expression we will regularly encounter throughout the remaining parts of this chapter on ac circuit analysis.

$$v(t) = V_P \cdot \sin(\omega \cdot t \pm \phi)$$

$$i(t) = I_{max} \sin(\omega \cdot t \pm \phi) \ .$$

Note the suggested compatibility between the subscripts '$_P$' (for peak) and '$_{max}$' (for maximum value). They are often interchanged, but they mean the same thing.

Phase angle can, unfortunately, sometimes be quoted in either degrees or radians, and since the multiple $\omega.t$ always results in radians, it is advisable to develop an early predisposition to working with radians when dealing with angular displacement. Unfortunately, we cannot demand this of others, and we must be versatile in both methods.

The above equations indicate that sinusoids may differ from each other in:

(a) peak value (V_P or I_{max})

(b) frequency (ω or f)

(c) phase angle (ϕ or Θ or $\ldots\beta$) .

The frequency in most of the cases considered in this book is consistent throughout the circuit being analyzed, and can therefore be considered to be constant. Thus in most circuits the sinusoidal currents and voltages throughout the networks will differ only in terms of their peak value and phase angle.

Worked examples 7.2 to 7.5 will take the student through the necessary appreciation of variations in peak value and phase angle.

7.7 GRAPHICAL SUMMATION OF AC WAVEFORMS

In the chapters that dealt with dc circuit analysis we saw that there was often a need to add, subtract, multiply, and divide electrical quantities. The only representation we have at present for the ac sinusodial waveforms is the time domain expressions like:

$$v(t) = V_P . \sin(\omega . t \pm \phi_1) \quad \text{and} \quad i(t) = I_P . \sin(\omega . t \pm \phi_2) .$$

If we have two quantities of the form shown above, it is not easy to see how we can operate upon them mathematically in the ways already found in the dc circuit theorems. There is a need to devise some simple method of describing the ac quantities that allows us to treat them with the same simple techniques devised for the dc cases. For the moment let us consider Kirchhoff's second law concerning the summation of voltages and show how we can achieve a result by graphical methods.

In Fig. 7.8(a) we can see that the summation of two sinusoids that are in phase is a

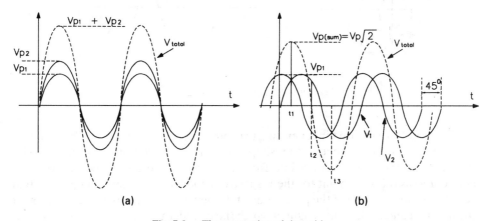

(a)   (b)

Fig. 7.8 — The summation of sinusoids.

relatively simple matter, and the final result is easily seen to be the summation of the peak values to give:

$$v_{(total)} = (V_{P1} + V_{P2}) . \sin . (\omega . t) ,$$

In Fig. 7.8(b), however, we see that the summation of two out of phase sinusoids must be arrived at through the summation of instantaneous values as seen at the sample times t_1, t_2, t_3, etc. This is obviously not going to be the preferred way of mathematically operating upon sinusoids. It is of interest to note that a sinusoid (the dashed curve in Fig. 7.8(b)) is generated through this form of addition, and that this sinusoid has a peak value of V_P. $\sqrt{2}$ (geometry), and this generated summation has a phase displacement of 45° ($\pi/4$ radians) relative to the curve of v_2.

7.8   PHASOR DIAGRAM REPRESENTATION OF AC SINUSOIDS

7.8.1   Phasor diagram development

In the simple generator shown in Fig. 7.4 we can see that the instantaneous value of the emf is dependent upon the position of the conductor relative to the magnetic field. The two voltages v_1 and v_2 shown in Fig. 7.8(b) could have been generated in the way suggested in Fig. 7.9.

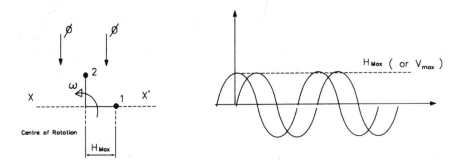

Fig. 7.9 — Generation of two sinusoids.

This is not a real form for generating two independent ac waveforms, but it allows us to see how we can progress to a simple form for representing ac sinusoids with differing phases. If we draw a line from the centre of rotation to the positions considered as the start point for the respective conductors we get a magnitude that could be representative of the peak value of the generated emfs. If we accept this for the moment and look at the height at which the conductor is standing above the axis X–X, we can see that for conductor No. 1 the height of the conductor relative to this axis is given by the equation:

$$h_{y1} = H_{max} . \sin(\omega . t) \ .$$

Similarly, the displacement between the two conductors of ϕ radians can be allowed for, and we can state the height of conductor No. 2 to be given by the equation:

$$h_{y2} = H_{max} \cdot \sin(\omega \cdot t + \phi) \; .$$

The similarlity between these two equations and the generated emf equations allows us to deduce that we can represent our ac sinusoidal waveforms as rotating lines of fixed magnitude set by the respective peak (or maximum) values of the ac wave-forms. Fig. 7.10 shows how we can use this technique to predict the instantaneous

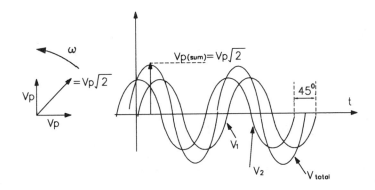

Fig. 7.10 — The summation of out of phase sinusoids.

values of our two out of phase sinusoids, and it is also obvious that there is a fixed pattern rotating as the time frames are stepped through. If the two lengths are treated as being vectors and added together, we get a vector of length $V_P \cdot \sqrt{2}$ and phase displacement from signal No. 2 of $\pi/4$ radians (or 45°).

Fig. 7.10 also shows how this vector summation rotates with two original vectors, and how its effective height above the X–X' axis describes a sinusoid that is directly comparable to the results shown in Fig. 7.8(b). This result is exactly what we want in that we have added two sinusoids of differing phases and successfully predicted a result that we know to be correct.

The relationship between the three rotating vectors does not alter throughout the continued rotations. The rotations only succeed in generating the graphic versions of the sinusoids.

If we can now accept that these rotating vectors can successfully represent the production of ac waveforms, we can dispense with the rotational movement and deal with them at a single frozen moment, and notate our diagram to indicate that these are rotating vectors and not static vectors. This is not an invention of ours; the idea already exists and is known as 'phasors'. Fig. 7.11 shows three separate examples of phasors and their respective time domain equational representation.

7.8.2 (r, ϕ) representation of phasor quantities

The phasor diagram representation of ac quantities contains only two distinct pieces of information. The peak or maximum value and the phase angle of the quantity relative to some arbitrary reference position. An agreed form of representation has grown into common use amongst engineers when it is accepted that ac vector

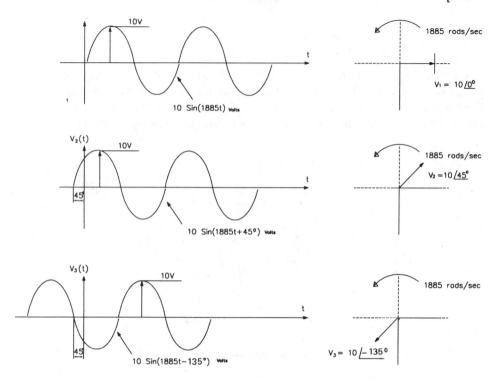

Fig. 7.11 — Phasor diagrams and equivalent time domain equations.

quantities are being described or analyzed or otherwise dealt with. Instead of having to draw the diagrams every time we wish to represent ac vector quantities we can adopt the shorthand form of notation shown in Fig. 7.12.

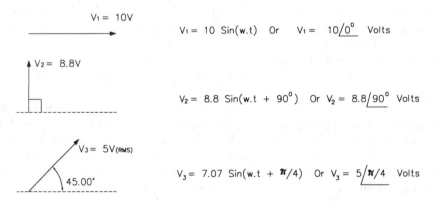

Fig. 7.12 — (r, ϕ) Representation of phasor quantities.

It is of importance to notice that the peak (or maximum) value is sometimes dropped in favour of the rms value, but this represents only a minor discomfort since, as we will later find, a clear relationship exists between these values. $V_{rms} = V_P/\sqrt{2}$).

7.8.3 Phasor summation of ac sinusoids

In Fig. 7.13, v_1 and v_2 are repeats of the generated sinusoids already given in Fig. 7.9,

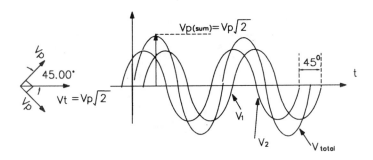

Fig. 7.13 — Phasor summation of two sinusoids.

and we can also see the phasors that we can now consider to be representative of them in all ways. If the phasors are treated as vectors and added vectorially, we get a resultant vector v_{12} which is shown on Fig. 7.13 as v_t and v_{total}.

If this resultant vector is allowed to generate a sinusoid in the normal manner we get the result as given. This is a confirmation of the result already found by graphical means, and the conclusion is that we can use vector addition techniques when we have to add or subtract any ac sinusoidal waveforms. It is reasonable to deduce that all other vector mathematics can be applied to ac sinusoids, and thus vector mutliplication and division are now also part of our arsenal of mathematical techniques in the manipulation of ac sinusoidal waveforms.

Worked examples 7.6 and 7.7 will consolidate the use of phasor diagrams, and the concepts of phase lead and lag are introduced by example rather then verbosity.

A short self-test review is given after the examples to allow consolidation of student confidence concerning the introductory ac topics.

WORKED EXAMPLES

Example 7.1

Q. A 60 Hz, 10 V peak sinewave voltage is available from a signal generator. Sketch the voltage with the horizontal axis labelled in:

(a) units of time
(b) units of degrees
(c) units of radians

A. Since the frequency is 60 Hz the period is:

$$T = 1/f = 1/60 = 16.68 \text{ mS}$$

Clearly the time required to complete $\frac{1}{4}$, $\frac{1}{2}$, and $\frac{3}{4}$ of a cyclé equals the times 4.17, 8.34,

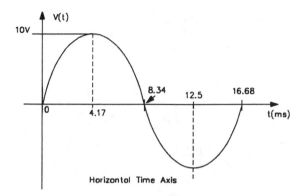

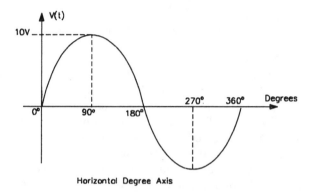

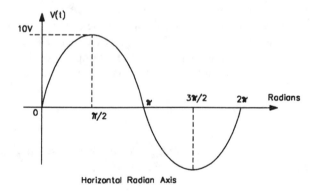

Fig. 7.14.

and 12.5 mS respectively as shown in Fig. 7.14(a). The degree axis and the radian axis graphs in Fig. 7.14(b) and (c) respectively are similarly annotated at their quarter, half, and three-quarter positions.

Example 7.2

Q. Most electrical appliances in the United Kingdom are designed to operate from a 240V rms, 50 Hz source. From this information determine:

(a) The peak voltage
(b) The peak-to-peak voltage
(c) The effective voltage
(d) The average voltage
(e) The cyclic frequency
(f) The period
(g) The radian frequency
(h) An equation that describes the voltage. Assume the phase angle is 0°.

A. (a) $V_P = \sqrt{2} \cdot V_{rms} = 1.414 \times 240 = 339.4\,V$.
(b) $V_{P-P} = 2 \cdot V_P = 2 \times 339.4 = 678.8 \cdot V$.
(c) The effectie voltage is just another name for the rms voltage, therefore $V_{eff} = V_{rms} = 240\,V$.
(d) $V_{av} = 0.0\,V$, since the voltage is sinusoidal.
(e) The cyclic frequency was given as 50 Hz.
(f) $T = 1/f = 1/50 = 20\,ms$.
(g) $\omega = 2 \cdot \pi \cdot f = 100 \cdot \pi = 314.16$ rad/s
(h) $v(t) = V_P \cdot \sin(\omega \cdot t + \phi) = 339.4 \sin(314.2 \cdot t)\,V$.

Example 7.3

Q. Sketch the following voltages:

(a) $v_1(t) = 10\sin 1885t$
(b) $v_2(t) = 10\sin(1885t + 45°)$
(c) $v_3(t) = 10\sin(1885t - 135°)$

How do these voltages differ from each other?

A. In each case the peak voltage (10 V), and radian frequency (1885 rads/s) are the same. Thus, the voltages are identical exccept for their respective phase angles. Fig. 7.15 illustrates a sketch of the three sinusoids. Note that $v_2(t)$ *leads* $v_1(t)$ by 45°, while $v_3(t)$ lags $v_1(t)$ by 135°.

Example 7.4

Q. Write the equations that describe the currents in Fig. 7.16(a) and (b).

A. Note that the period of each current is 8.33 ms. Thus:

$$f = 1/T = 1/(8.33 \times 10^{-3}) = 120\,Hz \ .$$

The radian frequency is therefore:

$$\omega = 2 \cdot \pi \cdot f = 240 \cdot \pi = 754 \cdot \text{rad/s} \ .$$

In Fig. 7.16(a) $I_M = I_P = 10\,A$ and $\phi = 90°\ (\pi/2\,\text{rad})$.

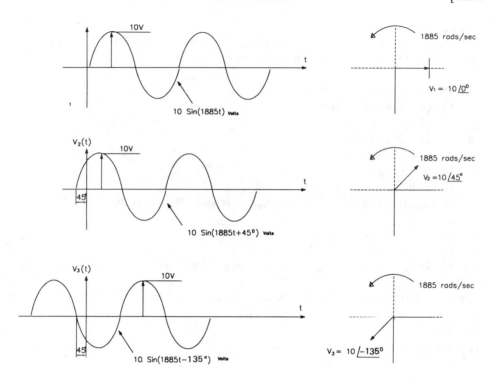

Fig. 7.15.

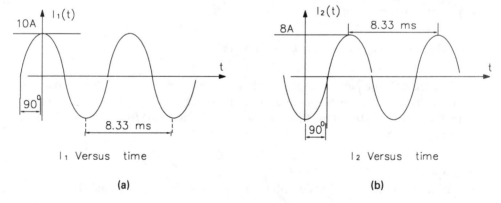

Fig. 7.16.

Thus: $i_1(t) = I_P . \sin(\omega . t + \phi) = 10 . \sin(754 . t + \pi/2)$ A.
In Fig. 7.16(b)$I_M = I_P = 8$ A and $\phi = -90° (-\pi/2 \text{ rad})$.
Thus: $i_2(t) = I_P . \sin(\omega . t + \phi) = 8 . \sin(754 . t - \pi/2)$ A.

Incidentally, $i_1(t)$ may be described by:

$$i_1(t) = 10 \cdot \cos(754 \cdot t) \text{ A}.$$

This is valid because the only difference between a sinewave and a cosine wave is that a cosine wave starts 90° ($\pi/2$ rads) earlier than a sinewave. In these chapters we will express all sinusoids as sine functions by default. However, if there is ever a need to convert from sine to cosine notation or vice versa, the following trigonometric identities can be used.

$$\cos(\omega \cdot t + \phi) = \sin(\omega \cdot t + \phi + \pi/2)$$
$$\sin(\omega \cdot t + \phi) = \cos(\omega \cdot t + \phi - \pi/2)$$

Thus to convert from cosine to sine we add $\pi/2$ rad (90°), and to convert sine to cosine we subtract $\pi/2$ rad (90°).

Example 7.5
Q. Convert:

(a) $20\cos(100t - 30°)$ to sine notation.
(b) Convert $16\sin(50t + 60°)$ to cosine notation.

A. (a) $20 \cdot \cos(100 \cdot t - 30°) = 20 \cdot \sin(100 \cdot t - 30° + 90°).$
$$= 20 \cdot \sin(100 \cdot t + 60°).$$
(b) $16\sin(50 \cdot t + 60°) = 16\sin(50 \cdot t + 60° - 90°)$
$$= 16 \cdot \cos(50 \cdot t - 30°).$$

Example 7.6
Q. Convert the following time domain expressions to frequency domain expressions (i.e. express them as vectors):

(a) $v_1(t) = 10\sin 1885t.$
(b) $v_2(t) = 10\sin(1885t + 45°).$
(c) $v_3(t) = 10\sin(1885t - 45°).$

A. In each case $V_P = 10$ V therefore $V_{rms} = 7.07$ V, therefore:

(a) $V_1 = 7.07 \angle 0$ V.
(b) $V_2 = 7.07 \angle \pi/4$ V.
(c) $V_3 = 7.07 \angle -\pi/4$ V.

Fig. 7.17 shows the time and frequency domain sketches of the voltages in Example 7.6.

Example 7.7
Q. Convert the following frequency domain expressions to time domain expressions — assuming $\omega = 754$ rad/s.

(a) $I_1 = 7.07 \angle 0°$ A.
(b) $I_2 = 3.55 \angle 45°$ A.
(c) Sketch the phasor diagram and the time domain waveforms.

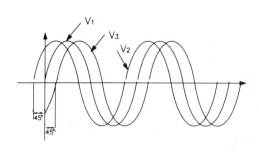

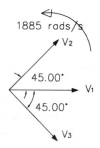

TIME DOMAIN SKETCH   PHASOR DIAGRAM

V_1 lags V_2 by 45^0
V_1 leads V_3 by 45^0
V_2 leads V_1 by 45^0
V_2 leads V_3 by 90^0
V_3 lags V_1 by 45^0
V_3 lags V_2 by 90^0

Fig. 7.17.

A. (a) $I_{1(\text{rms})} = 7.07\,\text{A}$, thus $I_{1(\text{peak})} = 10\,\text{A}$,
           therefore $i_1(t) = 10\sin(754 \cdot t + 0)$
(b) $I_{2(\text{rms})} = 3.535\,\text{A}$, thus $I_{2(\text{peak})} = 5\,\text{A}$,
       therefore $i_1(t) = 5 \cdot \sin(754 \cdot t + \pi/4)$
(c) See Fig. 7.18.

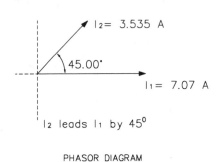

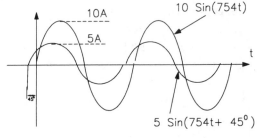

PHASOR DIAGRAM   TIME DOMAIN WAVEFORM

Fig. 7.18.

REVIEW QUESTIONS AND TUTORIAL EXAMPLES

(7.1)   A 50 Hz, 440 V peak sinewave voltage is available from a generator. Sketch the voltage with the horizontal axis lebelled in:

(a) units of time
(b) units of degrees
(c) units of radians

(7.2) Most appliances in the United States are designed to operate from a 115 V
rms, 60 Hz source. From this information determine:

(a) The peak voltage   (162.61 V)
(b) The peak-to-peak voltage   (325.22 V)
(c) The effective voltage   (115 V)
(d) The average voltage   (0.0 V)
(e) The cyclic frequency   (60 Hz)
(f) The period   (16.67 ms)
(g) The radian frequency   (377 rad)
(h) An equation that describes the voltage.
     Assume the phase angle is 0°. $(162.6 \sin\{377t\})$

(7.3) Sketch the following voltages, to a time base:

(a) $v_1(t) = 110 . \sin 377t$
(b) $v_2(t) = 250 . \sin(314.2t + \pi/3)$

(7.4) Write the equations that describe the currents in Fig. 7.19(a) and (b).

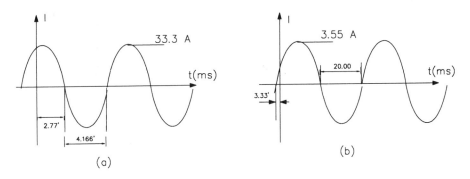

Fig. 7.19.
$(I_1 = 33.3 . \sin(754t + \pi/3), I_2 = 3.55 . \sin(157t + \pi/6)$

(7.5) Convert:

(a) $220 \cos(100t - \pi/3)$ to sine notation.
(b) Convert $160 \sin(500t + \pi/3)$ to cosine notation.

$(220 . \sin(100t + \pi/6), 160 . \cos(500t - \pi/6))$

(7.6)   Convert the following time domain expressions to frequency domain expressions and show the results on a phasor diagram:

(a) $v_1(t) = 66.66 \cdot \sin 850t$ $(47.14 \angle 0 \text{ V})$
(b) $v_2(t) = 20.03 \sin(2000t + 45°)$ $(14.16 \angle \pi/4 \text{ V})$
(c) $v_3(t) = 55.2 \sin(66.66t - 45°)$ $(39 \angle -\pi/4 \text{ V})$

(7.7)   Convert the following frequency domain expressions to time domain expressions — assuming $f = 159 \text{ Hz}$

(a) $I_1 = 14.14 \angle 60° \text{ A}$
(b) $I_2 = 20.55 \angle -30° \text{ A}$
(c)   Sketch the phasor diagrams and time domain waveforms for (a) and (b).

        $(I_1 = 20 \cdot \sin(1000t + \pi/3), I_2 = 29 \cdot \sin(1000t - \pi/6)]$

8

Voltages and currents in linear networks

8.1 AC VOLTAGES AND CURRENTS IN RESISTIVE CIRCUITS

8.1.1 Voltages and currents in a resistor, using Ohm's law

If an ac emf, or voltage, is applied to a purely resistive network, we can use Ohm's law to determine the current taken from this voltage source. We must remember that our voltage is time-variant and thus our equations are applicable only to instantaneous values. That is,

$$v = i.R \quad \text{or} \quad i = v/R$$

(where $v = V_P . \sin(\omega . t \pm \Phi)$.

Thus $$i = \frac{V_P}{R} . \sin(\omega . t \pm \Phi) \ .$$

We can combine V_P and R into a current maximum I_P to get the current time domain equation:

$$i = I_P . \sin(\omega . t \pm \Phi) \ .$$

Both the voltage and current equations are shown in Fig. 8.1 on an X axis of time

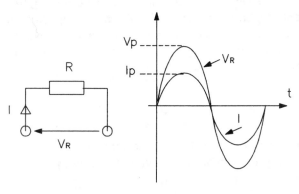

Fig. 8.1 — The V and I waveforms in a resistive network.

to show how the instantaneous value of current tracks the applied voltage with no delay, thus the current is in phase with the voltage in a purely resistive circuit. There is no magic in this, since the laws relating current and voltage in any resistive circuit, being governed by Ohm's law, contain no differential relationships and hence no delay relationship. When we look at inductors and capacitors where a differential relationship does exist, we will find that a delay or advance effect does exist, but that's for later.

8.1.2 (r,θ) representation and vector diagrams

Fig. 8.2(a) shows the vector diagrams associated with applied voltage and current in a

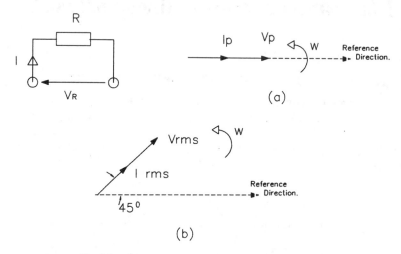

Fig. 8.2 — Vector diagram for resistive circuit.

purely resistive circuit. Fig. 8.2(a) shows the vector diagrams where the applied voltage is assumed to have no phase component. Fig. 8.2(b) shows the vector diagrams where the applied voltage is assumed to have $\pi/4$ radians (45°) phase shift with respect to an assumed reference vector. In both cases Ohm's law dictates that the current is considered to be in phase with the applied voltage.

8.1.3   Power in ac circuits (resistance only)

If we wish to know the power developed in a dc circuit we must multiply the relevant voltage and current together $(p = v \cdot i)$. This rule can be applied to ac circuits if we remember that what we get is instantaneous power and not average power. This consideration is highlighted in Fig. 8.3. A few observations are easily made concerning Fig. 8.3.

$$P_{max} = V_{max} \cdot I_{max} = V_p \cdot I_p$$

The average power developed (P_{av}) over a complete cycle, and hence over any number of complete cycles, can be easily seen to be given by:

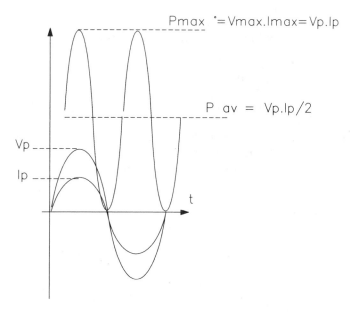

Fig. 8.3 — Instantaneous power in resistive circuit.

$$P_{\text{av}} = \tfrac{1}{2}(P_{\text{max}}) = \frac{V_{\text{p}} \cdot I_{\text{p}}}{2} = \frac{V_{\text{p}}}{\sqrt{2}} \frac{I_{\text{p}}}{\sqrt{2}} \; .$$

$V_{\text{p}}/\sqrt{2}$ and $I_{\text{p}}/\sqrt{2}$ are called the rms values of the applied voltage and current, thus we can write:

$$P_{\text{av}} = V_{\text{rms}} \cdot I_{\text{rms}} \; .$$

The full meaning of rms values is covered in Annex F, but we can see from the above result that if we wish to calculate the effective power developed in a resistor when an ac sinusoidal waveform is applied to it, we can either draw the waveforms and determine the average power over each cycle by graphical techniques or we can accept that a value called the rms value can be used to calculate the power direct, where the rms value is related to the peak value by the relationship given above.

The $\sqrt{2}$ relationship between V_{p} and V_{rms} is applicable only to sinusoids, and this must always be remembered when the term rms is used in ac circuits. Square wave and triangular wave ac waveforms, and in fact any non-sinusoidal waveforms are not covered by this simple relationship. A quick look at Fig. 8.3 and the ensuing observations clearly shows the sinusoidal to $\sqrt{2}$ dependence.

8.2 AC VOLTAGES AND CURRENTS IN INDUCTIVE CIRCUITS

8.2.1 Voltages and currents in an inductor, using Lenz's law
The law which governs the relationship between voltage and current in an inductive

circuit such as that given in Fig. 8.4 is Lenz's law, which we have already used to evaluate the operation of transient circuit analysis in section 5.3. It is given below.

$$\text{emf} = \upsilon = L \cdot \frac{di}{dt}$$

If we presume either υ or i to be a sinusoidal ac waveform, we can apply Lenz's law to determine the result for the remaining variable. For ease of deduction we will presume our current i to be an in-phase sinusoid given by:

$$i = I_\text{p} \cdot \sin(\omega \cdot t)$$

therefore

$$\frac{di}{dt} = \frac{d}{dt} [I_\text{p} \cdot \sin(\omega \cdot t)]$$

or

$$\frac{di}{dt} = I_\text{p} \cdot \frac{d}{dt} [\sin(\omega \cdot t)] \ ,$$

giving

$$\frac{di}{dt} = I_\text{p} \cdot \omega \cdot \cos(\omega t) \ .$$

But

$$\cos(\omega \cdot t) = \sin(\omega t + \pi/2) \ ,$$

therefore

$$\frac{di}{dt} = I_\text{p} \cdot \omega \cdot \sin(\omega \cdot t + \pi/2) \ ,$$

giving

$$\upsilon = L \cdot \frac{di}{dt} = I_\text{p} \cdot \omega \cdot L \cdot \sin(\omega \cdot t + \pi/2)$$

or

$$\upsilon = I_\text{p} \cdot \sin(\omega \cdot t + \pi/2) \cdot (\omega \cdot L) \ .$$

8.2.2 Inductive reactance

Now the $I_\text{p} \cdot \sin(\omega \cdot t + \pi/2)$ term is our original current waveform phase shifted by $\pi/2$ radians (90°), and Fig. 8.4 shows how this appears in the time domain once the

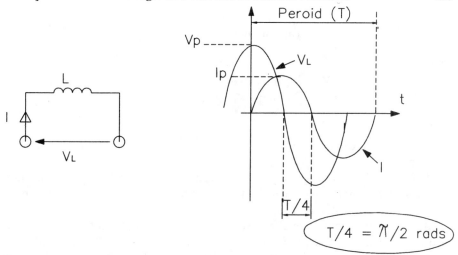

Fig. 8.4 — Voltage and current waveforms in pure inductive circuit.

multiplying factor of $[\omega . L]$ is taken into account. The left-hand side of the final equation has units of volts and the right-hand side of the equation is amps multiplied by a factor $\omega . L$. It is logical to deduce that this factor must have units of ohms.

The term $\omega . L$ is called the inductive reactance of the inductor, and is a measure of how much opposition to current flow the inductor is liable to produce when an ac voltage is applied across its terminals. The term $\omega . L$ is often gathered into a variable name of X_L when the inductive reactance of an inductor is being discussed, but we must never lose sight of the fact that the following is true:

$$X_L = \omega . L. \text{ ohms.}$$

8.2.3 (r, Φ) representation and phasor diagrams
If the (r, ϕ) method of describing an ac sinusoid is employed, we can write our voltage equation as follows:

$$v = i . X_L \angle \pi/2 \text{ V} .$$

This means that our resultant voltage is related to the current flowing through the inductor by a multiplying factor of X_L and a phase-shifting factor of $\pi/2$ radians. Both these effects are directly related to the fact that we are trying to push current through the inductor, and it is therefore common practice to combine both effects into X_L and to quote the inductive reactance to be given by:

$$X_L = \omega . L \angle \pi/2 .$$

We can therefore quote the whole effect of pushing current through an inductor by the following formula which has a useful resemblance to Ohm's law.

$$v = i \cdot X_L \qquad \text{(instantaneous effect)}$$

or

$$V_{rms} = I_{rms} \cdot X_L \qquad \text{(rms values)}$$
$$\text{(where } X_L = \omega \cdot L \ \angle \pi/2) \ \Omega$$

Thus an inductor can be seen to have two distinct effects upon the current-to-voltage relationship.

The size of the voltage required to push a current of i amperes through an inductor of L henry is governed by the magnitude of the inductive reactance X_L which in turn is equal to $\omega \cdot L$ ohms.

As well as the magnitude effect we must be aware of the fact that the inductor is also introducing a phase shift effect of $+\pi/2$ radians upon the applied voltage relative to the current which we will presume to be our reference signal having 0° phase shift.

Fig. 8.5 shows the phasor diagram representation of the voltage and current

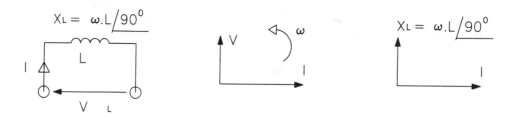

Fig. 8.5 — (r, Φ) representation and vector diagrams.

found in an inductor, from which we can see that for the voltage to be given by the multiplication of the current and the inductive reactance, our reactance must be a vector that moves the current vector by $\pi/2$ radians and affects its size by a factor of X_L ohms. This means that our inductive reactance must be a vector of magnitude $X_L = \omega \cdot L$ ohms and phase angle $\pi/2$ radians, as shown in Fig. 8.5.

Note that the current is a phasor quantity in that it is a rotating vector. The inductive reactance is a vector and not a phasor since it contains no sinusoidal components, that is no $\sin(\omega t)$ term.

Thus to an ac waveform the inductor can be considered to be a phase shifting and impeding element not unlike the resistor which is impeding but non-phase shifting. Both components can be treated by using Ohms law if we accept that they have the above distinguishing features.

When we talk about resistance and inductive reactance and wish to generalize about their commonality we talk about their impedance. This is the accepted form of talking about the general effect of component impedance to current flow. It will be used more productively when we investigate the combination of resistors, inductors, and capacitors in later chapters.

8.2.4 The frequency response of an inductor's reactance
Fig. 8.6 shows how the inductive reactance of an inductor varies as we change the

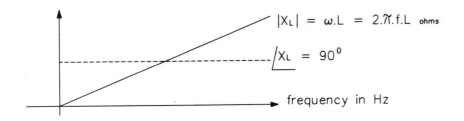

Fig. 8.6 — Inductive reactance versus frequency.

generator frequency from 0 Hz to the high-frequency range. The phase shift properties of the inductor can be seen to remain constant over the whole range, and both these effects are a result of the equation alrady given as $X_L = \omega . L \angle \pi/2 \; \Omega$. Although not a terribly exciting piece of deduction, this idea of frequency response must be examined in later chapters. The inductor is a principal building block in our analysis, and we must appreciate its ideal frequency response characteristics.

8.2.5 Power in a purely inductive circuit
The power developed in a pure inductor is calculated by multiplying the instantaneous voltage and current associated with the inductor. The result of this is shown in Fig. 8.7 which is a graph of instantaneous power over a full cycle of applied ac. The power waveform straddles the X axis symmetrically, thus we can deduce that the power over a full cycle of ac is zero. The power waveform is actually telling us that the inductor receives power during one cycle of its waveform and sends it back to the supply during the second part of the waveform. Thus we get an overall full cycle result of zero power dissipation. The only result of any significance is the peak power developed during this shuffle of power, and it is calculated as follows:

$$\text{Peak power} = i \times v \; (\text{at } t = t_2)$$

$$I_m . \sin(\pi/4) \times V_m . \sin(3\pi/4) = \frac{I_m . V_m}{2} = I_{rms} . V_{rms}$$

But

$$V_m = I_m . \omega L, \text{ therefore:}$$

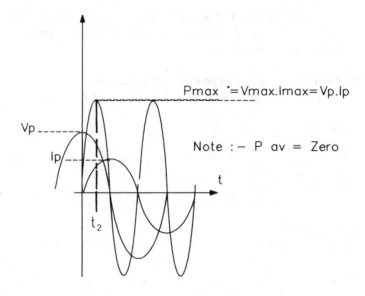

Fig. 8.7 — Instantaneous power in a purely inductive circuit.

Peak power also equals $I_m^2 \dfrac{(\omega . L)}{2}$

Worked examples 8.1 and 8.2 allow consolidation of the points raised here.

8.3 AC VOLTAGES AND CURRENTS IN CAPACITIVE CIRCUITS

8.3.1 Voltage and current in a capacitor, using the capacitor law
The law which governs the relationship between voltage and current in a capacitive circuit (Fig. 8.8) has already been encountered in section 5.7.2 where it was used to evaluate the operation of transient circuit analysis. It is given below:

$$v = \frac{1}{C} i . dt \quad \text{or} \quad i = C . \frac{dv}{dt} \ .$$

If we presume either v or i to be a sinusoidal ac waveform,. we can apply the above relationship to determine the result for the remaining variable. For ease of deduction we will presume our voltage v to be an in-phase sinusoid given by:

$$v = V_p . \sin(\omega . t)$$

therefore

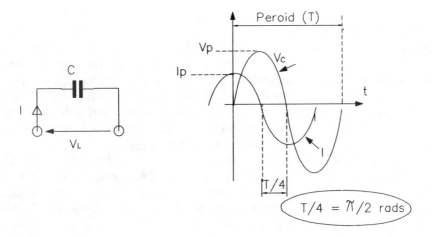

Fig. 8.8 — Voltage and current waveforms in pure capacitive circuit.

$$\frac{d\upsilon}{dt} = \frac{d}{dt}\,[V_p . \sin(\omega . t)]$$

or

$$\frac{d\upsilon}{dt} = V_p . \frac{d}{dt}\,[\sin(\omega . t)]\ ,$$

giving

$$\frac{d\upsilon}{dt} = V_p . \omega . \cos(\omega t)\ .$$

But $\cos(\omega . t) = \sin(\omega t + \pi/2)$,
therefore

$$\frac{d\upsilon}{dt} = V_p . \omega . \sin(\omega . t + \pi/2)\ ,$$

giving

$$i = C . \frac{d\upsilon}{dt} = V_p . \omega . C . \sin(\omega . t + \pi/2)$$

or

$$i = V_p . \sin(\omega . t + /2) . [\omega . C]$$

or

$$i . \frac{1}{[\omega . C]} = V_p . \sin(\omega . t + \pi/2)\ .$$

8.3.2 Capacitive reactance

A comparison with the work already completed for inductive circuits should suggest the next steps in our procedure. We have used exactly the same mathematical development in both cases, with simple switching between variables ω and i. The resultant equation can be split easily into three distinct elements as follows.

$V_p . \sin(\omega . t + \pi/2)$ is the applied voltage with a phase shift factor now included. $1/[\omega . C]$ is the ohmic effect of the capacitor which, when divided into the voltage part of the equation, will give us i, the resulting current flow.

The term $1/[\omega . C]$ is called the capacitive reactance of the capacitor and has units of ohms, as the equation implies. It is a measure of how much opposition to current flow the capacitor is liable to produce when an ac voltage is applied across its terminals. The term $1/[\omega . C]$ is often gathered into a variable name of X_c when the capacitive reactance of a capacitor is being discussed, but we must never lose sight of the fact that:

$$X_c = 1/[\omega . C] \ \Omega \ .$$

8.3.3 (r, Φ) representation and phasor diagrams

If the (r, Φ) method of describing an ac sinusoid is employed, we can write our current equation as:

$$i . X_c = v \ \angle \pi/2 \ .$$

If we move the phase shift effect next to the capacitive reactance where it belongs, since this is the reason for the effect, our equation becomes:

$$i . X_c \ \angle - \pi/2 = v$$

or

$$v = i . X_c \ \angle - \pi/2 \ .$$

This means that our resultant voltage is related to the current flowing through the capacitor by a multiplying factor of X_c and a phase-shifting factor of $-\pi/2$ radians. Both these effects are directly related to the fact that we are trying to push current through the capacitor, and it is therefore common practice to combine both effects into X_c ands quote the capacitive reactance given by:

$$X_c = \frac{1}{[\omega . C]} \ \angle - \pi/2 \ .$$

We can therefore quote the whole effect of pushing current through a capacitor by the following formula which has a useful resemblance to Ohm's law:

$$v = i \cdot X_c \qquad \text{(instantaneous effect)}$$

or

$$V_{rms} = I_{rms} \cdot X_c \qquad \text{(rms values)}$$

$$\left(\text{where } X_c = \frac{1}{[\omega \cdot C]} \angle -\pi/2\right).$$

Thus a capacitor can be seen to have two distinct effects upon the current-to-voltage relationship.

The size of the voltage required to push a current of i amperes through a capacitor of C farad is governed by the magnitude of the capacitive reactance X_c, which in turn is equal to $1/[\omega \cdot C]$ Ω.

As well as the magnitude effect we must be aware of the fact that the capacitor is also introducing a phase shift effect of $-\pi/2$ radians upon the voltage relative to the current which we will presume to be our reference signal having 0 radians phase shift.

Fig. 8.9 shows the phasor diagram representation of the voltage and current

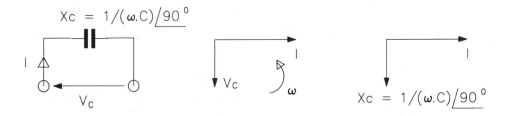

Fig. 8.9 — (r, Φ) representation and vector diagrams.

found in a capacitor. From this we can see that for the voltage to be given by the multiplication of the current and the capacitive reactance, our reactance must be a vector that moves the current vector by $-\pi/2$ radians and affects its size by a factor of X_c ohms. This means that our capacitive reactance must be a vector of magnitude $X_c = 1/[\omega \cdot C]$ ohms and phase angle $-\pi/2$ radians, as shown in Fig. 8.9.

Note that the current is a phasor quantity in that it is a rotating vector. The capacitive reactance is a vector and not a phasor since it contains no sinusoidal components.

Thus to an ac waveform the capacitor can be considered to be a phase-shifting and impeding element not unlike the resistor which is impeding and the inductor which is both impeding and phase-shifting. All three components can be treated by using Ohm's law if we accept that they have the distinguishing features suggested.

When we talk about resistance and reactance and wish to generalize about their commonality we talk about their impedance. This is the accepted form of talking about the general effect of component impedance to current flow. It will be used more productively when we investigate the combination of resistors, inductors, and capacitors in later chapters.

8.3.4 The frequency response of a capacitor's reactance
Fig. 8.10 shows how the capacitive reactance of a capacitor varies as we change the

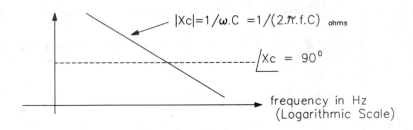

Fig. 8.10 — Capacitive reactance versus frequency.

generator frequency from 0 Hz to the high-frequency range. The phase shift properties of the capacitor can be seen to remain constant over the whole range. Both these effects are a result of the equation already given as $X_c = 1/[\omega . C] \angle - \pi/2$ Ω. Although not a terribly exciting piece of deduction, this idea of frequency response will be examined in later chapters, and the capacitor is a principal building block in our analysis and we must appreciate its ideal frequency response characteristics.

Note that the use of log scales linearises the response, $\log_{10}(1/\omega C)$ for variations in ω is a straight line graph.

8.3.5 Power in a purely capacitive circuit
The power developed in a pure capacitor is calculated by multiplying the instantaneous voltage and current associated with the capacitor. The result of this is shown in Fig. 8.11 which is a graph of instantaneous power over a full cycle of applied ac. As in the case for the inductor the power waveform straddles the X axis symmetrically, and thus we can again deduce that the power over a full cycle of ac is zero. Thus we can deduce that for all purely reactive components there will never be a development of real power over the continuous application of an ac signal. We can once again calculate the peak power of the instantaneous power waveform:

Peak power $= i \times v$ (at $t = t_2$)

$$V_m . \sin(\pi/4) \times I_m . \sin(3\pi/4) = \frac{V_m . I_m}{2} = V_{rms} . I_{rms} \ .$$

But $V_m = I_m/(\omega . C)$ therefore:

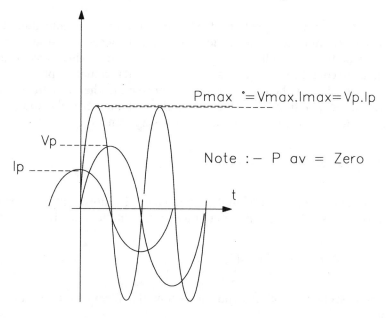

Fig. 8.11 — Instantaneous power in a purely capacitive circuit.

Peak power also equals $\dfrac{I_m^2}{2(\omega . C)}$

Worked examples 8.3. and 8.4 allow consolidation of the points raised here.

8.4 THE MEANING OF 'j' NOTATION IN AC CIRCUIT ANALYSIS

8.4.1. The resolution of phasors into horizontal and vertical components

A considerable amount of unnecessary mathematical grief can be created when it comes to the use of the 'j' or 'i' operator in the analysis of ac circuits.† It is hoped that this short digression into mathematics will exorcise any lingering fears about the use of 'j' notation, since it really is nothing more than a form of representing a quantity that has vector (or phasor) qualities, i.e. magnitude and direction.

The work so far completed in ac analysis has introduced the idea of vector (or phasor) representation of ac quantities, and this is necessary because we have found that ac quantities have two parts to their successful representation: a magnitude part and a phase angle part. We have chosen to represent only these two parts in r,Φ form so far, but another representation form is when we resolve our phasor quantities into vertical and horizontal components with the horizontal axis being the base or reference vector direction.

---

† The 'j' is, by convention, roman (upright), not italic. The use of 'i' in electrical work has been dropped because of potential confusion with *i* for current.

Fig. 8.12 shows a selection of phasors being resolved into their vertical and horizontal components, and it is clear that our two pieces of information concerning the ac quantities are still intact if slightly transformed. This transformation is not intended to complicate the analysis of ac circuits; it is actually a progression toward a more amenable mathematical form of representing them. With the information about our ac quantities now stored in horizontal and vertical component form we could write down the quantities in the following manner:

$$5.0 \ \angle \pi/4 = 3.54(\text{H}) \text{ and } 3.54(\text{V})$$

This is unnecessary since complex mathematical representation already exists to achieve successful representation of the quantity in the following manner:

$$5.0 \ \angle \pi/4 = 3.54 + j(3.54) \ .$$

The next section introduces and shows how this form of representation is totally valid.

8.4.2 Introduction to the 'j' operator

The 'j' operator is universally known to be the square root of -1 ($\sqrt{-1}$). In simple real number terms this is a meaningless statement, and this is where the problems begin. The use of the j operator term is unreasonable in mathematics that is based upon real numbers or scalar quantities.

We need it only where we process vector (or phasor) quantities, and this is known as 'complex' mathematics. In electrical and electronic circuits we use complex numbers to represent the two piece information content of ac quantities. In the following section we will discover the validity of the j operator.

8.4.3 The use of the j operator to represent a π/2 phase shift

To support the validity of the use of the j operator, a minor digression into the mathematics of r,Φ representation is necessary. Consider the multiplication of a current vector by itself to determine, say, the power developed in a component.

$$\text{Power} \propto I \ \angle \theta \times I \ \angle \theta$$

$$\propto I^2 \ \angle 2.\theta.$$

So, in general, when two vector quantities are multiplied together we can write the solution as:

$$R \ \angle \beta = r \ \angle \theta \times s \ \angle \Phi$$

where

$$R = (r \times s) \quad \text{and} \quad \beta = (\theta + \Phi) \ .$$

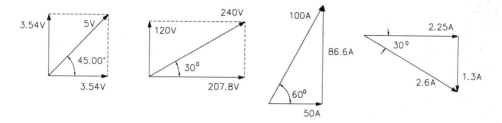

Fig. 8.12 — Resolution of vectors into vertical and horizontal components.

This means that we are multiplying the vector lengths and adding the vector phase angles. An interesting result is obtained when we look at the reversal of multiplication of a quantity by itself as in the above current case. We can observe that:

$$I \angle \theta \times I \angle \theta = I^2 \angle 2.\theta \ ,$$

and reversal, that is square root, $\sqrt{(I^2 \angle 2\theta)} = I \angle \theta$, that is, we square root the vector length and half the vector phase angle.

If we presume our current to be 1 amp length vector with a phase angle of $\pi/2$ radians, the squared-up effect of this will be:

$$1 \angle \pi/2 \times 1 \angle \pi/2 = 1 \angle \pi \ (\pi \ \text{rads} = 180°)$$

The phasor diagram, Fig. 8.13, shows what we have done, and we can see that by

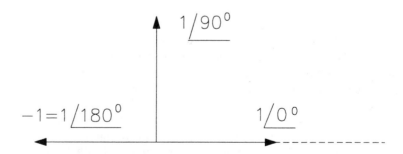

Fig. 8.13 — Phasor representation of unit length phasors.

multiplying vector 1 $\angle \pi/2$ by itself we have moved through a rotation of $\pi/2$ radians (90°). The result of this multiplication is a vector of length 1 amp in a direction of π radians (180°), or a vector of -1 amp in relation to the 1 amp reference vector shown in the diagram. This means that the following deduction can be achieved:

$$-1 = -(1) = 1 \angle \pi$$
$$\sqrt{-1} = \sqrt{(1 \ ^A[\pi])} = 1 \angle \pi/2 \ .$$

That is,

$$j = \sqrt{-1} = 1 \angle \pi/2 \ .$$

This means that the square root of -1 is a vector quantity given by a vector of length 1 unit and phase angle $\pi/2$ rad (90°).

If we multiply any vector quantity by j, we can see from Fig. 8.14 that it does

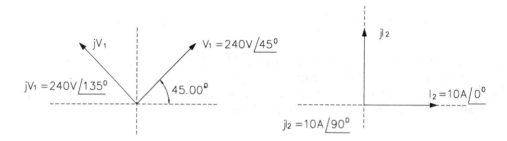

Fig. 8.14 — The j operator on a vector diagram.

nothing more dramatic than move it through a phase angle displacement of $\pi/2$ rads (90°). Thus we can consider our j quantity to be nothing more than a $\pi/2$ radian (90°) phase-shifting vector.

8.4.4   Resolution of vectors into complex form

If we choose to represent our vector quantities as horizontal and vertical components we can let our horizontal component remain as calculated and annotate our vertical component with a j to indicate its $\pi/2$ phase shift relative to the horizontal reference axis.

Fig. 8.15 is a repeat of Fig. 8.12 which now contains the vector quantities in complex form or $a + jb$ form. When vectors are represented in this style, where the vertical or out-of-phase components are annotated with a j, it is commonly known as complex number form. This may not seem to be of any overall advantage when it comes to operating upon ac quantities, but a few worked examples on the work already covered should highlight the simple application of the complex number method of representing ac quantities, although the use of j notation in problem solving will not be covered until chapter 9.

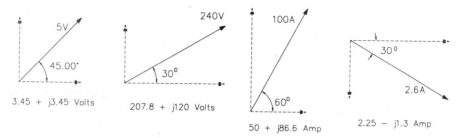

Fig. 8.15 — Resolution of vectors into complex form.

8.4.5 Multiples of j and their meaning
A further result concerning the use of the j operator will be of value, and it is represented in Fig. 8.16.

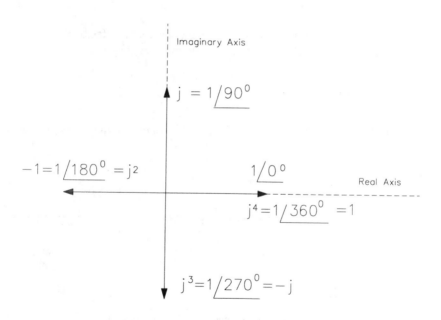

Fig. 8.16 — The j operator and its multiples.

If j is a vector $1 \angle \pi/2$ and its first self-multiple is a vector j^2 or -1, then from Fig. 8.16 we can see that as we progressively multiply j by itself we make $\pi/2$ (90°) steps around the phasor diagram. The following observed results are of value.

$$j = j^5 = j^9 = j^{13} \ldots = j^{(1+4 \cdot n)}$$
$$-1 = j^2 = j^6 = j^{10} \ldots = j^{(2+4 \cdot n)}$$

$$-j = j^3 = j^7 = j^{11} \ldots = j^{(3+4 \cdot n)}$$
$$1 = j^4 = j^8 = j^{12} \ldots = j^{(4 \cdot n)}$$

Thus we can see that all multiples of j reduce to only one of four options, and this result is of significant importance when it comes to manipulating complex numbers and their multiples.

8.4.6 The use of j in inductive reactance

It is hoped that at the conclusion of section 8.3 it was understood that the inductive reactance of a coil was representable by the vector quantity:

$$X_{\mathrm{L}} = \omega \cdot L \; \angle \pi/2$$

Since the j operator is nothing more than a $\pi/2$ phase shift effect we can absorb it into our expression for inductive reactance in the manner suggested below.

$$X_{\mathrm{L}} = j(\omega \cdot L) \; .$$

Both expressions are represented in Fig. 8.17 on separate diagrams, and we can see

Fig. 8.17 — Representations of inductive reactance.

that they both mean the same thing. $X_{\mathrm{L}} = j(\omega \cdot L)$ is the universally accepted method of mathematically representing the inductive reactance of a coil.

8.4.7 The use of j in capacitive reactance

It is hoped that at the conclusion of section 8.4 it was understood that the capacitive reactance of a capacitor was representable by the vector quantity:

$$X_{\mathrm{C}} = \frac{1}{\omega \cdot C} \; \angle -\pi/2 \; .$$

Since the j operator is nothing more than $\pi/2$ phase shift effect, and if we remember that $-$ j is a $-\pi/2$ phase shift operator, we can absorb this result into our expression for capacitive reactance in the manner suggested in Fig. 8.18.

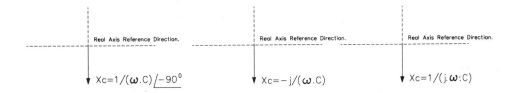

Fig. 8.18 — Representation of capacitive reactance.

$$X_C = -\,j \cdot \frac{1}{\omega \cdot C}$$

A more tidy solution can be obtained if we multiply the top and bottom of our RHS by j to get:

$$X_C = -\,j \cdot \frac{1}{\omega \cdot C} \frac{(j)}{(j)} = \frac{1}{j(\omega \cdot C)} \quad .$$

All three representations of capacitive reactance are represented in Fig. 8.18 on separate diagrams, and we can see that they all mean the same thing. $X_C = 1/j(\omega \cdot C)$ is the universally accepted method of mathematically representing the capacitive reactance of a capacitor.

Worked examples 8.5 and 8.6 will help to consolidate the work introduced in this section.

WORKED EXAMPLES

Example 8.1
Q. A voltage source $v(t) = 11.3 \sin (800t)$ is connected across a 5 mH inductor as illustrated in Fig. 8.19. Calculate the current flowing through the inductor. Also sketch the time and frequency domain responses.

A. First convert the problem into the vector form:

$$v(t) = 11.3 \sin (800t) = 8.0 \;\angle 0 \; \text{V (rms)}$$

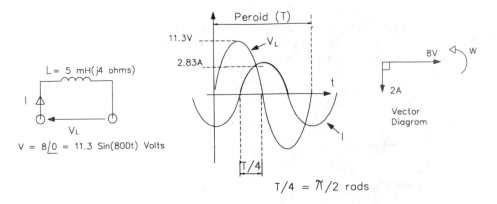

Fig. 8.19 — Time response and vector diagrams for Example 8.1.

$$X_L = j(\omega . L) = j(800) . (5 \times 10^{-3}) = j4 \; \Omega$$

Thus:

$$I = \frac{V}{X_L} = \frac{8.0}{j4} = -j2 \; A = 2.0 \; \angle -\pi/2 \; A \; \text{(rms)}$$

Current as a time domain expression is:

$$i(t) = I_p . \sin(\omega . t \pm \Phi) = 2\sqrt{2} . \sin(800t - \pi/2)$$
$$= 2.83 . \sin(800t - \pi/2) \; A$$

Example 8.2
Q. An emf of 100 V (50 Hz) is applied to a coil of negligible resistance and inductance 0.2 H. Find the current drawn at 50 Hz. Repeat the calculations for double the operating frequency and half the operating frequency.

A. First of all we must calculate the inductive reactance.

$$X_{L(50\,Hz)} = j(\omega . L)j(2 . \pi . 50)(0.2) = j62.83 \; \Omega$$
$$X_{L(100\,Hz)} = j(\omega . L)j(2 . \pi . 100)(0.2) = j125.66 \; \Omega$$
$$X_{L(25\,Hz)} = j(\omega . L)j(2 . \pi . 25)(0.2) = j31.42 \; \Omega \; .$$

Current in all cases is given by $I = V/X_L$:

$$I_{(50\,\text{Hz})} = \frac{100}{\text{j}62.83} = -\text{j}1.59 \text{ A} = 1.59 \angle -\pi/2$$

$$I_{(100\,\text{Hz})} = \frac{100}{\text{j}125.66} = -\text{j}0.795 \text{ A} = 0.795 \angle -\pi/2$$

$$I_{(25\,\text{Hz})} = \frac{100}{\text{j}31.42} = -\text{j}3.18 \text{ A} = 3.18 \angle -\pi/2$$

Example 8.3
Q. Calculate the reactance of a 2 μF capacitor at a frequency of 1 kHz.

A. $$X_\text{C} = \frac{1}{\text{j}(\omega\,.\,C)} = \frac{-\text{j}}{2\,.\,\pi\,.\,10^3(2\times 10^{-6})} = -\text{j}79.6\,\Omega = 79.6 \angle -\pi/2\,\Omega$$

Example 8.4
A 2 μF capacitor is driven from an ac current source $i(t) = 178.2\,.\,\sin\,(6280t)$ mA as shown in Fig. 8.20. Calculate the voltage across the capacitor. Show the result in both time response and vector form.

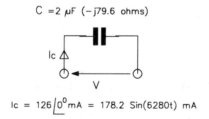

C = 2 μF (−j79.6 ohms)

Ic

V

Ic = 126 $\angle 0^0$ mA = 178.2 Sin(6280t) mA

Fig. 8.20.

A. First of all convert the current to vector form:

$$i(t) = 178.2\,.\,\sin\,(6283t) \text{ mA} = 126 \angle 0 \text{ mA} = 126 \text{ mA (rms)}$$

Next we must calculate X_C, but this is already known from the previous example as $X_\text{C} = -\text{j}79.6\,\Omega$.

$(1 \text{ kHz} \equiv 6283 \text{ rad/s})$ (check it!)

And now we calculate the voltage, using Ohm's law.

$$V = I . X_C = (126 \times 10^{-3}) . (-j79.6) = -j10 \text{ V (rms)}$$

To show the voltage in the time domain we must convert our result to $v(t) = V_m . \sin(\omega . t \pm \Phi)$ form.

$$v(t) = 14.14 . \sin(6283t - \pi/2) = 14.14 . \sin(6283t - \pi/2) \text{ V} \quad.$$

The full result is shown in Fig. 8.21.

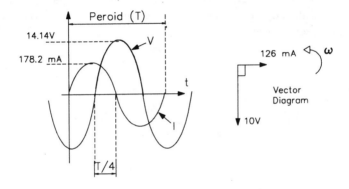

Fig. 8.21 — Full result for Example 8.4.

Example 8.5
The voltage applied to a resistor $(100 \, \Omega)$, an inductor (0.2 H), and a capacitor $(40 \, \mu\text{F})$ in turn is defined by $v(t) = 155.6 . \sin (377t + \pi/3)$ V. Calculate the current drawn in all three cases, showing both its magnitude and phase in both time domain form and phasor form.

A. Firstly, from the voltage equation we get:

$$V_{rms} = 110 \text{ V}$$

and

$$\omega = 377 \text{ rad/s,}$$

giving
$$f = 60 \text{ Hz. } (T_{(\text{Period})} = 16.66 \text{ ms}).$$

We also find that $\angle \Phi = \pi/3$ (60°).
Thus $v(t)$ in vector form is given by:

$$v(t) = 110 \ \angle \pi/3 \ \text{V (rms)}$$

Secondly, we determine the component 'impedances':

$$R = 100 \ \Omega$$

$$X_L = j(377) \cdot (0.2) = j75.4 \ \Omega$$

$$X_C = \frac{1}{j(\omega \cdot C)} = \frac{-j}{(377) \cdot (40 \times 10^{-6})} = -j66.3 \ \Omega \ .$$

Thirdly, we calculate the current drawn in each case:

$$I_R = \frac{V}{R} = \frac{110 \ \angle \pi/3}{100} = 1.1 \ \text{A} \ \angle \pi/3 \ \text{(rms)}$$

$$I = \frac{V}{X_L} = \frac{110 \ \angle \pi/3}{j75.4} = \frac{110 \ \angle \pi/3}{75.4 \ \angle \pi/2} = 1.46 \ \angle -\pi/6 \ \text{A (rms)}$$

$$I_C = \frac{V}{X_C} = \frac{110 \ \angle \pi/3}{-j66.3} = \frac{110 \ \angle \pi/3}{66.3 \ \angle -\pi/2} = 1.66 \ \angle 5\pi/6 \angle \ \text{A (rms)}$$

Finally, we can show the results on the vector diagram given in Fig. 8.22.
Fig. 8.22 shows us that the applied voltage phase angle of $\pi/3$ rad was a bit of a red herring since it does not substantially affect the result of the current magnitude. If we realign our voltage along the reference vector we see the familiar resistor, inductor, and capacitor voltage-to-current vector diagrams.

Example 8.6
q. The voltage across a component is measured as $V = 60 \ \angle -\pi/2$ V and the current through the same component is measured as $i = 15 \ \angle \pi$ mA. Given that the frequency is 318.3 Hz, determine the nature of the component.

A. The quickest and most graphic of discovering what is being measured is simply to draw both vectors on a vector diagram. This is done in Fig. 8.23. It is easy to see that since the voltage leads the current by $\pi/2$ radians we have an inductor component, and the following calculation gives us its reactance and its inductive value.

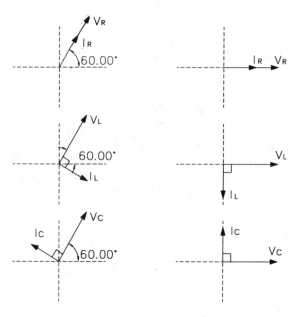

Fig. 8.22 — Vector diagram of results for Example 8.5.

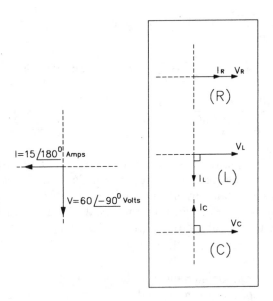

Fig. 8.23.

$$X_{L} = \frac{V}{I} \text{ (magnitude only)} = \frac{60}{15} = 4 \ \Omega$$

$$X_{L} = \frac{V}{I} \text{ (magnitude and phase)} = \frac{60 \ \angle - \pi/2}{15 \ \angle \pi} = 4 \ \angle \pi/2 = j4 \ \Omega$$

The j confirms the inductive nature of our component

$$X_{L} = 2 . \pi . f . L, \text{ thus } L = \frac{X_{L}}{2 . \pi . f} = \frac{4}{2 . \pi . 318.3} = 2 \text{ mH} \ .$$

REVIEW QUESTIONS AND TUTORIAL EXAMPLES

(8.1) For the waveform given in Fig. 8.24 obtain:

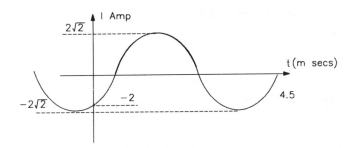

Fig. 8.24.

(a) the maximum value,
(b) the phase angle in degrees, (hint, draw the vector diagram)
(c) the phase angle in radians,
(d) the rms value,.
(e) the expression for the phasor in the form: $I = I \ \angle \Phi$,
(f) the period,
(g) the frequency in hertz,
(h) the angular frequency in radians per second,
(i) the current in the form: $i(t) = I_{max} \sin (\omega t + \Phi)$ A
(j) the current after 11 milliseconds.

(2.83 A, $- 45°$, $- \pi/4$, 2 A, $I = 2 \ \angle - \pi/4$ A, 4 ms, 250 Hz, 1571 rad/s, $i(t) = 2.83 \sin (1571t - \pi/4)$ A, $- 2$ A).

(8.2) The current waveform of problem (8.1) is applied to R, to L, and to C in Fig. 8.25. Obtain the maximum value of the voltage across each component.

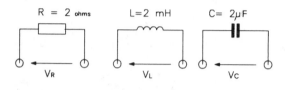

Fig. 8.25.

(5.657 V, 8.88 V, 0.9 kV)

(8.3) Obtain the phase angles of V_R, V_L, and V_C in problem (8.2)

$(-\pi/4, +\pi/4, -3\pi/4)$

(8.4) Obtain expressions for $v_R(t)$, $v_L(t)$, and $v_C(t)$ in problem (8.2)

(5.66 . sin $(1571t - \pi/4)$ V, 8.88 . sin $(1571t + \pi/4)$ V, and
0.9 . sin $(1571t - 3\pi/4)$ kV) .

(8.5) Obtain vector quantity expressions for V_R, V_L, and V_C in problem (8.2).

(4 $\angle - \pi/4$ V, 6.28 $\angle \pi/4$, 0.636 $\angle - 3\pi/4$ kV)

(8.6) A voltage $v = 12 \sin (1000t + \pi/2)$ v is applied to R, to L, and to C in problem (8.2). Obtain the current in each case.

(6 . sin $(1000t + \pi/2)$ A, 6 . sin $(1000t)$ A, 24 . sin $(1000t + \pi)$ mA) .

(8.7) A current $I = 6 \angle \pi/6$ mA is applied to R, L, and C in problem (8.2). Obtain v (vector form) in each case, given that the period of the waveform equals 0.1 seconds.

$(12 \angle \pi/6, 0.754 \angle 2\pi/3 \text{ mV}, 47.75 \angle -\pi/3 \text{ kV})$

(8.8) Obtain the component with the black box of Fig. 8.26, given that the frequency

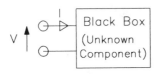

Fig. 8.26.

equals 50 Hz, $V = 250 \angle \pi/6$ V, and $I = 15 \angle 2\pi/3$ A .

$(190.9 \ \mu\text{F})$

(8.9) Prove that when a sinusoidal voltage is applied to a capacitance or an inductance; the average power developed equals 0 watts. (Draw instantaneous power waveforms).

(8.10) A current $i = I_{max} \sin \omega t$ is applied to:

(a) a resistance R
(b) an inductance L
(c) a capacitance C.

In each case, obtain the maximum instantaneous power supplied to the component.

$I_m^2 . R$ W, $I_m^2 . \omega . L/2$ W, $I_m^2/(2 . \omega . C)$ W .

(8.11) Draw the frequency response graph of the capacitive reactance of a 0.1 μF capacitor over the frequency range 100 Hz to 100 kHz. State the range of frequencies between which it is within $\pm 10\%$ of 1.0 kΩ reactance. (Hint: use log–log paper)

(1.447 kHz to 56.56 kHz)

9

Series combinations of *R*, *L*, and *C*

The possible circuit combinations of *R*, *L*, and *C* are obviously limitless. We will learn the rules about combination by first of all looking at the more common series combinations that are possible. Since we will be considering only the series form of circuit first, this means we must consider any supplying source to be a Thévénin source. If this is not the case in practice, then a simple conversion can be applied in the manner already discussed in the dc circuits chapters.

9.1   *R* AND *L* IN SERIES

There are four variable quantities in the circuit shown in Fig. 9.1 (v_S, v_R, v_L, i). Since

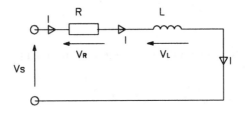

Fig. 9.1 — *R* and *L* in series.

i is common to all of the three circuit voltages we will use it as the reference variable. Kirchhoffs voltage summation law which we used extensively in the chapter about dc circuit analysis can now be applied to the circuit given in Fig. 4.1. We must remember that we are dealing with phasor quantities, and our variables have two components of magnitude and phase, thus simple magnitude addition is not applicable except in the unusual case of in-phase variables.

We must first of all determine the three voltages relationships to the suggested common variable of current i.

9.1.1 Phasor diagram solution

Fig. 9.2(a) and (b) shows the results already obtained for the two linear elements,

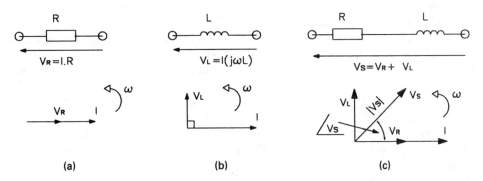

Fig. 9.2 — Phasor diagrams for the resistor and inductor with respect to current i.

and it also summarizes the relevant formulae. If we now align the current phasor on a single diagram we can see the phase relationship between the resistor voltage and the inductor voltage. Fig. 9.2(c) shows this alignment and also shows the Kirchhoff summation to give v_S. That is,

$$v_S = v_R + v_L \qquad \text{(phasor summation)} \ .$$

We now use Pythagoras's theorem and a bit of simple trigonometry to determine the magnitude and phase of our applied voltage v_S. That is,

$$|v_S| = \sqrt{(|v_R|^2 + |v_L|^2)}$$

and

$$\angle v_S = \tan^{-1}(|v_L|/|v_R|) \ .$$

Thus if we know the applied current we can calculate v_R and v_L, using our adapted Ohm's law rules, and we can also calculate the applied·voltage by using the above formulae.

We must now become fully aware that what we mean by calculating a variable's value when we are dealing with ac quantities is that we must calculate both magnitude and phase. This is because phasor quantities are effectively two-dimensional.

Unfortunately, most series circuits are supplied from a voltage source and not a current source. We must therefore devise a means of calculating our circuit variables from the start point of knowing only the supply voltage and the circuit component values. To do this we have to become familiar with the concept of circuit impedance.

9.1.2   The circuit impedance and the impedance diagram

The supply voltage will find a current being drawn from it when the resistor and inductor network is connected across it. Logic dictates that if we divide the supply voltage vectorily by this current, we get something that must have units of ohms, and it will be some vector combination of R and X_L. This is commonly known as the circuit impedance and is given the symbol Z. Z is a vector and has units of ohms and is a combination of the impedance effects of all the circuit components connected across the supply voltage. In our case, Z could be defined as the supply voltage divided by the supply current, but we will sometimes be calculating the impedance of, say, part of a network, and the impedance is thus generally defined as the voltage across a network divided by the current drawn by the network.

In the series R and L circuit given we can devolve a useful diagram called the impedance diagram by dividing all our phasors by the reference current phasor i. Since i has no phase angle, purely because we chose it as reference, this division is simple, and the result is shown in Fig. 9.3.

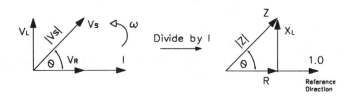

Fig. 9.3 — Development of the impedance diagram.

Fig. 9.3 shows how we get from the phasor diagram to the impedance diagram. It is of interest to note that since we have divided the phasors of frequency ω by a phasor of frequency ω we get a vector diagram of impedances that no longer must be considered to be rotating, thus the circuit impedance diagram is a vector diagram and not a phasor diagram. The impedance diagram allow us to develop the following formulae.

$$|Z| = \sqrt{(R^2 + X_L^2)} \qquad \text{and} \qquad \theta = \tan^{-1}(X_L/R) \ .$$

If we are now required to calculate the circuit variables when we are given a supply voltage of, say, $250\,V_{(rms)}$ we adopt the procedure shown in Fig. 9.4.

An example of the method is given in worked example 9.1.

9.1.3   Complex numbers solution

The description of the circuit components in their complex form (Fig. 9.5) significantly reduces the amount of geometry and diagram drawing. The circuit impedance Z can be easily stated to be as follows.

$$Z_T = Z_R + Z_L \ ,$$

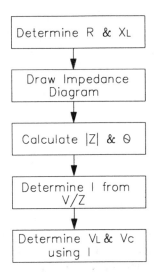

Fig. 9.4 — Procedure for determining the circuit variables in a series R and L circuit.

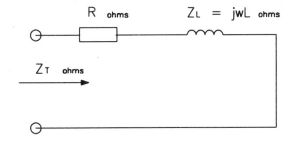

Fig. 9.5 — Complex number form of the R and L series circuit.

but

$$Z_R = R\,\Omega \quad \text{and} \quad Z_L = j\,.\,X_L = j\,.\,\omega\,.\,L\,\Omega$$

therefore

$$Z_T = Z = R + j\,.\,X_L$$

Note that Z is complex, that is, a vector.

Z is stated here in complex form where its two factors are given as a real part (R) and an imaginary part $(j \cdot X_L)$. If we require to know the magnitude and phase form of the variable Z we use the standard complex-to-polar transformation:

$$r = \sqrt{(a^2 + b^2)} \quad \text{and} \quad \theta = \tan^{-1}(b/a)$$

and in our case

$$|Z| = \sqrt{(R^2 + X_L^2)} \quad \text{and} \quad \theta = \tan^{-1}(X_L/R) .$$

The above result is a conformation of the result already obtained by using the impendance diagram, and it is clear that the complex form of notation has significant advantages over the diagramatic methods but this all supposes that the student is comfortable with complex number manipulation. The early worked examples (9.1 to 9.3) will use both the diagramatic and complex number methods, and the worked examples that come thereafter continue in this technique, and this parallel processing method should familiarize the student with the required practices.

9.2 R AND C IN SERIES

We shall now consider the R and C series circuit shown in Fig. 9.6.

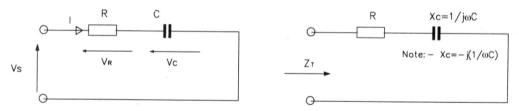

Fig. 9.6 — R and C in series.

9.2.1 Phasor diagram solution

Once again we will take the current phasor as our reference phasor since it is again common to all other circuit variables. Fig. 9.7 shows the phasor relationships for the

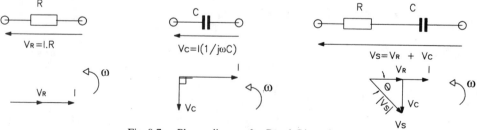

Fig. 9.7 — Phasor diagram for R and C in series.

individual circuit components and it also shows how they are added vectorily to get
the total voltage applied to the series combination of R and C.

It is of interest to note that the phasor diagram for a series combination of R and C
is very similar to the phasor diagram for a series combination of R and L. The
patterns are a reflection of each other about the current reference phasor.

We can once again use simple trigonometry to calculate the magnitide and phase
angle of the applied voltage, which is given here for reference purposes only:

$$|v_S| = \sqrt{(|v_R|^2 + |v_C|^2)}$$

and

$$\angle v_S = \tan^{-1}(|v_C|/|v_R|) \ .$$

This result, whilst being totally true, should be seen to be immaterial to the practical
cases where the supply voltage is normally the reference phasor.

9.2.2 Impedance diagram for R and C in series
The impedance diagram for R and C in series is shown in Fig. 9.8. It was, once again,

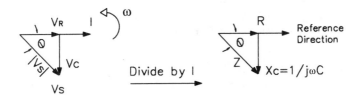

Fig. 9.8 — Impedance diagram for R and C in series.

obtained by dividing the circuit variables by the reference phasor 'i', as suggested in
the diagram.

$$\frac{v_R \angle 0°}{i} = R \angle 0 \qquad \frac{v_c \angle -\pi/2}{i} = X_c \angle -\pi/2 \qquad \frac{v_S \angle \theta}{I} = Z \angle \theta \ .$$

The calculations for the characteristics of the circuit impedance Z are similar to those
used in the R and L case:

$$|Z| = \sqrt{(R^2 + X_C^2)}$$

and

$$\angle Z = \tan^{-1}(-X_C/R)$$
$$= -\tan^{-1}(X_C/R)$$
$$= -\tan^{-1}(1/\omega \,.\, CR) \ .$$

This once again gives us a method for approaching our circuit analysis without having to make the current the reference phasor. The preferred method for dealing with ac analysis should now begin to suggest itself, and the next section, on complex number, should drive home this accepted wisdom.

9.2.3 Complex numbers solution
In Fig. 9.9, circuit impedance $Z = Z_R + Z_C$

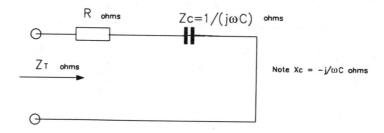

Fig. 9.9 — R and C in series with complex notation.

$$= R - j \,.\, X_C$$
$$= R - j \,.\, \frac{1}{\omega \,.\, C} \ ,$$

and again we use $r = \sqrt{(a^2 + b^2)}$ with $\angle\theta = \tan^{-1}(b/a)$ to determine $|Z|$ and $\angle Z$, thus

$$|Z| = \sqrt{(R^2 + X_C^2)}$$

and

$$\angle Z = \tan^{-1}(-X_C/R)$$
$$= -\tan^{-1}(1/\omega \,.\, CR) \ .$$

Once again the use of the the complex form of circuit analysis arrives at the result significantly faster and mathematically tidier.

9.3   R, L, AND C IN SERIES
We shall now consider the R, L, C series circuit shown in Fig. 9.10.

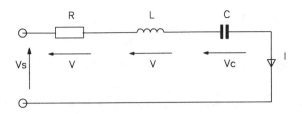

Fig. 9.10 — R, L , and C in series.

9.3.1 Phasor diagram solution

The circuit current is still the common variable to all the series components, and we will therefore use it as the reference vector to introduce the phasor diagram solution of the circuit analysis.

Fig. 9.11 shows how the individual component voltages are related to the

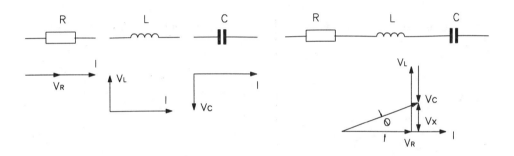

Fig. 9.11 — Phasor diagram of R, L, and C in series.

reference current phasor, and it also shows how they are combined under the guidance of Kirchhoff's voltage summation law to determine the overall supply voltage phasor. From this resultant phasor diagram we can determine the magnitude and phase of this supply voltage:

$$|v_S| = \sqrt{(|v_R|^2 + |v_X|^2)} \qquad \text{where } v_X = |v_L| - |v_C|$$

and

$$\angle v_S = \tan^{-1}(v_X/v_R) \ .$$

The circuit impedance diagram can, once again, be found by dividing the voltage phasor diagram through by the reference current phasor, see figure 9.12. The impedance diagram allows us to deduce the magnitude and phase of the overall circuit impedance Z:

$$|Z| = \sqrt{(R^2 + X^2)}$$

and

$$\angle Z = \tan^{-1}(X/R) \qquad [\text{where } X = X_L - X_C] \,.$$

Figs 9.11 and 9.12 show the condition on the phasor diagram where X_L is greater than

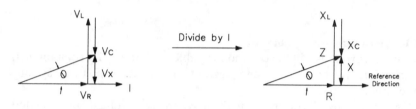

Fig. 9.12 — Impedance diagram for the R, L, and C series circuit.

X_C. This is obviously not always going to be the case, and Fig. 9.13 shows the three

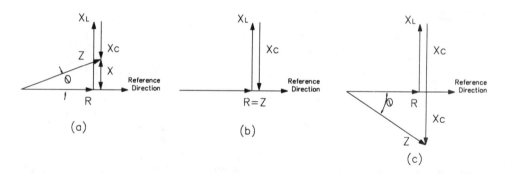

Fig. 9.13 — Series combination of R, L, and C for the three ranges of X_L relationship to X_C.

conditions for the series combination of R, L, and C that are commonly encountered.

(a) $X_L > X_C$, therefore X is positive ($+$ve).
(b) $X_L = X_C$, therefore X is zero.
(c) $X_L < X_C$, therefore X is negative ($-$ve).

All of the three ranges of conditions stated above still respond to the stated formulae for $|Z|$ and $\angle Z$, but we must remember to work with any negative values of X that might result. This means we can always be sure that the correct phase result is obtained.

The condition shown as Fig. 9.13(b) when X is zero is a special condition known as series resonance. This condition has such special features that it is dealt with separately in section 9.4.

9.3.2 Complex numbers solution
In the circuit shown in Fig. 9.14,

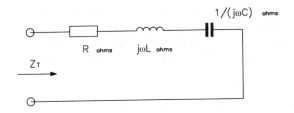

Fig. 9.14 — Complex notation on our R, L, and C series circuit.

$$Z = Z_R + Z_L + Z_C$$

that is,

$$Z = R + jX_L - jX_C$$

or

$$Z = R + j(X) \quad \text{(where } X = X_L - X_C) \text{ .}$$

Thus

$$|Z| = \sqrt{(R^2 + X^2)} \quad \text{and} \quad \angle Z = \tan^{-1}(X/R) \text{ .}$$

Once again we can see that the complex number form of solution has the advantage of mathematical simplicity, and it should now be clear that j notation is a valuable tool in the analysis of ac circuit. See worked example 9.7.

9.4 SERIES RESONANCE

9.4.1 Introduction

Resonance is defined as the vibration of a system at its natural frequency. In mechanical systems the natural frequency can be discovered by impulsing the system, for example by twanging a guitar string. If we listened to the sound of a guitar string being plucked we may be able to distinguish a main tone plus higher-frequency harmonics, and this means that even this simple mechanical system has a great many natural frequencies. This harmonic effect is significantly more evident in the sound emanating from a struck bell where a major frequency can be easily identified and the other natural frequencies can be recognized as background tones.

In electrical analaysis we can also impulse our systems, and we looked at the response of simple circuits in Chapter 6. In these early chapters we looked at the response of our circuits to the application of a step input from zero to some fixed dc level. The resultant circuit variable changes are known as the step response of the circuit under test.

We could have also looked at the effect of applying a sudden short-duration pulse of input and the resultant effects would have been called the impulse response. For the circuits considered in the previous chapters this would have been variations of simple exponential functions, as our step response results should suggest.

However, once we begin to build circuits including both inductors and capacitors we begin to get the possibility of energetic interaction between these opposing components. In the case where we apply an electrical impulse to circuits including L and C we can, under certain conditions, evoke a sinusoidal harmonic response in the circuit variables, and when this happens the circuit is said to resonate. The thoery to support this suggestion is rather complex, and outside the scope of this book, but for clarity a typical series L, C, and R impulse response is shown in Fig. 9.15.

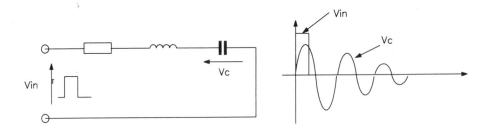

Fig. 9.15 — Series L, C, and R impulse response.

The sinusoidal oscillations are clearly seen in the above example, as is the exponential decay of the response. The frequency of the oscillations is related to the values of L and C as we will see later, and the exponential decay is directly due to the power dissipation effects of the resistor R. This regression to transient response effects is simply to make sense of the use of the term resonance when we consider the special case of the series L, C and R circuit for the condition suggested in Fig. 9.13(b). We will see that when we consider the frequency effects in our circuit around the resonant condition, a special frequency emerges that has a clear relationship to our circuit components.

9.4.2   The resonant or natural frequency in a series *R, L* and *C* circuit

Resonance in the series R, L, and C circuit is considered to be present when the supply current and the supply voltage are in phase. From the previous section we can see that this occurs when the reactance is zero, and that this in turn is a result of the inductive reactance and the capacitive reactance being equal in magnitude. Since they are always opposite in phase, this accounts for their self-cancellation when they are equal in magnitude. Fig. 9.16 shows the phasor and impedance diagrams for our series resonant circuit.

Fig. 9.16 — Phasor and impedance diagrams for series resonance.

The following observations are of use in calculating resonance parameters. At resonance

$$X_\text{L} - X_\text{C} = 0$$

that is,

$$X_\text{L} = X_\text{C} \qquad \text{(magnitude only)},$$

therefore

$$\omega \cdot L = \frac{1}{\omega \cdot C} \ ,$$

thus

$$\omega^2 = \frac{1}{L \cdot C}$$

giving

$$\omega = \frac{1}{\sqrt{(L \cdot C)}} \qquad \text{rad/s} \ .$$

Thus our radian frequency at the circuit condition called resonance is given in the above formula and is related to the two circuit reactive elements L and C. (This frequency is usually annotated with either the subscript 'n' to indicate the natural frequency or 'res' to indicate the resonant frequency of the series circuit. Both terms mean the same thing.) Thus,

$$\omega_n = \frac{1}{\sqrt{(L.C)}} \text{ rad/s} \quad \text{and} \quad f_n = \frac{1}{2.\pi\sqrt{(L.C)}} . \text{Hz} .$$

At resonance the circuit reactance (X) is zero ($X_L = X_C$), and the circuit impedance is now solely due to the circuit resistance R. That is,

$$Z = R\,\Omega .$$

In all circuits the definition of resonance (V_S and I_S in phase) is such that we can conclude that when resonance occurs the total circuit impedance can be assumed to be totally resistive. This is because the supply current and supply voltage are considered to be on phase for resonance to be happening, and voltage and current being in phase is a natural condition of purely resistive networks.

We will see later when we look at parallel circuit forms of resonance that the determination of circuit impedance at resonance is not as simple as purely considering the circuit resistance, and as the circuits become more complicated the evaluation of resonant impedance becomes less reliant upon simple deduction and more reliant upon the original definition which requires voltage and current to be in phase.

9.4.3   The series circuit voltage magnification factor (Q_0)

At resonance the inductor voltage and the capacitor voltage are equal in magnitude but opposite in direction, thus they cancel each other out completely. This is evident from the phasor diagram for resonance shown in Fig. 9.17. It must also be noted that

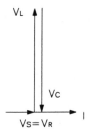

Fig. 9.17 — Resonance and voltage magnification.

all of the supply voltage now appears across R, thus $V_s = V_R$. The size of V_L and V_C is governed by the size of the current and the respective values of L and C. The current is now solely dependent upon V_s and R, but we can still alter the capacitor and inductor voltages by manipulating the L and C values to whatever we like, so long as they still satisfy the resonant frequency requirements. Thus we could achieve the situation shown in Fig. 9.17 where the inductor and capacitor voltages are significantly larger than the applied voltage.

It is important for us to appreciate the voltage magnification effect, since if it occurs it will cause practical design constraints on component operating voltages for our reactive elements.

This voltage magnification effect can be subdefined in terms of the relationship between the applied voltage and the voltage across either L and C at resonance. That is

$$Q_0 = \frac{v_L}{v_S} = \frac{v_C}{v_s} = \frac{v_X}{v_R} = \frac{i \cdot \omega_0 \cdot L}{i \cdot R} = \frac{L}{\sqrt{(L \cdot C)} \cdot R} \text{ ,}$$

giving us

$$Q_0 = \frac{1}{R} \cdot \frac{\sqrt{L}}{\sqrt{C}} \quad \text{(No units \dots volts/volts)}$$

The key points about this term Q_0 is that it is defined at resonance as it is not determinable at any other frequency. By this it is meant that v_L/v_S is equal to Q_0 only at $\omega = \omega_0$.

There are two distinct methods for making a series circuit resonate when this circuit is not currently resonating, and both techniques are derived from the resonant frequency equation.

$$\omega_n = \frac{1}{\sqrt{(L \cdot C)}} \quad \text{rad/s .}$$

If our current circuit frequency is not ω_n, we can simply alter it to achieve $\omega = \omega_n$. Or we can change L or C to bring about the condition where our current frequency is now the resonant frequency. Both methods are covered in the following sections.

9.4.4   Resonance through component balance

Fig. 9.18 shows how we must either increase the capacitance reactance or decrease the inductive reactance to make $X_L = X_C$. (Note system frequency $= 50$ Hz)

(a) Increasing X_C means decreasing C, since $X_C = \dfrac{1}{\omega \cdot C}$

The desired increase is to $500 \, \Omega$ (at 50 Hz) therefore

$$C_{(new)} = \frac{1}{\omega \cdot X_C} = 6.366 \, \mu F$$

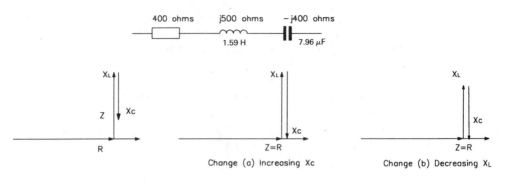

Fig. 9.18 — Phasor diagrams for before and after component change to achieve resonance.

(b) Decreasing X_L means decreasing L since $X_L = \omega \cdot L$

The desired decrease is to $400\,\Omega$ (at 50 Hz) therefore

$$L_{(new)} = X_L/\omega = 1.27\,H \ .$$

9.4.5   Resonance through variation of system frequency

We can also achieve resonance in our series R, L, *and* C circuit by varying the system frequency until $X_L = X_C$. This is achieved by setting $\omega = \omega_n$ (where $\omega_n = 1/\sqrt{(L \cdot C)}$).

$$\therefore \omega_n = 281.1 \text{ rads/s or } f_n = 44.74 \text{ Hz}$$

Worked example 9.7 covers the calculations necessary to complete your introduction to resonance.

9.5   POWER IN AC CIRCUITS

When we looked at power in dc circuits we discovered that the basic formulae for computing power were as follows.

$$\text{Power } P = I \cdot V = I^2 R = \frac{V^2}{R} \text{ W}$$

When we looked at power in ac circuits for purely resistive loads we found that the above formulae were applicable only if we were considering instantaneous power. If we adopted the use of rms values, we could use that above formulae to predict the average power developed over a sinusoidal cycle of ac waveform.

When we looked at pure inductance and capacitance we found that the ac power over a cycle of sinusoidal waveform was zero, but it did have the same shape as the power waveform for a purely resistive load. When we looked at combinations of resistive and reactive circuits the calculation of power was not covered, and this was because the rules about power in ac circuits with combinations of resistance and reactance are independent of the forms of combination, as the following sections should show.

9.5.1 Power waveforms in ac circuits

Fig. 9.19(a) shows the power dissipation waveform for a purely resistive circuit.

Fig. 9.19(b) shows the power dissipation waveform for a resistive and inductive combination circuit.

Fig. 9.19(c) shows the power dissipation waveform for a resistive and capacitive combination circuit.

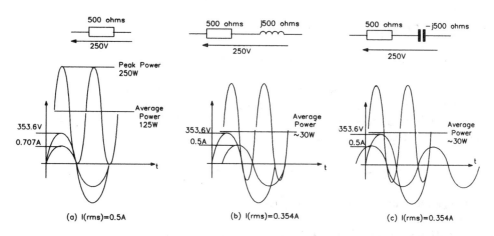

Fig. 9.19 — Power dissipation in resistive, inductive and capacitive circuits.

Whilst the shape of the power waveform remains the same in all three cases, we can see that the average power, that is, the effective power delivered to the circuit, is dependent upon the amount of the waveform that sits below the X axis.

If we calculate the power dissipated in the resistor of all three circuits by using the I^2R formula and thus avoiding L and C we can see that the average power in all three circuits is obviously due to the resistor alone.

(a) $I^2R = 125.0\,\text{W}$ (125.0 W from graph)
(b) $I^2R = 31.3\,\text{W}$ (≈ 30 W form graph)
(c) $I^2R = 31.3\,\text{W}$ (≈ 30 W from graph)

This consistent with the results obtained in Chapter 8 for the three pure components where we found that inductors and capacitors cannot dissipate power. Thus, as a general rule, we can say that only the resistive components in ac circuits can dissipate power, thus these are the only components we need to consider in our determination of power in ac circuits. This might suggest that in complicated circuits with lots of resistors, etc., we must identify the current flowing through each resistor in order to find the total power being dissipated. In fact this is not the case, and all we need to do is to determine the effective resistance connected across the circuit under examination. This can be achieved by resolving the current taken from the supply voltage into resistive and reactive components.

9.5.2 Resolution of current phasor into resistive and reactive components

In both the inductive (Fig. 9.20(a)) and the capacitive (Fig. 9.20(b)) circuits we can

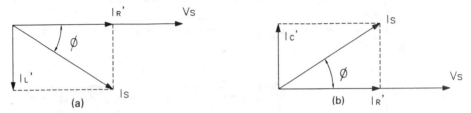

Fig. 9.20 — Current resolution in ac power circuits.

see that the current can be resolved into two components, one in phase with the applied voltage and therefore the effective resistive component, and the other at $\pm \pi/2$ rad to the applied voltage and therefore the reactive component. Thus we can say that the effective power in all ac circuits is given by:

$$\text{Power in ac circuits } 'P' = V \cdot I \cdot \cos(\phi)$$

where V and I are rms values and ϕ is the phase angle between the applied voltage and current.

Cos(ϕ) is universally known as the circuit power factor (pf), and it is the single most important factor when the design of a power system is being considered. We cannot calculate the power in ac systems without it, and it is the most common source of error in calculations carried out by novices in the manipulation of power systems formulae.

It is also of interest to look at the other V and I products possible in ac circuits, since they all have information to impart for consideration in power systems. To do this we will employ a vector diagram called the power phasor diagram.

9.5.3 The power phasor diagram

Fig. 9.21 shows the progression from impedance to power diagram through the

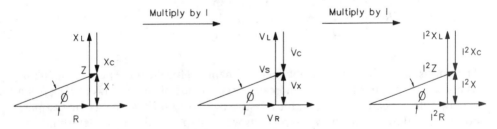

Fig. 9.21 — Voltage, impedance, and power diagrams.

repeated multiplication of the diagrams by the current phasor I:

$$Z_{(\text{diag})} \times I_S \gg V_{(\text{diag})}$$

$$V_{(\text{diag})} \times I_S \gg P_{(\text{diag})}$$

Now $|I_S|^2 . R = |I_S| . |V_R|$ we already know is real power.

The term $|I_S|^2 . X = |I_S| . |V_X|$ is called volt amperes reactive (or vars)

The term $|I_S|^2 . Z = |I_S| . |V_S|$ is called apparent power (or volt amperes)

The apparent power is so called because it is the product of V and I which traditionally indicates power calculations. It is important to know about the system's apparent power because this indicates the maximum current conditions and this allows us to determine the system's ratings for things like fuses and coil windings.

The Vars of a circuit is a measure of how much power in the circuit is being wasted. All reactive power is employed in charging and discharging either inductors or capacitors, thus it constitutes a waste of energy transfer. In power systems it is usually necessary to ensure that the Vars are kept to a minimum, and there is a process called power factor correction that is specifically employed to achieve this.

The power phasor diagram allows us to write down another set of formulae for real power and vars as follows:

$$\text{Real power} = |I_S|^2 . R = |I_S| . |V_R| = |I_S| . |V_S| . \cos(\phi)$$

and

$$\text{Vars} = |I_S|^2 . X = |I_S| . |V_X| = |I_S| . |V_S| . \sin(\phi) .$$

These results can be confirmed by looking at Fig. 9.21 and applying simple trignometric formulae.

9.5.4 Power factor correction

If the power factor is such that we get a large vars component of power, this indicates a waste of energy transfer, and in industrial power systems it is common to employ power factor correction techniques which reduce this Vars component to below a power factor ≈ 0.8.

Most industrial loads are inductive, owing to the common use of electrical machines which employ magnetic field windings. Thus power factor correction is normally a problem associated with the correction from an inductive current lag ($\omega . r . t.$ supply voltage) to a current lag of less than $36.87°$. (pf = 0.8). This is achieved by the use of a power factor correction capacitor as shown in Fig. 9.22.

The current drawn by the capacitor is at $+\pi/2$ rads ($+90°$) phase angle with respect to the applied voltage. Thus the total current I_T drawn from the supply voltage is seen to be the vector sum of I_L and I_C. If we assume that a correction to a pf = 0.8 is acceptable, the following calculation for the capacitor value is of interest.

Presuming we know I_L and ϕ we can calculate I_L' and I_R', using:

$$I_L' = I_L . \sin(\phi) \qquad \text{(see phasor diagram)}$$

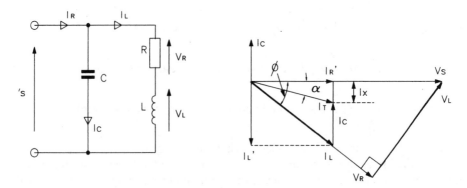

Fig. 9.22 — The use of a power factor correction capacitor.

$$I_R' = I_L \cdot \cos(\phi) \qquad \text{(see phasor diagram)}$$

and

$$I_X = I_R \cdot \tan(\alpha) \qquad \text{(where } \cos(\alpha) = 0.8) \; .$$

Now

$$I_C = I_L' - I_X \; ,$$

which allows us to calculate X_C as follows:

$$X_C = \frac{V_S}{I_C}\Omega \; ,$$

hence the value of C in farads is:

$$C = \frac{1}{2 \cdot \pi \cdot f \cdot X_C} \qquad \text{(where } f = \text{supply frequency)} \; ,$$

This is the traditional technique for the determination of the power factor correction capacitor, but a simpler method exists if we use parallel circuit theory instead of the series circuit theory so far encountered. This leads us nicely into the next chapter where we investigate the analysis of circuits that are parallel in nature, and obviously we must also look at circuits that are combinations of both parallel and series circuits.

WORKED EXAMPLES

Example 9.1

Q. For the circuit shown in Fig. 9.23; calculate the current drawn from the 50 V (50 Hz) supply and hence calculate the voltage dropped across the resistor and the

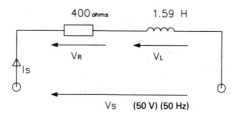

Fig. 9.23.

voltage dropped across the inductor. Show your results in phasor diagram form and Argand (complex diagram) form. The phasor and impedance diagrams for the circuit are shown in Fig. 9.24.

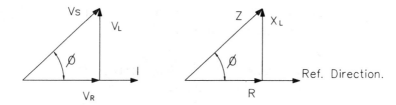

Fig. 9.24 — Phasor and impedance diagrams for the circuit.

A. *Solution using phasor diagrams*

$$L = 1.59\,\mathrm{H}$$

Thus

$$X_L = 2 \times \pi \times 50 \times 1.59$$
$$= 500\,\Omega$$

and, since

$$R = 400\,\Omega \ ,$$

we get

$$|Z| = \sqrt{(R^2 + X_L^2)} = 640.3\,\Omega$$

and

$$\angle Z = \tan^{-1}(X_L/R) = 0.896 \, \text{rad} \ (51.34°) \ ,$$

thus

$$Z = 640.3 \ \angle 0.896 \, \Omega.$$

Finally,

$$i = \frac{v_S}{Z} = \frac{50}{640.3 \ \angle 0.896} = 78.09 \ \angle -0.896 \, \text{mA} \ .$$

To complete the example we will calculate the resistor and inductor voltages, using Ohm's law.

$$v_R = i \cdot R = 78.09 \times 10^{-3} \ ^\wedge[-0.896] \times 400 \ ^\wedge[0]$$
$$= 31.236 \ \angle -0.896 \, \text{V}.$$

$$v_L = i \cdot X_L = 78.09 \times 10^{-3} \ \angle -0.896 \times 500 \ \angle \pi/2$$
$$= 39.05 \ \angle 0.675 \, \text{V}. \qquad (0.675 \, \text{rad} = 38.67°)$$

Fig. 9.25 shows the final result of all our work, and we can see that the supply voltage

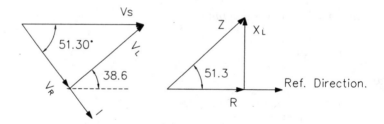

Fig. 9.25 — Phasor diagram for the worked example.

is now our reference phasor, but the phasor diagram shape is consistent with the theory covered in the preceding section. If we rotate that phasor diagram until the current vector is in line with 0 radians (0°) we get our familiar phasor diagram as shown in Fig. 9.24.

Solution using complex numbers

$$Z = 400 + j \cdot 500 \, \Omega \ ,$$

therefore

$$i = \frac{v_S}{Z} = \frac{50}{400 + j500} = 48.78 - j60.98 \, \text{mA} \; (78.09 \; \angle - 51.3° \, \text{mA})$$

$$v_R = i \cdot R = (48.78 - j60.98) \times 10^{-3} \times 400$$
$$= 19.512 - j24.39 \, \text{V} \; (31.23 \; \angle - 51.34° \, \text{V}) \; .$$
$$v_L = i \cdot X_L = (48.78 - j60.98) \times 10^{-3} \times j.500$$
$$= 30.49 + j24.39 \, \text{V} \; (39.05 \; \angle 38.65° \, \text{V}) \; .$$

Fig. 9.26 shows the results for the circuit on an Argand diagram. When we compare

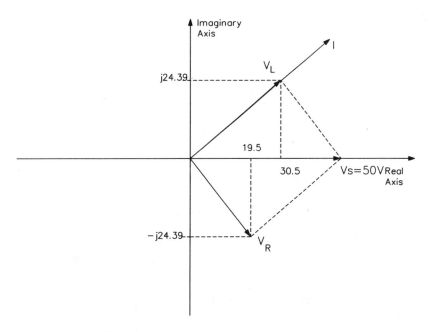

Fig. 9.26 — Argand diagram of worked example.

this to the phasor diagram we can see the compatibility of the results. It is of interest to perform complex-to-polar transformations upon our complex number solutions for i, v_R, and v_L which should give us the results obtained in the phasor solution. See above.

It is clear that we have two closely related techniques for the solution of ac circuits, but as the circuits become more complicated, the complex number method of analysis begins to become the more useful since it is independent of graphical analysis. All of the dc analysis techniques translate in method to ac analysis if we make the simple rule that for all dc cases where an R occurred we now must talk of Z in the ac equivalent analysis technique. We can do this if we accept that Z is a complex number value, whereas R was simply a real number value. This converts ac circuit analysis difficulties into complex number difficulties which are significantly easier to solve.

The final chapters of this book will perform this dc to ac analysis conversion to confirm the validity of this simple idea.

Example 9.2
Q. Calculate the current drawn from the 50 V (50 Hz) supply and hence calculate the voltage dropped across the resistor and the voltage dropped across the capacitor in the Fig. 9.27 circuit. Show your results in phasor diagram form and Argand (complex diagram) form.

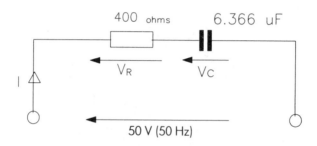

Fig. 9.27 — *R* and *C* in series.

A. *Solution using phasor diagrams*
The phasor diagram is shown in Fig. 9.28

$$C = 6.366 \,\mu\text{F} \ ,$$

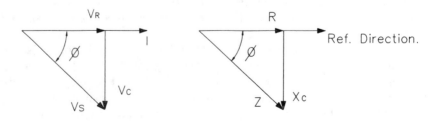

Fig. 9.28 — Phasor diagram for *R* and *C* in series.

Thus

$$X_C = 1/(2 \times \pi \times 50 \times 6.366 \times 10^{-6})$$
$$= 500\,\Omega \ ,$$

and since

$$R = 400\,\Omega \ ,$$

we get

$$|Z| = \sqrt{(R^2 + X_C^2)} = 640.3\,\Omega$$

and

$$\angle Z = -\tan^{-1}(X_C/R) = -0.896\,\text{rad}\ (-51.34°)\ ,$$

thus

$$Z = 640.3 \ \angle -0.896\,\Omega \ .$$

Finally,

$$i = \frac{v_S}{Z} = \frac{50}{640.3 \ \angle -0.896} = 78.09 \ \angle 0.896\,\text{mA} \ .$$

To complete the example we will calculate the resistor and inductor voltages, using Ohm's law.

$$v_R = i \cdot R = (78.09 \times 10^{-3} \ \angle 0.896) \times (400 \angle 0°)$$
$$= 31.236 \ \angle 0.896\,\text{V} \ .$$
$$v_C = i \cdot X_C = (78.09 \times 10^{-3} \ \angle 0.896) \times (500 \ \angle -\pi/2)$$
$$= 39.05 \ \angle -0.675\,\text{V} \ .$$
$$(-0.675\,\text{rad} = -38.65°)$$

Fig. 9.29 shows the final result of all our work, and we can see that the supply voltage is now our reference phasor, but the phasor diagram shape is consistent with the theory covered in the preceding section. If we rotate the phasor diagram until the current vector is in line with 0 radians (0°) we get our familiar phasor diagram as shown in Fig. 9.28.

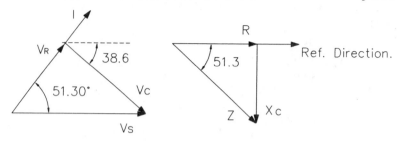

Fig. 9.29 — Phasor diagram for the worked example.

Solution using complex numbers

$$Z = 400 - \mathrm{j} . 500\,\Omega \ ,$$

therefore

$$i = \frac{v_S}{Z} = \frac{50}{400 - \mathrm{j}500} = 48.78 + \mathrm{j}60.98\,\mathrm{mA} \ .$$

$$v_R = i . R = (48.78 + \mathrm{j}60.98) \times 10^{-3} \times 400$$
$$\qquad = 19.512 + \mathrm{j}24.39\,\mathrm{V} \ .$$

$$v_C = i . X_C = (48.78 + \mathrm{j}60.98) \times 10^{-3} \times -\mathrm{j}.500$$
$$\qquad = 30.49 - \mathrm{j}24.39\,\mathrm{V} \ .$$

Fig. 9.30 shows the results for the circuit on an Argand diagram. When we compare this to the phasor diagram we can see the compatibility of the results. It is once again of interest to perform complex-to-polar transformations upon our complex number solutions for i, v_R, and v_C, which should give use the results obtained in the phasor solution. Try it for you own satisfaction.

Once again complex mathematics appears to provide the preferred method of solution.

Example 9.3
Q. Calculate the circuit supply current of the series circuit shown in Fig. 9.31 for the three values of capacitor given below. Give both phasor diagram and complex number forms of solution.

(a) $C = 12.732\,\mu\mathrm{F}$
(b) $C = 3.183\,\mu\mathrm{F}$
(c) $C = 6.366\,\mu\mathrm{F}$

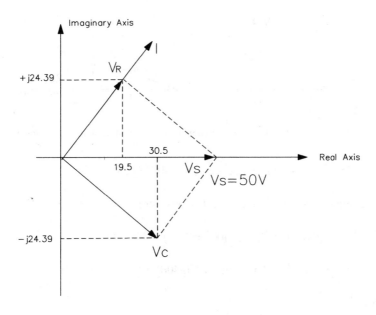

Fig. 9.30 — Argand diagram of worked example.

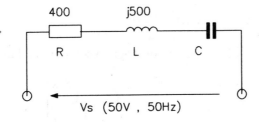

Fig. 9.31 — *R*, *L*, and *C* in series.

Note: we have already calculated $|X_L|$ to be $500\,\Omega$ at the supply frequency.

A.

(a) $C = 12.732\,\mu\text{F}$ $(|X_C| = 250\,\Omega)$

Fig. 9.32 shows the basis of the phasor diagram solution, and the complex number form of solution is given below.

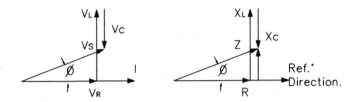

Fig. 9.32 — Phasor diagram and impedance diagram for worked example (a).

$$Z = R + j(X) = R + j(X_L - X_C) = 400 + j250 \ .$$

Whichever procedure we adopt, the next steps are the same.

$$|Z| = \sqrt{(R^2 + X^2)} = \sqrt{(400^2 + 250^2)} = 471.7\,\Omega \ ,$$

$$\angle Z = \tan^{-1}(X/R) = \tan^{-1}(250/400) = 0.559\,\text{rad}\,(32°) \ ,$$

therefore

$$|i| = v_S/|Z| = 106\,\text{mA}$$

and

$$\angle i = -0.559\,\text{rad relative to } V_S.$$

(b) $C = 3.183\,\mu\text{F}\ (|X_C| = 1000\,\Omega)$

Fig. 9.33 shows the basis of the phasor diagram solution, and the complex number

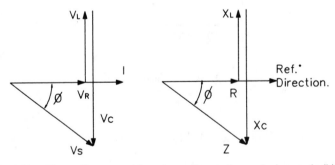

Fig. 9.33 — Phasor diagram and impedance diagram for worked example (b).

form of solution is given below.

$$Z = R + j(X) = R + j(X_L - X_C) = 400 - j500 \ .$$

Whichever procedure we adopt, the next steps are the same.

$$|Z| = \sqrt{(R^2 + X^2)} = \sqrt{(400^2 + 500^2)} = 640.31\,\Omega$$

$$\angle Z = \tan^{-1}(X/R) = \tan^{-1}(-500/400) = -0.895\,\text{rad}\ (51.3°)\ ,$$

therefore

$$|i| = v_S/|Z| = 78.09\,\text{mA}$$

and

$$\angle i = 0.895\,\text{rad relative to } V_S\ .$$

(c) $C = 6.366\,\mu\text{F}\ (|X_C| = 500\,\Omega)$

Fig. 9.34 shows the basis of the phasor diagram solution, and the complex number

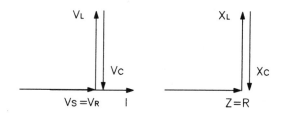

Fig. 9.34 — Phasor diagram and impedance diagram for worked example (c).

form of solution is given below.

$$Z = R + j(X) = R + j(X_L - X_C) = 400 + j0 = 400\,\Omega$$

Whichever procedure we adopt, the next steps are the same.

$$|Z| = \sqrt{(R^2 + X^2)} = 400\,\Omega\ .$$

$$\angle Z = \tan^{-1}(X/R) = \tan^{-1}(0/400) = 0\,\text{rad}\ (0°)\ ,$$

therefore

$$|i| = v_S/|Z| = 125\,\text{mA}$$

and

$$\angle i = 0 \text{ rad relative to } V_s \text{ (that is, in phase)}$$

As stated before, this condition is called resonance.

Example 9.4

Q. A series circuit consists of $R = 20\,\Omega$, $L = 20\,\text{mH}$, and an ac supply of 60 V with $f = 100\,\text{Hz}$. Calculate the current taken from the supply, the voltage across R, the voltage across L, and the phase angle of the current with respect to the supply voltage. Hence determine the power taken from the supply and also the apparent power and the Vars.

A. $\qquad X_L = j(\omega . L) = j . 2 . \pi . f . L = j . 2 . \pi . 100 . (20 \times 10^{-3}) = j12.57\,\Omega$

$$Z = R + jX_L = 20 + j12.57\,\Omega \ .$$
$$|Z| = \sqrt{(R^2 + X_L^2)} = 23.6\,\Omega$$

and

$$\angle Z = \tan^{-1}(X_L/R) = 0.561\,\text{rad} \ (32.1°)$$

$$I_S = V_S/Z = \frac{60}{20 + j12.57} = \frac{60(20 - j12.57)}{20^2 + 12.57^2} = 2.15 - j1.344$$

$$|I_S| = 2.54\,\text{A} \qquad \text{and} \qquad \angle I_S = -32.1° \ (\text{lagging } V_S)$$

$$V_R = I . R = (2.15 - j1.344) \times 20 = 43 - j26.88 = 50.71 \ \angle -32.1°\,\text{V} \ .$$
$$V_L = I . X_L = (2.15 - j1.344) \times j12.57$$
$$= 16.89 + j27.03 = 31.87 \ \angle 58°$$

Real power $= I^2R$ or $|I_S| . |V_R|$ or $|I_S| . |V_S| . \cos\phi$, where $\phi = 32.1°$.

Therefore real power $= 2.54 \times 60 \times \cos(32.1°) = 129\,\text{W}$.

Apparent power $= I^2Z$ or $|I_S| . |V_S| = 2.54 \times 60$

$$= 152 . \text{VA (volt amperes) (can't use watts)}$$

Vars $= I^2X_L$ or $|I_S| . |V_L|$ or $|I_S| . |V_L|$ or $|I_S| . |V_S| . \sin\phi$)

therefore Vars $= 2.54 \times 60 \times \sin(32.1°) = 81$ Vars.

Note: App power $= \sqrt{(\text{real power}^2 + \text{Vars}^2)}$ (power phasors)

(Use the above to check the results).

Example 9.5

Q. A 64 mH inductor with a winding resitance of $R_w = 700\,\Omega$ is connected in series with a resistor $R_1 = 3.3\,\mathrm{k}\Omega$. A 10 V supply with a frequency of 5.0 kHz is connected to the series circuit. Calculate the circuit current and the terminal voltage across the inductor. Hence, or otherwise, determine the percentage of the supplied power that is lost in heating the inductor's windings.

The first step in solving this example is the drawing of an explanatory circuit diagram. This will allow us to identify the variables being asked for. The phasor diagram can also be sketched to outline the circuit conditions. See Fig. 9.35.

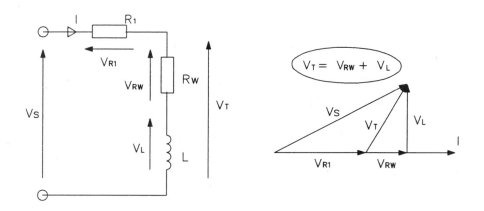

Fig. 9.35 — Circuit diagram and phasor diagram.

$$jX_L = j.2.\pi.f.L = j.2.\pi.(5 \times 10^3).(64 \times 10^{-3}) = j2.0\ \mathrm{k}\Omega.$$

The total circuit resistance R_T is given by the sum of the inductor's winding resistance and the resistor R_1.

$$R_T = R_w + R_1 = 4.0\,\mathrm{k}\Omega \ .$$

Now

$$I_S = V_S/Z \qquad \text{where} \qquad Z = R_T + jX_L \ ,$$

Therefore

$$I_S = \frac{V_S}{R_T + jX_L} = \frac{10\,\mathrm{V}}{4.0 + j2.0\,\mathrm{k}\Omega} = 2.0 - j1.0\,\mathrm{mA} \ ,$$

giving

$$I_S = 2.24\ \angle -26.56°\,\mathrm{mA} \ .$$

Now V_T, the terminal voltage across the inductor, must include an appreciation of the winding resistance R_w. Thus,

$$V_T = I_S \cdot Z_T = (2.0 - j1.0 \,\text{mA}) \times (0.7 + j2.0 \,\text{k}\Omega)$$
$$= (1.4 + 2.0) + j(-0.7 + 4.0) \,\text{V}$$
$$= 3.4 + j3.3 \,\text{V}$$
$$= 4.74 \angle 44.1° \,\text{V} \qquad \text{(phase angle with respect to } V_S\text{)}$$
$$= 4.74 \angle 70.7° \,\text{V} \qquad \text{(phase angle with respect to } I_S\text{)}$$

The phasor diagram for the final result is now given in Fig. 9.36.

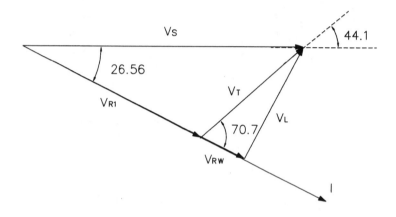

Fig. 9.36 — Phasor diagram for the final result.

Total Power Supplied $= |I_S| \cdot |V_S| . \cos\phi = 2.24 \times 10^{-3} . 10 . \text{Cos}(26.56°)$
$$= 20.04 \text{ mW.}$$

Power in Inductor $= |I_S| \cdot |V_T| . \cos\phi_L = 2.24 \times 10^{-3} . 4.74 . \text{Cos}(70.7°)$
$$= 3.51 \text{ mW.}$$

$\therefore$ % lost in heating inductor $= 17.5\%$

Use I^2R to confirm these results.

Example 9.6
Q. A series circuit (Fig. 9.37) consists of $R = 47 \,\Omega$ and $C = 10 \,\mu\text{F}$ connected across an ac supply of 100 V (300 Hz). Calculate the supply current, the voltage across R, and the phase angle of the current with respect to the supply voltage. Hence determine the real power developed in the resistor and the Vars lost in the capacitor.

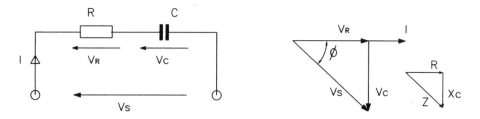

Fig. 9.37 — Circuit diagram and sketch phasor diagram.

A. $X_C = 1/(j.2.\pi.f.C) = 1/(j.2.\pi.300.\{10^{-5}\}) = -j53.1\,\Omega$

$Z = R + X_C = 47 - j53.1\,V$,

therefore

$$I_S = V_S/Z = \frac{100}{47 - j53.1} = 0.935 + j1.056\,A$$

$$= 1.41\,\angle\,48.5°\,A$$,

giving

$$V_R = I.R = 1.41\,\angle\,48.5° \times 47 = 66.3\,\angle\,48.5°\,V$$.

We can observe that ϕ (phase angle) $= \angle\,48.5°$, thus

$$\text{real power} = |I_S|.|V_S|.\cos(\phi) = 93.43\,W,$$

and

$$\text{Vars} = |I_S|.|V_S|.\sin(\Phi) = 105.6\,\text{Vars}$$,

CHECK:

$$VA = 141 ,\qquad \sqrt{(\text{real power}^2 + \text{Vars}^2)} = 141.04\qquad \text{'OK'}$$

Example 9.7
Q. A series R, L, *and* C circuit (Fig. 9.38) has a supply voltage of 75 V with a frequency of 200 Hz. Calculate the following circuit conditions.

(a) Supply current I_S.

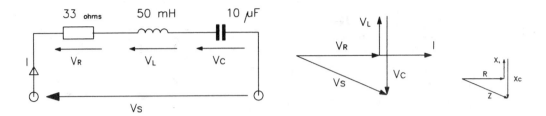

Fig. 9.38 — R, L, and C circuit diagram and phasor diagram.

(b) V_R, V_L, and V_C.
(c) The circuit phase angle and power factor (ϕ and $\cos(\phi)$).
(d) The apparent and real power and the Vars.
(e) The circuit resonant frequency f_n.
(f) The Q_0 at resonance.
(g) The current drawn at resonance.
(h) The value of a power factor correction capacitor if R and L were as given above at a frequency of 200 Hz. (i.e. no series capacitor).

A. (a) Supply current I_S.

$$X_L = j(\omega \cdot L) = j \cdot 2 \cdot \pi \cdot 200 \cdot (50 \times 10^{-3}) = j62.8\,\Omega$$

$$X_C = 1/j(\omega \cdot C) = 1/j(2 \cdot \pi \cdot 200 \cdot \{10^{-5}\} = -j79.6\,\Omega$$

$$Z = R + j(X_L - X_C) = 33 - j16.8\,\Omega = 37 \angle -27°\,\Omega$$

$$I_S = \frac{V_S}{Z} = \frac{75}{37 \angle -27°} = 2.03 \angle 27°\,\text{A} \quad.$$

(b) V_R, V_L, and V_C.

$$V_R = I_S \cdot R = 2.03 \angle 27° \times 33 = 67\,\text{V} \angle 27°$$

$$V_L = I_S \cdot X_L = 2.03 \angle 27° \times 62.8 \angle 90° = 127 \angle 117°\,\text{V}$$

$$V_C = I_S \cdot X_C = 2.03 \angle 27° \times 79.6 \angle -90° = 162 \angle -63°\,\text{V}$$

(c) The circuit phase angle and power factor (ϕ and $\cos(\phi)$)

By observation $\phi = 27°$, therefore $pf = \cos(\phi) = 0.89$

(d) The apparent and real power and the Vars

Apparent power $= |I| \cdot |V| = 152\,\text{VA}$
Real power $= |I| \cdot |V| \cdot \cos(\phi) = 135.5\,\text{Watts}$
Vars $= |Z| \cdot |V| \cdot \sin(\phi) = 69\,\text{Vars}$

(e) The circuit resonant frequency f_n.

$$\omega_n = 1/\sqrt{(L \cdot C)} = 1.414 \times 10^3\,\text{rad/s}$$

$$f_n = \omega_n/(2 \cdot \pi) = 225\,\text{Hz}$$

Observation of the phasor diagram calculated values suggests that the resonant frequency should not have been far away from 200 Hz.

(f) *The Q_0 at resonance.*

$$Q_0 = \frac{1 \cdot \sqrt{L}}{R\sqrt{C}} = 2.143 \qquad \text{(You can't use } V_L \text{ and } V_R \text{ from (b))}$$

(g) The current drawn at resonance

$$I_{res} = \frac{V_S}{Z_{res}} = \frac{V_S}{Z_R} = \frac{75}{33} = 2.273\,\text{A}$$

(h) The value of a power factor correction capacitor if R and L were as given above at a frequency of 200 Hz (i.e., no series capacitor). The circuit is shown in Fig. 9.39.

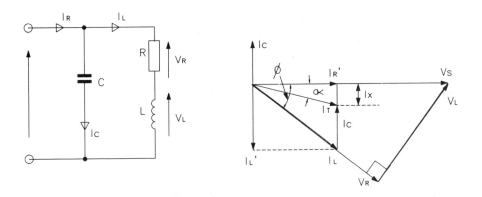

Fig. 9.39 — Circuit for part (h).

$$I_L = \frac{V_S}{Z_L} = \frac{75}{33 + j62.8} = 0.492 - j0.936\,\text{A} = 1.057\,\angle -62.2°\,\text{A}\ ,$$

therefore,

$$I_L' = I_L \cdot \sin(\phi) = 1.057 \cdot \sin \cdot (62.2) = 0.936\,\text{A}\ ,$$

and

$$I_R' = I_L \cdot \cos(\phi) = 1.057 \cdot \cos \cdot (62.3) = 0.492\,\text{A}$$

Now

$$I_X = I_R' \cdot \tan \cdot (\alpha)$$

where α is the desired phase angle and $\cos(\alpha) = 0.8\,(\text{pf})$

$$\alpha = \cos^{-1}(0.8) = 36.87°\ ,$$

therefore,

$$I_X = 0.492 \cdot \tan(36.87°) = 0.37\,\text{A}$$

Now

$$I_C = I_L' - I_X = 0.566\,\text{A}\ ,$$

therefore

$$X_C = \frac{V_S}{I_C} = \frac{75}{0.5653} = 132.6\,\Omega\ ,$$

giving

$$C = \frac{1}{2 \cdot \pi \cdot f \cdot X_C} = \frac{1}{2 \cdot \pi \cdot 200 \cdot (132.6)} = 6.0\,\mu\text{F}\ .$$

As a check of this result we can evaluate the total circuit impedance, and if our result is correct the phase angle of this impedance should satisfy a power factor requirement of 0.8, that is, the phase angle should be $+36.87°$.

$$Z_T = \frac{Z_C . Z_L}{Z_C + Z_L}$$

where $Z_C = -j132.6\,\Omega$ and $Z_L = 33 + j62.8\,\Omega$.

Try it and see.

$$Z_{CCT} = 121.8 \ \angle 36.98° \ \Omega$$

∴comparable.

REVIEW QUESTIONS AND TUTORIAL EXAMPLES

(9.1)   Calculate the current in an inductive load of resistance $5\,\Omega$ ohms and inductance $0.02\,H$, when supplied from a 200 V (50 Hz) supply. Also determine the load phase angle (24.91 A, 51.5°).

(9.2)   An inductive coil of resistance $40\,\Omega$ and inductance $0.2\,H$ is connected to a 500 V (50 Hz) supply. Calculate the coils impedance, the supply taken, and its phase angle. ($74.5\,\Omega$, 6.714 A, $-57.5°$).

(9.3)   An inductive coil of resistance $4\,\Omega$ takes a current of 8 A when connected to a 100 V (50 Hz) supply. Calculate the impedance of the coil, its inductive reactance element, and thus the coils inductance. Also determine the supply current phase angle. ($12.5\,\Omega$, $11.84\,\Omega$, $0.0377\,H$, $-71.3°$).

(9.4)   A purely resistive load takes 10 A at 100 V (50 Hz). Calculate the value of an inductor that is intended to be connected in series with this resistor in order that the same current be supplied from a new voltage source of 200 V (50 Hz). Also determine the phase angle between the 200 V supply and the required current. ($0.055\,H$, 60°).

(9.5)   When a resistor and an 'impure' inductor are connected in series and placed across a supply of 240 V (50 Hz) a current of 3 A flows at a lagging phase angle of 37°. The voltage across the inductor is measured to be 171 V (magnitude only). Determine the resistance of the resistor and the resistance and inductance of the inductor. ($33.4\,\Omega$, $30.5\,\Omega$, and $0.153\,H$). (Hint, Worked example 9.5)

(9.6)   A resistor of $100\,\Omega$ is connected in series with a capacitor of $50\,\mu F$ to a supply of 200 V (50 Hz). Determine the circuit impedance, the supply current, the circuit pf, the supply current phase angle, the voltage across the resistor, and voltage across the capacitor. ($118.5\,\Omega$, 1.69 A, 0.844, 32.48°, 169 V, 107 V).

(9.7)   A resistor in series with a capacitor is connected to a 240 V (60 Hz) supply. Find the value of C so that the resistor absorbs 300 W at 100 V. (36.5 μF).

(9.8)   An inductive load takes a 10 A current and disspates 1000 W when connected across a supply of 250 V (50 Hz). Calculate the impedance of the load, the effective resistance of the load, the inductance of the load, its power factor pf, and the angle of current lag. (25 Ω, 10 Ω, j22.9 Ω (73 mH). 0.4, 66.4°).

(9.9)   In a series R and L circuit the current is measured at 100 $\angle$ $-25°$ mA to a supply voltage of 50 V. Calculate the apparent power, real power and Vars supplied to the circuit. (5.0 VA, 4.5 W, 2.1 Vars).

(9.10)   A series circuit consisting of $R = 1.2$ kΩ and $C = 0.1 \mu$F is supplied with a voltage of 45 V (1 kHz). Determine the apparent and real power and the Vars. (1 VA, 0.6 W, 0.8 Vars).

(9.11)   The current taken from a 115 V (60 Hz) supply is measured as 20 A with a lagging power factor of 75%. Calculate the apparent power, real power, and Vars. Also determine the amount of capacitance that must be connected in parallel to correct the power factor to 95% lagging. (2.3 kVA, 1.725 kW, 1.52 kVars, 191 μF).

(9.12)   A series circuit has $L = 85 \mu$H, $C = 298$ pF, and $R = 100 \Omega$. If this circuit was connected across a 10 V supply of variable frequency, determine the supply frequency to achieve resonance. Also calculate the circuit current at $0.25 f_n$, $0.5 f_n$, $0.8 f_n$, f_n, $1.25 f_n$, $2 f_n$, and $4 f_n$. Plot a graph of I versus f to a logarithmic base. ($f_n = 1$ MHz, $I = \{5, 12.4, 38.3, 100, 38.3, 12.4, 5\}$ mA).

(9.13)   A series LCR circuit has $L = 100 \mu$H, $C = 1000$ pF, and $R = 25 \Omega$. Determine the f_n and Q_0 for the circuit. Also determine the new value of C required for resonance at 500 kHz when the value of L is doubled, and calculate the new Q_0. (500 kHz, 12.6, 500 pF, 25.3).

10

Parallel circuit analysis

10.1 INVERSE CIRCUIT PARAMETERS

All of the rules and techniques used so far in ac circuit analysis have relied heavily upon the fact that we have been dealing with primarily 'series' circuits. Once we begin to look at circuits that have parallel limbs, the simple formulae which employ R, X_L and X_C that we have previously used, begin to become complicated. For example, consider the simple combination of R and L in parallel, shown in Fig. 10.1.

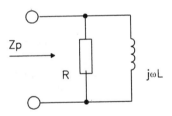

Fig. 10.1 — R and L in parallel.

$$Z_P = R \| j X_L = \frac{R \cdot j X_L}{R + j X_L} \qquad \text{(product over sum rule)}.$$

Reorganizing this into $a + jb$ form gives

$$Z_P = \frac{j R \cdot X_L (R - j X_L)}{R^2 + X_L^2}$$

or

$$Z_P = \frac{R(X_L)^2 + jR^2X_L}{R^2 + X_L^2},$$

thus

$$Z_P = R^* + jX^*$$

where

$$R^* = \frac{R(X_L)^2}{R^2 + X_L^2} \quad \text{and} \quad jX^* = \frac{jR^2X_L}{R^2 + X_L^2}.$$

This result highlights the sort of complications we can expect if we continued to use R, X, and Z in our analysis of parallel circuits. However, fear not, because a technique exists, and it is called the inverse parameter method. If it isn't, it should be. In this method we use the inverses of R, X, and Z to analyze our parallel circuits, and the results are significantly easier than those obtained by using the standard methods.

To start this method we will look at the suggested inverse parameters of R, X, and Z.

10.1.1 Conductance (G), the inverse of resistance

For Fig. 10.2, R is defined as follows:

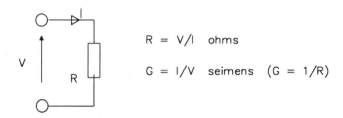

R = V/I   ohms

G = I/V   seimens   (G = 1/R)

Fig. 10.2 — Simple resistor and its voltage and current.

$$R = V/I\,\Omega \qquad \text{(Ohm's law)}$$

G is defined as:

$$G = I/V \text{ siemans},$$

thus $$G = I/R \qquad \text{(the inverse of } R\text{)}$$

Certain variations of Ohm's law are now apparent.

$$\textit{Resistor-based formulae} \qquad\qquad \textit{Conductance-based formulae}$$
$$R = V/I \qquad\qquad\qquad\qquad G = I/V$$
$$V = I \cdot R \qquad\qquad\qquad\qquad I = V \cdot G$$
$$I = V/R \qquad\qquad\qquad\qquad V = I/G$$

The use of these inverse versions of Ohm's law is not apparent as yet, but when we look at parallel combinations where the voltage is common to all components and the currents are added together to determine total current, the advantages should be self evident.

10.1.2 Susceptance (*S*), the inverse of reactance
In Fig. 10.3, X_L and X_C are both defined as follows:

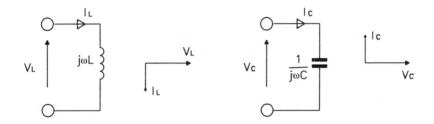

Fig. 10.3 — Simple inductor and capacitor and their voltages and currents.

$$X = V/I \, \Omega \qquad \text{(Ohm's law)}$$

S is defined as

$$S = I/V \text{ siemens},$$

that is,

$$S_L = I_L/V \qquad \text{and} \qquad S_C = I_C/V,$$

thus, $S = 1/X$ (the inverse of *X*)

More specifically, if we are using complex number forms for our reactive components we can state that:

if $X_L = j(\omega \cdot L)$,   then $S_L = \dfrac{1}{j(\omega \cdot L)} = \dfrac{-j}{(\omega \cdot L)}$,

and,

if $\quad X_C = \dfrac{1}{j(\omega . C)}, \quad$ then $\quad S_C = j(\omega . C)$.

The previously mentioned variations in Ohm's law are still applicable if we replace R with X, and G with S_L or S_C. Remember, S is complex, like X.

10.1.3 Admittance (Y), the inverse of impedance

In Fig. 10.4, Z is defined as follows:

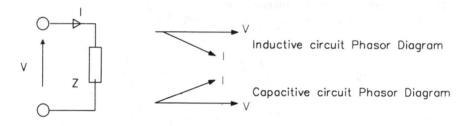

Fig. 10.4 — Simple impedance and its voltage and currents.

$$Z = V/I\,\Omega \qquad \text{(Ohm's law)}$$

Y is defined as:

$$Y = I/V \text{ siemens,}$$

thus, $\quad Y = 1/Z \qquad$ (the inverse of Z).

The Ohm's law variations are once again applicable if we use the relevant substitutions of Z for R and Y for G. For example:

$$V = I.R \qquad \text{becomes} \qquad V = I.Z$$
and $\quad V = I/G \qquad \text{becomes} \qquad V = I/Y$

Remember, Y is complex, like Z.

We will now employ these new-found versions of Ohm's law to analyze simple parallel circuits.

10.2 ANALYSIS OF PARALLEL CIRCUITS

10.2.1 R in parallel with L

The applied voltage V is common to both components in Fig. 10.5, and it is therefore

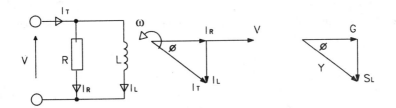

Fig. 10.5 — R and L in parallel, with phasor and admittance diagrams.

used as the reference vector. We can see from the phasor diagram that I_T is found by summating I_R and I_L. If we divide the current phasors by the common voltage phasor we get the admittance diagram.

It must now be apparent that we are using developments very similar to those used in the series combination of R and L, and thus the maths is as simple here as it was in the series case, if we use admittance-based formulae. Using complex number notation is equally easy, and we can see that the total admittance of the circuit is easily deduced:

$$I_T = I_R + I_L \qquad \text{(Kirchhoff current law)}$$

dividing through by V gives

$$\frac{I_T}{V} = \frac{I_R}{V} + \frac{I_L}{V}$$

or $\qquad Y_T = Y_R + Y_L, \qquad$ that is, $\qquad Y_T = G + S_L$

and $\qquad Y_T = G + \dfrac{1}{j(\omega . L)}$

Now compare this to the impedance style of development seen in section 10.1. The complexity is significantly reduced.

If we now wish to calculate the circuit values like I_T. I_L, etc., we can apply our revised Ohm's law equations as the need dictates. For example,

$$I_T = V . Y_T \qquad \text{and} \qquad I_L = V . S_L = \frac{V}{j(\omega . L)}$$

Review example 10.1 will reinforce this first use of the admittance style of circuit analysis.

10.2.2   *R* in parallel with *C*

The total admittance of the circuit in Fig. 10.6 is once again easily deduced.

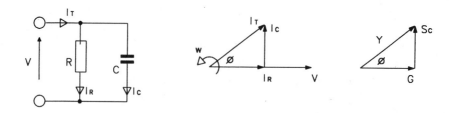

Fig. 10.6 — *R* and *C* in parallel, with phasor and admittance diagrams.

$$I_T = I_R + I_C \qquad \text{(Kirchhoff current law)}.$$

Dividing through by *V* gives:

$$\frac{I_T}{V} = \frac{I_R}{V} + \frac{I_C}{V}$$

or $\qquad Y_T = Y_R + Y_C,\qquad$ that is, $\qquad Y_T = G + S_C$

and $\qquad Y_T = G + j(\omega . C).$

Again we can deduce all other circuit variables by using our revised Ohm's laws. For example,

$$I_T = V . Y_T \qquad \text{and} \qquad I_C = V . S_C = V . j(\omega . C).$$

10.2.3   *R* in parallel with *L* and *C*

The total admittance of the circuit shown in Fig. 10.7 is once again easily deduced.

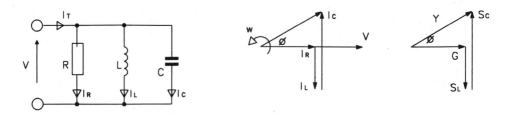

Fig. 10.7 — *R, L,* and *C* in parallel, with phasor and admittance diagrams.

$$I_T = I_R + I_L + I_C \qquad \text{(Kirchhoff's current law)}.$$

Dividing through by V gives:

$$\frac{I_T}{V} = \frac{I_R}{V} + \frac{I_L}{V} + \frac{I_C}{V}$$

or $\qquad Y_T = Y_R + Y_L + Y_C, \qquad$ that is, $\qquad Y_T = G + S_L + S_C,$

giving

$$Y_T = G + \frac{1}{j(\omega . L)} + j(\omega . C),$$

thus $\qquad Y_T = G + j(\omega . C - 1/[\omega . L])$

or $\qquad Y_T = G + j(S'), \qquad$ where $\qquad S' = \omega . C - 1/[\omega . L].$

Again we can deduce all other circuit variables by using our revised Ohm's laws. For example,

$$I_T = V . Y_T \qquad \text{and} \qquad I_C = V . S_C = V . j(\omega . C).$$

10.3 PARALLEL RESONANT CIRCUIT

Resonance is defined as the condition where the supply current is in phase with the supply voltage, and this can be true only when the circuit impedance or admittance is totally real, that is, without imaginary parts. Thus

$$Y_T = G + j(S')$$

gives $\qquad Y_T = G \qquad$ at resonance, therefore $\qquad S' = 0,$

or $\qquad \omega . C = 1/(\omega . L),$

thus $\qquad \omega_n = \dfrac{1}{\sqrt{(L . C)}} \qquad$ (where ω_n = resonant frequency)

Thus the resonant frequency of a circuit which is made up of pure R, L, and C in parallel has the same resonant frequency as that found in the series circuit. We will look at resonance in complex combinations of R, L, and C in worked examples, and later we will see this expression for ω_n recurring at great length.

There is also a current magnification factor along the same lines as the voltage magnification factor found in series circuits. It is defined by using very similar reasoning.

$$Q_O = \frac{I_L}{I_R} = \frac{V \cdot S_L}{V \cdot G} = \frac{S_L}{G} = \frac{R}{\omega_n \cdot L} = R \cdot \frac{\sqrt{C}}{\sqrt{L}}$$

Compare this to the voltage magnification factor, and we can see a not unexpected inverse relationship.

The use of these deductions about parallel circuits is best covered by example, and the section that follows on complex circuits with both series and parallel circuits will highlight the advantages and disadvantages of having the impedance and admittance forms of circuit analysis combined in an overall system analysis. In general, we try to keep them separate where possible, and when we must combine them we make one form convert to the other before combination.

A simple application of the admittance form of analysis is given in the next section, where we reconsider the power factor correction problem.

10.3.1 Power factor correction, using parallel rules
The current and voltage phasor found in inductive loads is shown in Fig. 10.8, which

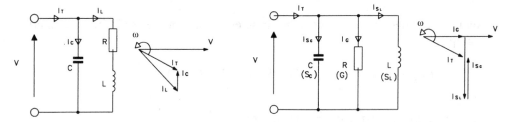

Fig. 10.8 — Power factor correction circuits (series and parallel forms).

also shows how they can be equally resolved into either an equivalent circuit in series form or an equivalent circuit in parallel form

We have already looked at the problem by using impedance-based reasoning. Let us now consider it from an admittance-based stance. To do this we must generate the admittance diagram from the current phasor diagram by simply dividing through by V. Thus, in Fig. 10.9,

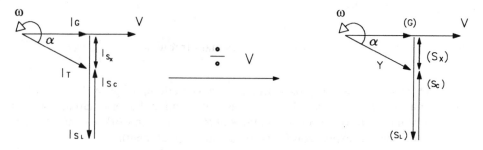

Fig. 10.9 — Admittance diagram for pf correction.

$$S_C = S_L - S_X \qquad \text{(where } S_X = G . \tan(\alpha))$$

$$\text{(and } \alpha = 0.8 \text{ typically).}$$

Thus $\omega . C = S_L - G . \tan(\alpha)$,

resulting in

$$C = \frac{1}{\omega}[S_L - G . \tan(\alpha)]$$

Thus, unlike the previous case where no simple expression for C was generated, we now have a single formula that allows us to calculate C directly from the effective parallel admittances of the circuit requiring correction.

If the circuit requiring correction is in fact a series combination of R and L, we must determine the supply current before correction and resolve it into I_L and I_G. We can then use these currents to calculate G and S_L and proceed with the calculation of the correction capacitor.

The tutorial example 9.13 given in chapter 9 will be reworked in example 10.10 to show the improved method.

10.4 COMPLEX CIRCUITS WITH SERIES AND PARALLEL COMBINATIONS

The earlier sections that dealt with dc circuit analysis introduced theorems that allowed us to simplify complicated forms of linear dc circuits and thus produce results with the minimum computational effort. The set of chapters on ac analysis completed so far has introduced only the relevant elements (R, L, and C) and the normal fundamental rules about dealing with their simple series circuit combinations. Unfortunately, ac circuits cannot always be relied upon to be either series or parallel. We must therefore develop ac circuit theorems that allow us to deal with complicated combinations of series and parallel circuits that include R. L. and C.

Fortunately, the groundwork set down in dc circuits is still valid, and we can use all of the theorems developed in dc circuit analysis and convert them for use in ac circuit analysis by employing some very simple and easily supportable substitutions.

The fundamental rules about conversion of dc theorems to ac theorems are that, firstly we must remember that we are now dealing with complex quantities ($a + jb$) and, secondly, if we now use Z in place of R we can reliably assume that we have covered the inclusion of L and C into all theorems. As we look at the ac versions of our theorems the rules suggested here should become clearer.

10.4.1 Impedance or admittance reduction techniques
Resistor reduction techniques applied to Fig. 10.10(a) will produce the following result:

$$R_{in} = R_1 + R_2 \| R_3 = R_1 + \frac{R_2 . R_3}{R_2 + R_3}.$$

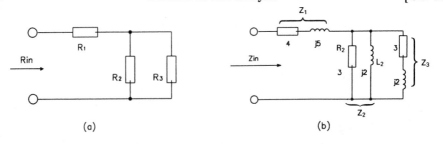

Fig. 10.10 — DC circuit and a similarly complicated ac circuit.

The ac circuit given in Fig. 10.10(b) can be treated in a very similar way by lumping our resistors and inductors into impedance elements as suggested, and we can therefore determine Z_{in} as follows:

$$Z_{in} = Z_1 + Z_P, \quad \text{where} \quad Z_P = Z_2 \| Z_3$$

This is a good point at which to introduce the use of inverse parameters, and we will evaluate Z_P via Y_P, its inverse.

Now, if $Z_3 = 3 + j2\,\Omega$,

then $$Y_3 = \frac{1}{3 + j2} = 0.231 - j0.154\,\text{S},$$

and $$Y_{R2} = G_2 = \frac{1}{R_2} = \frac{1}{3.0} = 0.333'\,\text{S},$$

and $$Y_{L2} = S_2 = \frac{1}{j.\omega.L_2} = \frac{1}{j.2} = -j0.5\,\text{S}.$$

Therefore

$$Y_P = G_2 + S_2 + Y_3 = 0.333' - j0.5 + 0.231 - j0.154$$
$$= 0.5643' - j0.654,$$

giving

$$Z_p = 0.7563 + j0.8765\,\Omega,$$

and since

$$Z_1 = R_1 + j\omega . L_1 = 4 + j5,$$

we get

$$Z_{in} = 4.756 + j5.876\,\Omega.$$

10.4.2 Mesh analysis

Mesh analysis in dc circuits carried with it a considerable scope for creating errors in

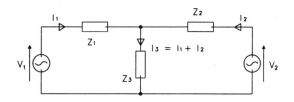

Fig. 10.11 — AC circuit mesh analysis problem.

calculations. If this is true for simple non-complex mathematics, then it is not surprising to find that ac circuits, with their dependence upon complex numbers and/ or vectors, have an even greater error-creating environment.

This problem was overcome in dc circuit analysis by avoiding the technique wherever possible, and employing the more manageable alternatives. This is even more the case in ac analysis, but for the pure in heart the circuit given in Fig. 10.11 is analyzed here by mesh analysis, purely to show how irritating the technique can be, and it is not the recommended method of solving ac circuits. Please note that this is only a two-loop mesh and has therefore only two complex unknowns.

The mesh analysis equations are:

$$V_1 = I_1(Z_1) + (I_1 + I_2)(Z_3) \qquad\qquad \dots \ (1)$$

$$V_2 = I_2(Z_2) + (I_1 + I_2)(Z_3) \qquad\qquad \dots \ (2)$$

$$[\text{remembering } I_3 = (I_1 + I_2)]$$

which reorganizes to give:

$$V_1 = I_1(Z_1 + Z_3) + I_2(Z_3) \qquad\qquad \dots \ (1.1)$$

$$V_2 = I_2(Z_2 + Z_3) + (I_1)(Z_3) \qquad\qquad \dots \ (2.1)$$

$$V_2 = I_1(Z_3) + I_2(Z_2 + Z_3) \qquad\qquad \dots \ (2.2)$$

Now (1.1) and (2.2) will eventually arrive at the following equations, once the summation of impedances required has been achieved.

$$V_1 = I_1(a + jb) + I_2(c + jd) \qquad \ldots (1.3)$$

$$V_2 = I_1(m + jn) + I_2(p + jq) \qquad \ldots (1.3)$$

To eliminate either I_1 or I_2 from our equations means we have to perform a complex multiplication of, say, $a + jb$ in such a way as to make it equal $m + jn$. We can then subtract the terms to leave us with a final equation for I_2. The multiplication of complex numbers is a pain, and it is much easier to convert back to vectors (r, ϕ) form) before attempting multiplication or division. Thus

$$V_1 = I_1(r \angle \phi) + I_2(p \angle \theta) \qquad \ldots (1.4)$$

$$V_2 = I_1(g \angle \alpha) + I_2(h \angle \beta) \qquad \ldots (2.4)$$

If we multiply (1.4) by $g \angle \alpha$ and (2.4) by $r \angle \phi$, the following solutions result:

$$V_1(r \angle \phi)(g \angle \alpha) = I_1(r \angle \phi)(g \angle \alpha) + (I_2(p \angle \theta)(r \angle \phi) \qquad \ldots (1.5)$$

$$V_2(r \angle \phi)(g \angle \alpha) = I_1(r \angle \phi)(g \angle \alpha) + (I_2(h \angle \beta)(g \angle \alpha) \qquad \ldots (2.5)$$

which eventually gives us:

$$I_2 = \frac{(V_2 - V_1)(rg \angle \phi + \alpha)}{(hg \angle \beta + \alpha) - (pr \angle \theta + \phi)},$$

which eventually becomes:

$$I_2 = (V_2 - V_1)(x + jy) \, \text{A},$$

where $\quad x + jy = \dfrac{(rg \angle \phi + \alpha)}{(hg \angle \beta + \alpha) - (pr \angle \theta + \phi)}.$

This final vector to complex transformation is not detailed because it is felt that the purpose of the exercise has been achieved.

It is self-evident that this mesh analysis of a simple (two-loop) ac circuit is potentially horrendous, and any student would seek an alternative wherever possible. These alternatives do exist, and as in dc circuits their operation is considerably less hazardous than mesh analysis. We will now look at the more common theorems and their application to the circuit given in Fig. 10.11.

10.4.3   Thévénin's and Norton's theorem

Let us presume that we are still interested in determining I_3 in the Fig. 10.11 circuit.

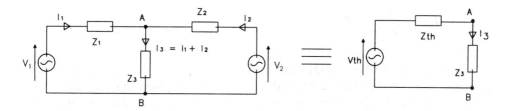

Fig. 10.12 — Thévénin's equivalent circuit in ac circuit analysis.

Thévénin's theorem suggests that the current I_3 can be considered to be provided from a single voltage source, as suggested in Fig. 10.12.

$$Z_{Th} = Z_1 \| Z_2 = \frac{Z_1 \cdot Z_2}{Z_1 + Z_2}$$

$$V_{Th} = V_1 - V_{Z1} = V_1 - \frac{(V_2 - V_1) \cdot Z_1}{(Z_1 + Z_2)}.$$

This calculation of V_{Th} is beginning to be unhelpful, so let's switch to $I_{S/C}$ as a route to V_{Th}. See Fig. 10.13.

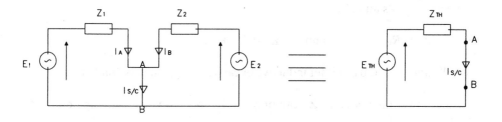

Fig. 10.13 — Determination of $I_{S/C}$ in ac circuit.

$$I_{S/C} = I_A + I_B = \frac{V_1}{Z_1} + \frac{V_2}{Z_2} \quad \cdots \quad (\text{much easier}),$$

and $\quad V_{Th} = I_{S/C} \cdot (Z_{Th}),$

and finally,

$$I_3 = \frac{V_{Th}}{(Z_{Th} + Z_3)} \, \text{A}.$$

It must be clear that this method of finding I_3 is significantly less hazardous than mesh analysis, and we therefore commend it to this house. Norton's theorem is so interchangeable with Thévénin's theorem, as we saw in the use of $I_{S/C}$, that it will be sufficient to state that it can be used as and when the need arises. Worked examples will highlight the interactiveness of Thévénin's and Norton's theorems.

10.4.3 Maximum power transfer theorem
If Z_L in Fig. 10.14 is variable in both its real and imaginary parts, we wish to know

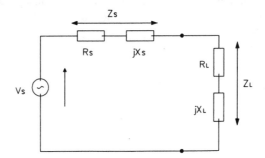

Fig. 10.14 — Maximum power transfer in ac circuits.

what these parts must be for Z_L to be developing its maximum possible power for the given values of Vs and Zs.

Let $\quad Z_S = R_S + jX_S \quad$ and $\quad Z_L = R_L + jX_L.$

Note: X_L and X_S could be either inductive or capacitive ('$_L$' means 'load' in this case).

Now the power dissipated in Z_L can only be that power which is dissipated in R_L. That is,

$$P = |I|^2 \cdot R_L \quad (I \text{ is rms}).$$

Now $I = \dfrac{V_S}{Z_S + Z_L} = \dfrac{V_S}{(R_S + jX_S) + (R_L + jX_L)}$

$\qquad\qquad = \dfrac{V_S}{(R_S + R_L) + j(X_S + X_L)}$,

but $|I| = \dfrac{|V_S|}{\sqrt{[(R_S + R_L)^2 + (X_S + X_L)^2]}}$

thus $|I|^2 = \dfrac{|V_S|^2}{(R_S + R_L)^2 + (X_S + X_L)^2}$,

giving $P = |I|^2 . R_L = \dfrac{|V_S|^2 . R_L}{(R_S + R_L)^2 + (X_S + X_L)^2}$.

Maximum power output occurs when the expression for P given above is a maximum. If we consider the reactive elements X_S and X_L in this expression we can see that if X_S is equal and opposite to X_L, P will be a maximum. Thus

$$P = \frac{|V_S|^2 . R_L}{(R_S + R_L)^2}.$$

Now this is exactly the expression we obtained in the dc circuit theorem, and we know that its solution for maximum power transfer (MPT) is $R_L = R_S$.

We can now conclude that maximum output power is transferred from a source when its load is the complex conjugate of the source's internal impedance. That is, if

$$Z_S = R_S + jX_S, \qquad \text{then} \qquad Z_L = R_S - jX_S \text{ for MPT}$$

The actual power developed in Z_L for this MPT condition is given by

$$P_{(MPT)} = \frac{|V_S|^2 . R_L}{4 . R_L^2} = \frac{|V_S|^2}{4 . R_L} \text{W}.$$

The efficiency of the power transfer in this condition is given as:

$$\text{Eff} = \frac{\text{power dissipated in load } (R_L)}{\text{power delivered by } V_S},$$

Now the power dissipated in the load $= \dfrac{|V_S|^2}{4 \cdot R_L} = P_{(MPT)}$,

and power delivered by $V_S = |I|^2 \cdot (R_L + R_S)$

$$= \frac{|V_S|^2 \times (2R_L)}{(2R_L)^2}$$

$$= \frac{|V_S|^2}{2R_L} = 2 \cdot P_{(MPT)}.$$

Thus   Eff $= 0.5$ or 50%.

If the load impedance is purely resistive, a special case must be determined since X_L can no longer be eliminated from the expression for P. We already have:

$$P = \frac{|V_S|^2 \cdot R_L}{(R_S + R_L)^2 + (X_S + X_L)^2},$$

and if we differentiate this with respect to R_L we get:

$$\frac{dP}{dR_L} = \frac{|V_S|^2[\{(R_L + R_S)^2 + (X_L + X_S)^2\} - \{2 \cdot R_L(R_L + R_S)\}]}{[(R_S + R_L)^2 + (X_S + X_L)^2]^2}.$$

But $X_L = 0$,   therefore:

$$\frac{dP}{dR_L} = \frac{|V_S|^2[\{(R_L + R_S)^2 + (X_S)^2\} - \{2 \cdot R_L(R_L + R_S)\}]}{[(R_S + R_L)^2 + (X_S)^2]^2}.$$

If we expand the numerator and set it to zero for the maximum turning point: (Note $V_S \neq 0$ for this analysis $\therefore$ ignore it)

$$0 = [\{(R_L + R_S)^2 + (X_S)^2\} - \{2 \cdot R_L(R_L + R_S)\}]$$
$$= R_L^2 + 2R_LR_S + R_S^2 + X_S^2 - 2R_L^2 - 2R_LR_S$$
$$= R_L^2 + R_S^2 + X_S^2 - 2R_L^2$$
$$= -R_L^2 + R_S^2 + X_S^2.$$

If we equate this to zero to find the turning points:

$$0 = -R_L^2 + R_S^2 + X_S^2$$

or $R_L{}^2 = R_S{}^2 + X_S{}^2$.

That is, $R_L = \sqrt{(R_S{}^2 + X_S{}^2)}$ (remembering that $X_S = |X_S|$).

That is, $R_L = |Z_S|$ (the magnitude of the source impedance).

A worked example will help to consolidate the theorem's rules.

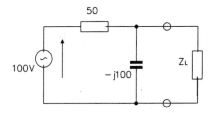

Fig. 10.15 — Maximum power transfer example.

In the Fig. 10.15 circuit, for P_{max} Z_L = conjugate of Z_S (that is, Z_{Th})

and $Z_{Th} = R_1 \| - jX_C = \dfrac{R_1 \cdot (-jX_C)}{R_1 - jX_C} = \dfrac{50(-j100)}{50 - j100}$,

therefore

$$Z_{Th} = 40 - j20\,\Omega$$

and $Z_L = 40 + j20\,\Omega$.

There is a danger of now assuming that $V_S = 100\,V$ and of using this to proceed to a calculation of P_{max},

where $P_{max} = \dfrac{|V_S|^2}{4 \cdot R_L}$ $(R_L = 40\ \Omega)$.

But the V_S used in the above formula is the voltage of the source given in Fig. 10.14, (ie. $V_{Th} = V_S$) and our problem circuit is not similar and we must complete the circuit conversion to match the circuit used to derive the formula.
    Thus in Fig. 10.16:

Fig. 10.16 — Determining V_{Th} for our example.

$$V_{Th} = \frac{V_S \cdot (Z_C)}{Z_{R1} + Z_C} = \frac{100 \cdot (-j100)}{50 - j100} = \frac{-j200}{1 - j2},$$

therefore $\quad |V_{Th}| = \dfrac{200}{\sqrt{5}} = 40\sqrt{5}\,\text{V},$

(V_{Th} phase ignored since we are only interested in $|V_{Th}|$)

therefore $\quad P_{max} = \dfrac{|V_{Th}|^2}{4 \cdot R_L} = \dfrac{200^2}{5 \times 4 \times 40} = 50\,\text{W}.$

If the load were purely resistive, the maximum power developed in it would come under different conditions.
For P_{max}

$$R_L = |Z_{Th}|,$$

but $\quad Z_{Th} = 40 - j20\,\Omega,$

giving $\quad R_L = |40 + j20| = \sqrt{(40^2 + 20^2)} = 44.72\,\Omega$

$$V_{Th} = \frac{-j200}{1 - j2} \quad \text{(as before)},$$

therefore $\quad |V_{Th}| = \dfrac{200}{\sqrt{5}} = 40\sqrt{5}\,\text{V},$

therefore $\quad P_{max} = \dfrac{|V_{Th}|^2}{4 \cdot R_L} = \dfrac{200^2}{5 \times 4 \times 44.73} = 44.72\,\text{W}.$

More worked examples about maximum power transfer will be given, at the end of this chapter.

10.4.5   Star $\equiv$ delta transformations

The conclusion of the section on dc circuit analysis that dealt with star to delta and delta to star transformations gave us two sets of formulae that could be easily applied to achieve successful transformation. These formulae are re-quoted below.

Delta to star (using R)

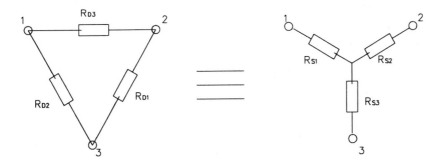

Fig. 10.17 — Delta to star transformation (resistors only).

In Fig. 10.17,

$$R_{S1} = \frac{R_{d3} \cdot R_{d2}}{R_{d3} + R_{d2} + R_{d1}}$$

$$R_{S2} = \frac{R_{d3} \cdot R_{d1}}{R_{d3} + R_{d2} + R_{d1}}$$

$$R_{S3} = \frac{R_{d1} \cdot R_{d2}}{R_{d3} + R_{d2} + R_{d1}}$$

If our circuit is an ac delta network, the formula changes simply by converting all Rs to Zs.

Delta to star (using Z)
In Fig. 10.18,

$$Z_{S1} = \frac{Z_{d3} \cdot Z_{d2}}{Z_{d3} + Z_{d2} + Z_{d1}}$$

$$Z_{S2} = \frac{Z_{d3} \cdot Z_{d1}}{Z_{d3} + Z_{d2} + Z_{d1}}$$

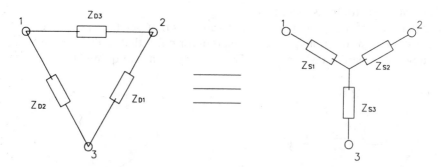

Fig. 10.18 — Delta to star transformation (ac impedances).

$$Z_{S3} = \frac{Z_{d1} \cdot Z_{d2}}{Z_{d3} + Z_{d2} + Z_{d1}}.$$

Remember that all Zs are complex and may be resistive, inductive, or capacitive.

We can now look at the second of these transformations, where we convert from a star network to a delta network.

Star to delta(d) (using G)

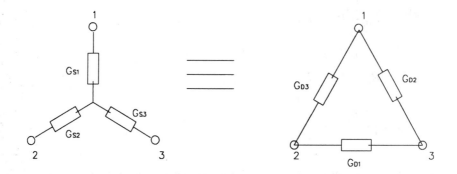

Fig. 10.19 — Star to delta transformation (conductances only).

In Fig. 10.19,

$$G_{d1} = \frac{G_{S3} \cdot G_{S2}}{G_{S3} + G_{S2} + G_{S1}}$$

$$G_{d2} = \frac{G_{S3} \cdot G_{S1}}{G_{S3} + G_{S2} + G_{S1}}$$

$$G_{d3} = \frac{G_{S1} \cdot G_{S2}}{G_{S3} + G_{S2} + G_{S1}}.$$

If our circuit is an ac star network, the formula changes simply by converting all G's (conductances), to Y's (admittances).

Star to delta (using Y)

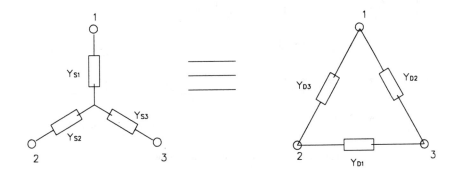

Fig. 10.20 — Star to delta transformation (ac admittances).

In Fig. 10.20,

$$Y_{d1} = \frac{Y_{S3} \cdot Y_{S2}}{Y_{S3} + Y_{S2} + Y_{S1}}$$

$$Y_{d2} = \frac{Y_{S3} \cdot Y_{S1}}{Y_{S3} + Y_{S2} + Y_{S1}}$$

$$Y_{d3} = \frac{Y_{S1} \cdot Y_{S2}}{Y_{S3} + Y_{S2} + Y_{S1}}$$

The transformation techniques are so straightforward that an example is really unecessary at this stage, but for those who feel the need, a worked example is given at the end of the chapter in example 10.7.

10.4.6 AC bridge circuits

A great many ac bridge circuits exist that are similar in principle to the dc Wheatstone bridge, but they are used to measure capacitance and inductance as well as resistance. Pages 91 to 94 of Reference (a) in the *Bibliography* cover the classic measurement bridges. The fundamental theory is given below with a full worked example of the results for the classic Wein bridge network.

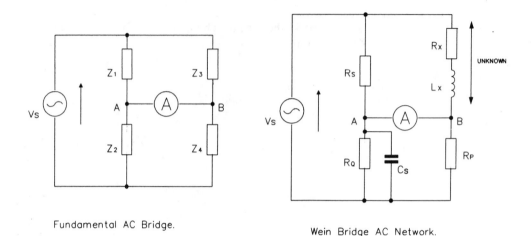

Fundamental AC Bridge.

Wein Bridge AC Network.

Fig. 10.21 — Fundamental ac bridge network.

The fundamental ac bridge network is shown in Fig. 10.21.

The general principle is the same in all ac bridges, that is to obtain a zero detection current through the central limb. In dc circuits this is achieved when $V_A = V_B$, but in ac circuits we must remember that this requirement includes both magnitude and phase.

At the null condition:

$$V_A = \frac{V_S(Z_2)}{(Z_1 + Z_2)} \quad \text{and} \quad V_B = \frac{V_S(Z_4)}{(Z_3 + Z_4)}.$$

Since $V_A = V_B$ we get

$$\frac{Z_2}{(Z_1 + Z_2)} = \frac{Z_4}{(Z_3 + Z_4)}$$

which gives

$$Z_2 \cdot (Z_3 + Z_4) = Z_4 \cdot (Z_1 + Z_2).$$

Thus $Z_2 \cdot Z_3 = Z_4 \cdot Z_1$ ($Z_2 \cdot Z_4$ cancels), giving the generalized bridge result of:

$$\frac{Z_1}{Z_2} = \frac{Z_3}{Z_4}.$$

The Wein bridge circuit shown in Fig. 10.21 allows us to say:

$$Z_1 = R_S \quad \text{and} \quad Z_4 = R_P$$

$$Z_3 = R_X + j\omega.L_X$$

$$Z_2 = R_Q \| 1/(j\omega.C_S) \quad \text{or} \quad Y_2 = G_Q + j\omega.C_S.$$

If we put this into the generalized result we get:

$$\frac{Z_1}{Z_2} = Z_1.Y_2 = R_S(G_Q + j\omega.C_S) = \frac{R_X}{R_P} + \frac{j\omega.L_X}{R_P}.$$

Equating the real and imaginary parts gives:

$$R_S.G_Q = \frac{R_X}{R_P} \quad \text{and} \quad R_S.C_S = \frac{L_X}{R_P},$$

or $\qquad R_X = R_P.R_S.G_Q = \dfrac{R_P.R_S}{R_Q} \qquad \text{and} \qquad L_X = R_P.R_S.C_S,$

Further ac bridge networks are offered for analysis in the tutorial examples section.

WORKED EXAMPLES

Example 10.1

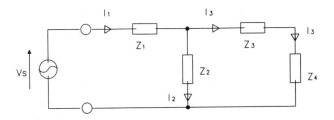

Fig. 10.22 — Circuit reduction.

Q.   For the circuit shown in Fig. 10.22, $Z_1 = 560 - j620\,\Omega$, $Z_2 = 330 + j470\,\Omega$, $Z_3 = 390 + j270\,\Omega$, and $Z_4 = 220 - j220\,\Omega$. Determine the effective impedance connected across the supply voltage V_S. ($V_S = 30\ \angle 0°$ Volts)

A.   The first step in solving this problem is to sketch the circuit reduction steps in a clear manner, as shown in Fig.20.23.

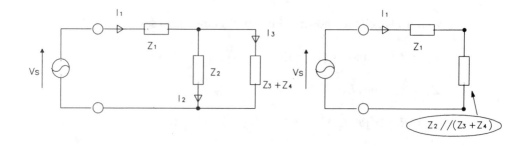

Fig. 10.23 — Circuit reduction procedure steps.

$$Z_3 + Z_4 = 610 + j50\,\Omega = 612\ \angle\,4.7°\,\Omega$$

and $Y_{3,4} = \dfrac{1}{612\ \angle\,4.7°} = 1.63\ \angle\,-4.7°\,\text{mS}.$

Now $Z_2 = 574\ \angle\,54.9°\,\Omega,$ thus $Y_2 = 1.74\ \angle\,-54.9°\,\text{mS}.$

Thus $Y_{2,3,4} = 1.74\ \angle\,-54.9° + 1.63\ \angle\,-4.7°$

$$= 1 - j1.424 + 1.625 - j.134$$

$$= 2.625 - j1.56\ \text{mS}$$

$$= 3.04\ \angle\,-30.6°\,\text{mS}.$$

Thus $Z_{2,3,4} = \dfrac{1}{3.04\ \angle\,-30.6°} = 329\ \angle\,30.6°\,\Omega$

$$= 283 + j167\,\Omega$$

Thus $Z_T = Z_1 + Z_{2,3,4} = 843 - j453\,\Omega = 957\ \angle\,-28.3°\,\Omega.$

The solution of this example illustrates the recommended occasions on which we should switch between j notation and polar form, and also when we should use the inverse parameter Y instead of Z. The problem can be solved by using only j notation and impedance equations, but it is advisable to develop versatility on simple problems and thus allow practice of the techniques required in the more complicated examples.

Example 10.2

Q.   For the example given in 10.1 determine the total current I_1 that flows through Z_1 and use the current divider rule described in section 2.12 of the dc theory discussion to determine the currents I_2 and I_3.

A. $I_1 = \dfrac{V_S}{Z_T} = \dfrac{30\,V}{957\,\angle -28.3°} = 31.3\,\angle 28.3°]\,mA$.

The current divider theorem suggests the following:

$$I_2 = I_1 \cdot \frac{Y_2}{Y_{2,3,4}} = 31.3\,\angle 28.3°\,mA \times \frac{1.74\,\angle -54.9°}{3.04\,\angle -30.6°}\,mS,$$

giving $I_2 = 17.9\,\angle 4.0°\,mA$.

To find I_3 we need only apply Kirchhoff's current summation law:

$$I_3 = I_1 - I_2 = 31.3\,\angle 28.3° - 17.9\,\angle 4.0°\,mA$$
$$= 27.56 + j14.84 - 17.86 - j1.25$$
$$= 9.7 + j13.59\,mA$$
$$= 18.7\,\angle 54.5°\,mA$$

Example 10.3

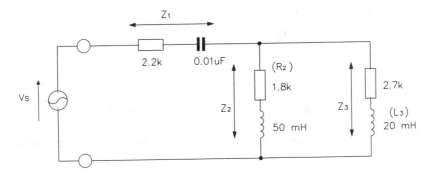

Fig. 10.24 — Circuit for reduction.

Q.   For the circuit shown in Fig. 10.24 determine the total equivalent impedance across the source voltage V_S. ($V_S = 72\,V\ \angle 0°$ (6 kHz))

A.   It is once again prudent to set out the style of circuit reduction technique, using diagrams as given in Fig. 10.25.

$$Z_3 = 2.7 + j0.754\,k\Omega = 2.803\,\angle 15.6°\,k\Omega,$$

thus $Y_3 = 0.3567\,\angle -15.6°\,mS = 0.3436 - j0.096\,mS,$

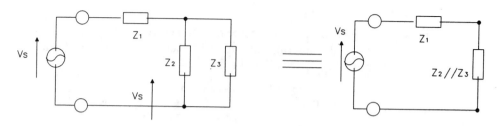

Fig. 10.25 — Circuit reduction methodology.

and $Z_2 = 1.8 + j1.885\,k\Omega = 2.606 \angle 46.32°\,k\Omega.$

Thus $Y_2 = 0.384\,^\wedge[-46.32°]\,mS = 0.265 - j0.2777\,mS,$

giving $Y_{2,3} = 0.3436 - j0.096 + 0.265 - j0.2777\,mS$
$$= 0.6086 - j0.3737\,mS = 0.714 \angle -31.55°\,mS.$$

Thus $Z_{2,3} = \dfrac{1}{0.714 \angle -31.55°\,mS} = 1.4 \angle 31.55°\,k\Omega,$

giving $Z_T = Z_1 + Z_{2,3}$
$$= 2.2 - j2.652 + 1.4 \angle 31.55°\,k\Omega$$
$$= 2.2 - j2.652 + 1.193 + j0.7325\,k\Omega$$
$$= 3.393 - j1.92\,k\Omega.$$
$$= 3.9 \angle -29.5°\,k\Omega.$$

Example 10.4

Q.   For the circuit in Fig. 10.24 calculate the currents that flow through R_2 and L_3 respectively.

The best way of determining these currents is to employ the current divider method:

$$I_2 = I_T \cdot \frac{Y_2}{Y_{2,3}} \quad \text{and} \quad I_3 = I_T \cdot \frac{Y_3}{Y_{2,3}}$$

Now $I_T = \dfrac{V_S}{Z_T} = \dfrac{72}{3.9 \angle -29.5°\,k\Omega} = 18.46 \angle 29.5°\,mA,$

And Y_2, Y_3, and $Y_{2,3}$ are already known.

Thus $\quad I_2 = I_T \cdot \dfrac{Y_2}{Y_{2,3}} = \dfrac{18.46 \angle 29.5° \, \text{mA} \times 0.384 \angle -46.32° \, \text{mS}}{0.714 \angle -31.55° \, \text{mS}}$

$\qquad\qquad = 9.93 \angle 14.73° \, \text{mA}.$

Thus $\quad I_3 = I_T \cdot \dfrac{Y_3}{Y_{2,3}} = \dfrac{18.46 \angle 29.5° \, \text{mA} \times 0.3567 \angle -15.6° \, \text{mS}}{0.714 \angle -31.55° \, \text{mS}}$

$\qquad\qquad = 9.22' \angle 45.45° \, \text{mA}.$

Example 10.5

Q.   Use Thévénin's or Norton's theorems to determine I_3 in the circuit given in Fig. 10.24, rearranged as in Fig. 10.26.

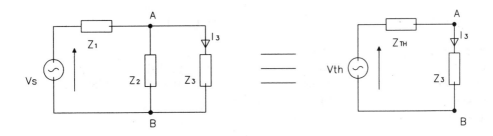

Fig. 10.26 — Circuit rearranged to show Thévénin analysis.

A. $\qquad V_{\text{Th}} = V_{\text{S}} \cdot \dfrac{Z_2}{Z_1 + Z_2} \qquad Z_{\text{Th}} = Z_1 \| Z_2,$

where $\quad Z_1 = 2.2 - j2.652 \, k\Omega = 3.445 \angle -50.32° \, k\Omega$

and $\quad Z_2 = 1.8 + j1.885 \, k\Omega = 2.606 \angle 46.32° \, k\Omega.$

Thus $\quad Z_1 + Z_2 = 4.0 - j0.767 \, k\Omega = 4.073 \angle -10.85° \, k\Omega.$

Now $\quad V_{\text{Th}} = \dfrac{72 \times 2.606 \angle 46.32° \, k\Omega}{4.073 \angle -10.85° \, k\Omega} = 46.07 \angle 57.17°$

and $\quad Z_{\text{Th}} = \dfrac{Z_1 \cdot Z_2}{Z_1 + Z_2} = \dfrac{3.445 \angle -50.32° \, k\Omega \times 2.606 \angle 46.32°}{4.073 \angle -10.85°} \, k\Omega$

$$= 2.204 \angle 6.85° \, k\Omega = 2.188 + j0.2629 \, k\Omega$$

Now $I_3 = \dfrac{V_{Th}}{Z_{Th} + Z_3} = \dfrac{46.07 \angle 57.17° \, V}{2.188 + j0.2629 + 2.7 + j0.754 \, k\Omega}$

$$= \frac{46.07 \angle 57.17° \, V}{4.888 + j1.017 \, k\Omega}$$

$$= \frac{46.07 \angle 57.17° \, V}{5.0 \angle 11.75° \, kV}$$

$$= 9.214 \angle 45.42° \, mA$$

(Compare this result with that obtained in Example 10.4.)

Example 10.6
Q. For the Thévénin circuit in Fig. 10.26 determine the optimum load for maximum power transfer to said load and determine the amount of power transferred for this condition. Also determine the component values and type that this load must be.

A. $Z_{Th} = 2.204 \angle 6.85° \, k\Omega = 2.188 + j0.2629 \, k\Omega$,

therefore

$$Z_L = 2.188 - j0.2629 \, k\Omega \qquad (2.188 \, k\Omega \text{ and } 0.1 \, \mu F).$$

$$P_{(MPT)} = \frac{|V_{Th}|^2}{4.R_L} = \frac{|46.07|^2}{4 \times 2.188 \, k\Omega} = 0.2425 \, W.$$

Example 10.7

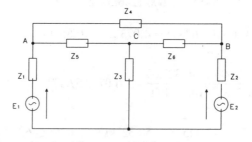

Fig. 10.27 — Delta to star transformation.

Q.   For the circuit shown in Fig. 10.27 convert the delta network of Z_4, Z_5, and Z_6 to their star equivalents Z_A, Z_B, and Z_C, as Fig. 10.28 implies. The impedance values are $Z_4 = 100 \angle 30° \Omega$, $Z_5 = 95 \angle 40° \Omega$, and $Z_6 = 60 \angle 20° \Omega$.

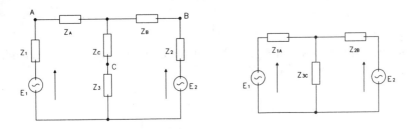

Fig. 10.28 — Transformation complete.

A.   Using the results obtained in section 10.4.5, we can perform the required transformations, but it must now be clear that we often require both polar and complex forms of impedance representation, and thus a useful exercise at the beginning of all problems is to create a set of impedance forms as given below:

$$Z_4 = 100 \angle 30° \Omega = 86.6 + j50 \, \Omega$$

$$Z_5 = 95 \angle 40° \omega = 72.77 + j61.06 \, \Omega$$

$$Z_6 = 60 \angle 20° \Omega = 56.38 + j20.52 \, \Omega.$$

We will also require $Z_T = Z_4 + Z_5 + Z_6$, therefore:

$$Z_T = 96.6 + j50 + 72.77 + j61.06 + 56.38 + j20.52 \, \Omega$$
$$= 215.75 + j131.58 \, \Omega = 252.7 \angle 31.38° \, \Omega.$$

We can now begin the conversions:

$$Z_A = \frac{Z_4 \cdot Z_5}{Z_4 + Z_5 + Z_6} = \frac{100 \angle 30° \times 95 \angle 40°}{252.7 \angle 31.38°}$$

$$= 37.6 \angle 38.6° \, \Omega = 29.38 + j23.46 \, \Omega$$

$$Z_B = \frac{Z_4 \cdot Z_6}{Z_4 + Z_5 + Z_6} = \frac{100 \angle 30° \times 60 \angle 20°}{252.7 \angle 31.38°}$$

$$= 23.74 \angle 18.62° \, \Omega = 22.5 + j7.58 \, \Omega$$

$$Z_C = \frac{Z_6 \cdot Z_5}{Z_4 + Z_5 + Z_6} = \frac{60 \angle 20° \times 95 \angle 40°}{252.7 \angle 31.38°}$$

$$= 22.56 \angle 28.62° \, \Omega = 19.8 + j10.8 \, \Omega.$$

Example 10.8

Q. For the circuit shown in Fig. 10.27, calculate the current flowing through Z_3 if $V_1 = 100 \, V$, $V_2 = 50 \, V$, and $Z_1 = Z_2 = Z_3 = 25 \, \Omega$.

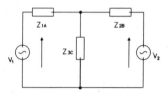

Fig. 10.29 — Two source network for analysis.

A. At first glance there are three possible methods for solving the problem. The superposition theorem would allow us to consider V_1 and V_2 separately, but the circuit would still be two loops and therefore require two separate attacks to get a result. Thévénin's theorem would eliminate Z_3 and Z_C from the analysis, and leave one loop for analysis. Nortons theorem would short-circuit Z_3 and Z_C and thus eliminate them, but it would also separate V_1 and V_2 into two unconnected loops and thus allow simple calculation of the short-circuit current. The Thévénin and Norton options are shown in Fig. 10.30, and it is proposed that the Norton option is tackled since it appears to require the least work.

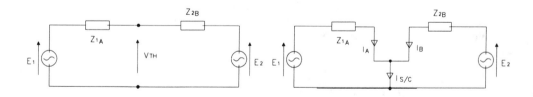

Fig. 10.30 — Thévénin and Norton options for Example 10.8.

Once again it is prudent to tabulate our impedance values.

$$Z_{1A} = Z_1 + Z_A = 25 + 29.38 + j23.46 \, \Omega$$

$$= 54.38 + j23.46 = 59.22 \angle 23.34° \Omega$$

$$Z_{2B} = Z_2 + Z_B = 25 + 22.5 + j7.58 \Omega$$
$$= 47.5 + j7.58 = 48.1 \angle 9.07° \Omega$$

$$Z_{3C} = Z_3 + Z_C = 25 + 19.8 + j10.8 \Omega$$
$$= 44.8 + j10.8 = 46.08 \angle 13.55° \Omega.$$

Thus $\quad I_{S/C}(V_1) = \dfrac{V_1}{Z_{1A}} = \dfrac{100}{59.22 \angle 23.34° \Omega}$

$$= 1.69 \angle -23.34° = 1.55 - j0.669 \, \text{A},$$

and $\quad I_{S/C}(V_2) = \dfrac{E_2}{Z_{2B}} = \dfrac{50}{48.1 \angle 9.07° \Omega}$

$$= 1.04 \angle -9.07° = 1.027 - j0.164 \, \text{A},$$

giving $\quad I_{S/C} = I_{S/C}(V_1) + I_{S/C}(V_2)$
$$= 1.55 - j0.669 + 1.027 - j0.164 \, \text{A}$$
$$= 2.577 - j0.833 = 2.708 \angle -17.9° \, \text{A}.$$

Now $\quad Z_N = Z_{Th} = Z_{1A} \| Z_{2B} = \dfrac{Z_{1A} \cdot Z_{2B}}{Z_{1A} + Z_{2B}}$

$$= \dfrac{59.22 \angle 23.34° \times 48.1 \angle 9.07°}{54.38 + j23.46 + 47.5 + j7.58}$$

$$= \dfrac{2848 \angle 32.41°}{101.88 + j31.04} = \dfrac{2848 \angle 32.41°}{106.5 \angle 16.94°}$$

$$= 26.74 \angle 15.47° \Omega = 25.77 + j7.13 \Omega.$$

To complete the analysis it is preferable to determine V_{Th}, and it is also helpful to draw our concluding circuit diagram, Fig. 10.31.

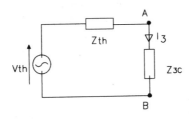

Fig. 10.31 — Concluding circuit Diagram for Example 10.8.

$$V_{\text{Th}} = I_{\text{S/C}} \cdot Z_{\text{N}} = 2.708 \angle -17.9° \, A \times 26.74 \angle 15.47° \, \Omega$$
$$= 72.41 \angle -2.43° \, V.$$

$$I_3 = \frac{V_{\text{Th}}}{Z_{\text{Th}} + Z_{3\text{C}}} = \frac{72.41 \angle -2.43° \, V}{25.77 + j7.13 + 44.8 + j10.8 \, \Omega}$$

$$= \frac{72.41 \angle -2.43° \, V}{70.57 + j17.93 \, \Omega}$$

$$= \frac{72.41 \angle -2.43° \, V}{72.81 \angle 14.26° \, \Omega}$$

$$= 0.995 \angle -16.19° \, A.$$

Example 10.9

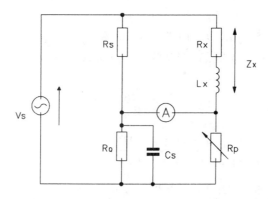

Fig. 10.32 — Maxwell Wien bridge circuit.

Q.   The Maxwell Wien bridge circuit shown in Fig. 10.32 uses a $0.1 \, \mu F$ standard capacitor (C_S) and a $1 \, k\Omega$ standard resistor (R_Q). Zero deflection of the null-detector is obtained when $R_P = 1.33 \, k\Omega$ and $R_S = 870 \, \Omega$. Calculate the impedance of the unknown impedance Z_X.

A.   The following formulae have been extracted from section 10.4.6 which dealt with the analysis of the above bridge.

$$R_X = R_P \cdot R_S \cdot G_Q = \frac{R_P \cdot R_S}{R_Q} \qquad \text{and} \qquad L_X = R_P \cdot R_S \cdot C_S,$$

thus $R_X = \dfrac{1.33\,\text{k}\Omega \times 870\,\Omega}{1\,\text{k}\Omega} = 1.157\,\text{k}\Omega$,

and $L_X = 133\,\text{k}\Omega \times 870\,\Omega \times 0.1\,\mu\text{F} = 115.7\,\text{mH}$.

Example 10.10

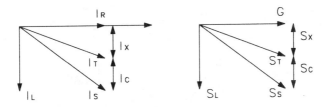

Fig. 10.33 — Supply phasor diagram and its resolved currents.

Q.   Fig. 10.33 shows a supply where the current taken from a 115 V (60 Hz) supply is 20 A with a lagging power factor of 0.75 or 75%. Determine the power factor correction capacitor necessary to correct the pf to 95% lagging.

We must first of all determine the present system's effective parallel admittances. This is done by resolving the supply current into I_R and I_L as shown. That is:

$$I_R = I_S \cos(\phi) \qquad \text{where } \cos(\phi) = 0.75$$
$$\quad\; = 15\,\text{A},$$

and $I_L = I_S \cdot \sin(\phi) = 13.23\,\text{A}$.

Therefore

$$G = \frac{I_R}{V_S} = \frac{15}{115} = 0.1304\,\text{S},$$

and $S_L = \dfrac{I_L}{V_S} = \dfrac{13.23}{115} = 0.115\,\text{S}$ (j notation omitted).

Thus $C = \dfrac{1}{\omega}\{S_L - G \cdot \tan(\alpha)\}$ where $\alpha = \cos^{-1}(0.95)$,

gives $C = \dfrac{1}{2 \cdot \pi \cdot 60}\{0.115 - 0.1304 \cdot \tan(18.19^{\circ})\}$

$$= 191\,\mu\text{F}.$$

(Compare this to the result obtained in tutorial example 9.11 in the previous chapter.)

REVIEW QUESTIONS AND TUTORIAL EXAMPLES

(10.1) In the Fig. 10.34 circuit determine the current I_1 flowing through the inductor of value $j3\,\Omega$. $(1.87 \angle 84.13°\,A)$.

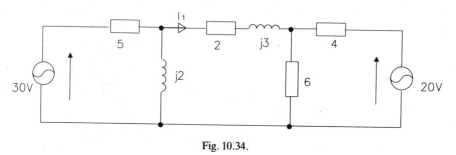

Fig. 10.34.

(10.2) In the Fig. 10.35 circuit determine the voltage V_1 by either Thévénin's or

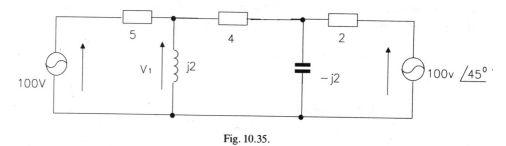

Fig. 10.35.

Norton's theorems. Note the phase difference in V_2 with respect to V_1. $(78.2 \angle 54°\,V)$.

(10.3) In the Fig. 10.36 circuit find the current flowing through the $(3+j4)$ impedance. $(0\,A)$.

(10.4) In the network shown in Fig. 10.37 determine the current I_1 $(7.91 \angle 73.7°\,mA)$.

(10.5) Determine the current I_1 shown in Fig. 10.38 by which ever method you think fit. $(22.4 \angle -25°\,A)$.

(10.6) Determine the voltage V_1 given in Fig. 10.39. It is strongly advised to use Thévénin's theorem. $(75.14 \angle 55.19°\,V)$.

(10.7) The circuit shown in Fig. 10.40 is commonly found in radio receivers in the

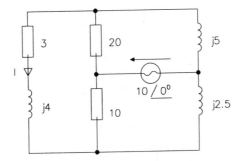

Fig. 10.36.

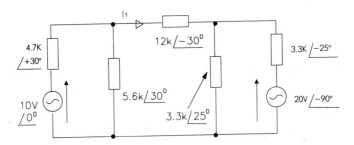

Fig. 10.37.

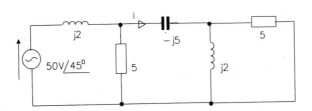

Fig. 10.38.

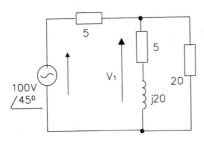

Fig. 10.39.

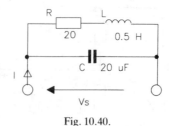

Fig. 10.40.

section that tunes in the required frequency. It exhibits certain effects at resonance that suit it most admirably for this function. Using the definition of the conditions for resonance, show that the resonant frequency is given by the expression:

$$f_N = (1/2 \, . \, \pi) \sqrt{\{1/LC - (R^2/L^2)\}}.$$

The total impedance of the circuit at resonance must be purely resistive. Show that the impedance of the parallel circuit in this condition is given by $Z_{RES} = L/CR\,\Omega$.

(10.8) Calculate the resonant frequency of the circuit given in Fig. 10.40 if the following conditions exist:

$$L = 0.5\,H, \qquad R = 20\,\Omega, \qquad \text{and} \qquad C = 20\,\mu F.$$

Also determine the total current drawn from the supply at resonance if the supply is 10 V. (50 Hz, 8.0 mA).

(10.9) Fig. 10.41 shows an ac measurement bridge known as the Schering bridge

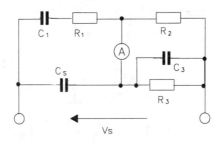

Fig. 10.41.

which is used to measure the capacitance and dielectric losses of the unknown impedance Z_X (C_1 & R_1). At balance the unknown impedance values are given by:

$$C_1 = \frac{C_s R_3}{R_2} \qquad \text{and} \qquad R_1 = \frac{R_2 C_3}{C_s}.$$

Prove the above result from first principles and calculate C_1 and R_1 if the following conditions exist at balance:

$$R_2 = 200\,\Omega, \quad C_S = 0.1\,\mu F, \quad R_3 = 1.21\,k\Omega, \quad \text{and} \quad C_3 = 165\,pF.$$

$(C_1 = 0.605\,\mu F, \ R_1 = 0.33\,\Omega)$.

(10.10)   Use Norton's theorem to determine the voltage drop across Z_4 in Fig. 10.42. $(1.517 \angle -30.3°\,V)$.

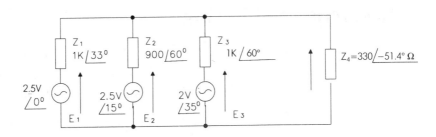

Fig. 10.42.

(10.11)   Apply delta–star transformation and Norton's theorem to determine the current through Z_4 in Fig. 10.43. $(0.1395 \angle 94.36°\,mA)$.
[Hint: see worked example 3.6]

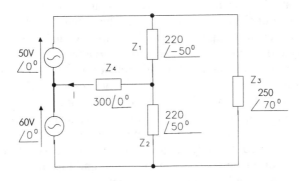

Fig. 10.43.

11

Frequency response in ac circuits and an introduction to filtering

11.1 THE TRANSFER FUNCTION OF AN AC CIRCUIT

If an ac voltage is applied to any linear network, all the components in the circuit will experience an ac sinusoidal voltage waveform across their terminals. If one of these voltage is viewed on an oscilloscope at the same time as the applied ac voltage, we can observe how it behaves in relationship to variations in this applied signal.

The response of this selected waveform in our circuit to the changes in the applied signal would allow us to observe and record and changes in magnitude and phase with respect to the applied signal, and we would build up an appreciation of how much of the changes in input signal are transferred to the output, or observed signal.

If the frequency of the applied input signal were varied, the output signal would again respond to this change, and we could observe the magnitude and phase of our output with respect to the input. From this practice of observation we would build up an appreciation of the chosen network's frequency response, that is, how our chosen network responded to changes in input signal frequency.

The frequency response of all linear networks is governed, not surprisingly, by what components are contained in the network and how these components are arranged or connected. Complex mathematics allows us to determine an equation that relates the output signal to the input signal, and this mathematical equation is called the network transfer function. The transfer function is not limited to purely determining the frequency response of a network, but this is what we will be using it for in this final chapter of our book.

Fig 11.1 shows the common method of representing a network when it is being analyzed in terms of its transfer function. The input port is two wires that are connected across some limb of the network, and the output port is again just two wires connected across some other limb of the network.

The transfer function (T.F) of the network is defined as the ratio of output signal to input signal and could be either a voltage T.F. or a current T.F. That is,

$$\text{T.F}_{(v)} = \frac{V_{out}}{V_{in}} \quad \text{and} \quad \text{T.F}_{(I)} = \frac{I_{out}}{I_{in}} \; .$$

When these transfer functions are emphasized with respect to frequency responses, we begin to move into the area called signal filtering.

11.2 FILTERS

Fig. 11.2 shows the classic 'brick wall' characteristics of the four main forms of filter. All signal frequencies that fall within the pass bands of our filters are theoretically passed through the network with no loss of magnitude and no change in phase angle. All signal frequencies that fall within the stop band or attenuation band are theoretically reduced to zero in magnitude, and thus phase angle information is irrelevant. In all practical forms of filtering these idealized options are not realizable, and we get four bands of filtering effect as shown in Fig. 11.3.

There are now transition bands between the pass and stop bands, and we can also see that the pass and stop bands are no longer ideal, and we usually have to accept these practical limitations in the real world of filter design. The design of filters is usually a trade-off between the reduction of transition bands and improvement in pass and stop band attenuation factors.

We will now look at the frequency response of the more common series circuit combinations, and from this we will build up an appreciation of how *R*, *L*, and *C* elements can be combined to form all four classic filter types.

11.3 FREQUENCY RESPONSE OF A SERIES *R* AND *L* CIRCUIT

If the applied supply voltage v_S is considered to have a variable frequency capability we can look at the effect this will have upon the circuit variables v_R and v_L and thus deduce the two transfer functions of the circuit suggested in Fig. 11.4. The only frequency-dependent component in the circuit is the inductor (L), and its effect is given in formula form via X_L:

$$X_L = j(\omega \, . \, L) \quad \text{or} \quad X_L = j(2 \, . \, \pi \, . f \, . \, L) \; .$$

For simplicity we will use radian frequency in our analysis, but please remember that the difference between radian frequency and cyclic frequency is nothing more than a multiplication factor of 2π.

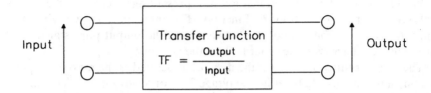

Fig. 11.1 — Block diagram of linear network.

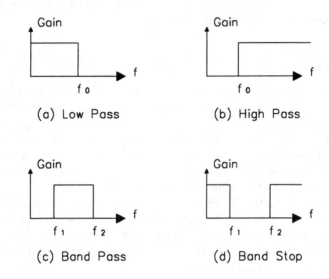

Fig. 11.2 — The four classifications of ideal filter frequency characteristics.

11.3.1　The resistor frequency response of the circuit (V_R/V_S)

$$\frac{V_R}{V_S} = \frac{R}{Z} = \frac{R}{R+jX_L} = \frac{R}{R+j(\omega.L)}$$

therefore

$$\left|\frac{V_R}{V_S}\right| = \frac{R}{\sqrt{(R^2+[\omega.L]^2)}}$$

and

$$\angle V_R/V_S = \tan^{-1}(\omega.L/R)$$

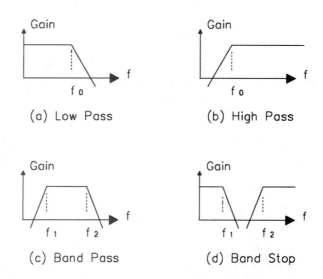

(a) Low Pass   (b) High Pass

(c) Band Pass   (d) Band Stop

Fig. 11.3 — The four classifications in a more practical form.

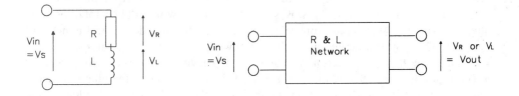

Fig. 11.4 — *R* and *L* in series (shown in transfer function form).

It is of advantage to rearrange our formulae into frequency terms since we intend to plot the frequency response. The following technique is a very common practice.
    We can say

$$R + \mathrm{j}(\omega . L) = R\left[1 + \mathrm{j}\left(\omega . \frac{L}{R}\right)\right] \ .$$

Now the term L/R is the circuit time constant, and we have encountered this already in the transient analysis section (6.3.5). Now frequency is nothing more than the inverse of time, so we can gather the time constant L/R into a frequency constant as follows. If

$$L/R = \tau \text{ (secs) then } 1/\tau = R/L = \omega_0 \text{ (Hz)} .$$

The transfer function can now be rewritten as follows.

$$\frac{V_R}{V_S} = \frac{R}{R[1 + j(\omega \cdot L/R)]} = \frac{1}{1 + j(\omega/\omega_0)} .$$

We can also say

$$\frac{V_R}{V_S} = \frac{1}{1 + j(f/f_0)} \qquad \begin{array}{l} (\qquad \omega = 2 . \pi . f) \\ (\text{and } \omega_0 = 2 . \pi . f_0) \end{array}$$

We now have a complex equational representation of how our simple circuit is going to affect the various frequencies that we may choose to apply to it. Note that we have converted the two circuit constants R and L into a frequency constant ω_0 via the circuit time constant $\tau = L/R$.

If we now imagine our frequency ω or f changing from a very small value to a very large value, we can use this transfer function to predict the changes in V_R $\omega . r . t$. V_S over the whole suggested range. Note that the constant ω_0 or f_0 gives us an indication of the range area of interest. If f_0 was, say, 1.0 kHz there wouldn't be a lot of point in investigating 100 MHz conditions since this is patently outside the frequencies of interest. This is not directly obvious from knowing simply R and L values.

Since the transfer function is complex we have, as always, two pieces of information to evaluate and display. It is traditional to evaluate the magnitude and phase angle of our transfer function and to display the results of these evaluations in graphical form to an X axis of frequency (ω or f). This form of representation is commonly called the Bode plot of the transfer function after the initiator of the method. We could also have looked at the real and imaginary results of our transfer function, and this is common practice to control engineers who need to be aware of these parameters. But we are limiting ourselves to a simple appreciation of filtering effects, and this is best seen by considering the magnitude and phase responses. Now

$$\left| \frac{V_R}{V_S} \right| = \frac{1}{\sqrt{[1 + (f/f_0)^2]}}$$

and

$$\angle V_R/V_S = -\tan^{-1}(f/f_0)$$

We can now plot the magnitude and phase of our transfer function as they vary with respect to frequency over the range already suggested. Note again that the term f now gives us an indication of the frequency range of interest. It is also common to present our magnitude in logarithmic form by the use of the decibel term, and we will now take a brief look at this form of representing the magnitude of our transfer function.

11.3.2   The use of decibel representation of magnitude responses
The ratio of power transferred from the input of our system (Fig. 11.5) to the output

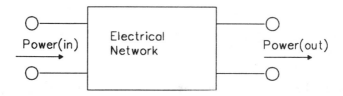

Fig. 11.5 — Black box representation of a system.

of our system is declared simply as:

$$\text{Power gain} = \frac{P_{out}}{P_{in}}$$

This result can be of such a large numeric value over a range of frequencies that is now common practice to present it in logarithmic form to reduce its presentable size.

$$\text{Log}_{10}(\text{power gain}) = \text{Log}_{10}(P_{out}/P_{in})$$

It is also common practice to multiply this result by a factor of 10 to bring it into a more useful range, thus we get the final definition of the decibel (dB) as follows:

$$10 \,.\, \text{Log}_{10}(\text{power gain}) = 10 \,.\, \text{Log}_{10}(P_{out}/P_{in})$$

$$= \text{power gain in dB's}$$

or
$$G_{P(dB)} = 10 \,.\, \text{Log}_{10}(P_{out}/P_{in})$$

The gain of any system can be declared in terms of power, voltage, or current, but if we wish to use the dB form of representation we can do so only if we are talking about power gain. We can, however, develop a bastardized form of the dB representation if we employ the following deception.

$$P_{out} = V_{out} \,.\, I_{out} = \frac{V_{out}}{R_{out}} \quad \text{and} \quad P_{in} = \frac{V_{in}}{R_{in}}$$

In some systems it is fair to assume that R_{in} could equal R_{out}, which would allow us to say the following.

$$\text{Power gain} = \frac{V_{out}^2}{V_{in}^2} \times \frac{R_{out}}{R_{in}} = \frac{V_{out}^2}{V_{in}^2} = \frac{[V_{out}]^2}{[V_{in}]}$$

and

$$G_{P(dB)} = 10 \cdot \text{Log}_{10} \frac{[V_{out}]^2}{[V_{in}]} = 20 \cdot \text{Log}_{10} \frac{[V_{out}]}{[V_{in}]} \quad .$$

It must always be remembered that this definition of power gain in dB, which is based upon voltage gain, is valid only when $R_{in} = R_{out}$ for the system under consideration.

When the dB gain is derived from voltage gain it is normal to declare it to be so, using the following notation form.

$$\left| \frac{V_R}{V_S} \right| \, dB = 20 \cdot \text{Log}_{10} \left| \frac{V_R}{V_S} \right|$$

Note that this is only a magnitude measurement, and we must still be aware that the system has a phase response to be considered. It is also necessary to note that the requirement for R_{in} to equal R_{out} for this result to be valid is very often ignored by engineers and equipment manufacturers. This erroneous practice is so widespread that it has almost become the standard, but we must in truth be aware of this regrettable practice and thus be armed against using the results too formally.

11.3.3   Frequency response of the transfer function (V_R/V_S) shown, using magnitude, phase, and dB scale representations

Now

$$\left| \frac{V_R}{V_S} \right| = \frac{1}{\sqrt{[1 + (f/f_0)^2]}}$$

giving

$$\left| \frac{V_R}{V_S} \right| \, dB = 20 \, \text{Log}_{10} \frac{1}{\sqrt{[1 + (f/f_0)^2]}}$$

and

$$\angle V_R/V_S = -\tan^{-1} (f/f_0) \quad .$$

Fig. 11.7 was based on the results from a proprietary circuit analysis software

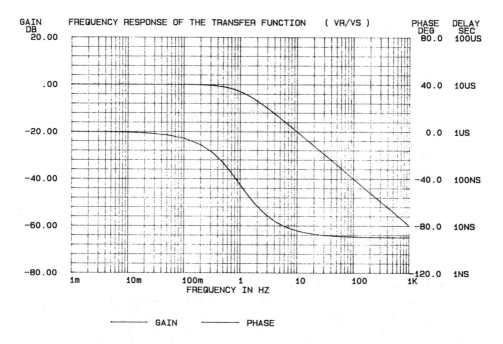

Fig. 11.6 — Frequency response of the transfer function (V_R/V_S).

package called Micro-cap©. The respons is shown normalised to an ω_0 of 1 Hz. The response is the same basic shape whatever ω_0 is deduced to be. There are a great many electrical & mathematical software packages available that reduce the amount of work involved in calculating the frequency response of circuits. The Bibliography lists two available options. There is, however, a simplified approximation technique that allows us to determine the frequency response in general form to a satisfactory degree. This will now be covered.

11.3.4 Simplified deduction of transfer function magnitude and phase responses (asymptotic approximations)

If we consider the two equations determined for our R and *L* circuit we can make logical and useful simplifications. To consider these simplifications it is best to start from the complex trransfer function, since the phase and magnitude information is easily deduced from this with the suggested simplifications.

$$\frac{V_R}{V_S} = \frac{1}{1 + j(f/f_0)}$$

As f tends toward zero:

$$\frac{V_R}{V_S} \approx 1.0 \ (0 \text{ dB}) \quad \text{and} \quad \angle V_R/V_S \approx 0 \text{ rad } (0°)$$

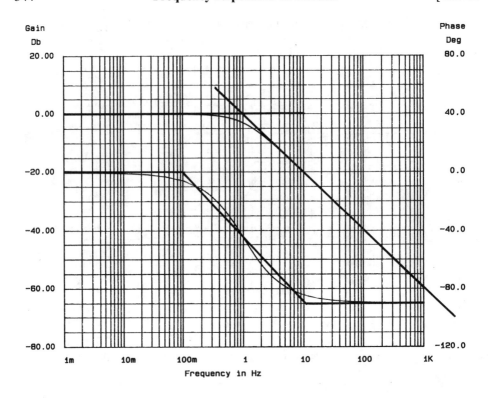

Fig. 11.7 — Approximate magnitude and phase responses.

At $f = f_0$:

$$\frac{V_R}{V_S} = \frac{1}{1 + j(1)} = \frac{1}{\sqrt{[1 + (1)^2]}} = \frac{1}{\sqrt{2}} \ (-3 \text{ dB})$$

$$\angle V_R/V_S = -\tan^{-1} = -\pi/4 \text{ rad } (-45°)$$

and as f tends toward infinity:

$$\frac{V_R}{V_S} \approx \frac{1}{j(f/f_0)} = -jf_0/f \ ,$$

giving

$$\left| \frac{V_R}{V_S} \right| = 20 \cdot \text{Log}_{10}(f_0/f)$$

and $\angle V_R/V_S = -\pi/2$ rad ($-90°$) (since V_R/V_S is $-$ve and complex).

The magnitude term as f tends toward infinity demands a further investigation. If we let f go up in steps of $f_0 \times 10^n$ we can see a useful result.

$$
\begin{array}{cccccc}
f = & f_0 & 10f_0 & 100f_0 & 1000f_0 & 10^4f_0 \\
dB = & 0 & -20 & -40 & -60 & -80
\end{array}
$$

That is, the magnitude rolls off at 20 dB per decade as the frequency tends toward infinity. This gives us three clear chunks of information about our frequency response, summarized below:

Low frequency asymptote   (0 dBs),   (0   rad)

Main frequency result   (-3 dBs),   ($-\pi/4$ rad)

High frequency asymptote   (-20 dB/dec), ($-\pi/2$ rad)

If these are combined on a sheet of log-linear graph paper we get a fair representation of our magnitude and phase responses, as in Fig. 11.7.

The true result is also shown, and we can see the closeness of the symptotic approximation. It is also possible to draw an improved phase response approximation as shown in Fig. 11.7 from which we can deduce a general rule about future phase response approximations. This rule is that we can draw a line from (0 rad, 0.1 ω_0) to ($-\pi/2$ rad, 10 ω_0) to achieve a closer approximation to the real phase response. This rule will be applied in later approximations, and we will find it is a valid technique. Remember that our frequency response is normalised to an ω_0 of 1 Hz.

11.3.5   Frequency response of series *R* and *L* circuit with respect to inductor voltage (V_L/V_S)

In the circuit given in Fig. 11.8,

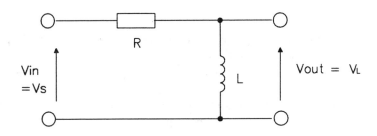

Fig. 11.8 — *R* and *L* in series (shown in transfer function form).

$$\frac{V_L}{V_Z} = \frac{Z_L}{Z_S} = \frac{j\omega \cdot L}{R + j\omega \cdot L}$$

This equation can be transformed by using the methods already covered for the resistor voltage transfer function to arrive at:

$$\frac{V_L}{V_S} = \frac{j(f/f_0)}{1 + j(f/f_0)} \qquad \left(\text{where } f_0 = \frac{1}{2 \cdot \pi \cdot \tau} \right)$$

(and $\tau = L/R$)

If we divide through by $j(f/f_0)$ we can get to a simpler result.

$$\frac{V_L}{V_S} = \frac{1}{1 - j(f_0/f)}$$

which we can now show in magnitude and phase form:

$$\left| \frac{V_L}{V_S} \right| = \frac{1}{\sqrt{[1 + (f_0/f)^2]}}$$

and

$$\angle V_L/V_S = - \tan^{-1}(-f_0/f) = \tan^{-1}(f_0/f)$$

Once again we can use Micro-cap© or some other software package to draw the actual frequency response. The result is given in Fig. 11.9 with the response normalised to $\omega_0 = 1$Hz.

11.3.6 Simplified deduction of transfer function magnitude and phase responses (asymptotic approximations)

Not surprisingly, we can again employ the asymptotic approximation technique to arrive at a quicker appreciation of the magnitude and phase responses. It is best to use the complex equation when we apply the simplifications, since the magnitude and phase angle information remains uncomplicated.

$$\frac{V_L}{V_S} = \frac{1}{1 - j(f_0/f)} \ .$$

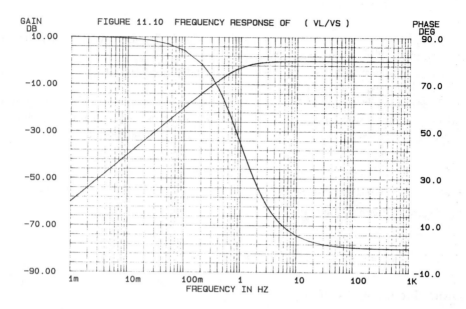

Fig. 11.9 — Frequency response of (V_L/V_S).

As f tends to infinity:

$$\left|\frac{V_L}{V_S}\right| \simeq 1.0\ (0\ \text{dB}) \ \text{ and } \ \angle\, V_L/V_S \simeq 0 \text{ rads } (0°)$$

at $f = f_0$:

$$\frac{V_L}{V_S} = \frac{1}{1-j}$$

and:

$$\left|\frac{V_L}{V_S}\right| = \frac{1}{\sqrt{(1+1)}} = \frac{1}{\sqrt{2}}\ (-3\text{dB})$$

and $\angle\, V_L/V_S = -\tan^{-1}(-1) = \pi/4 \text{ rad } (45°)$,

and as f tends toward zero:

$$\frac{V_L}{V_S} \simeq \frac{1}{-j(f_0/f)} = +j(f/f_0)$$

thus $$\left|\frac{V_L}{V_S}\right|_{\text{dB}} = 20\,.\,\text{Log}_{10}(f/f_0)$$

and $\angle\, V_L/V_S = +\pi/2 \text{ rads } (90°)$ (since V_L/V_S is $+$ve and complex).

The asympotic approximation is shown in Fig. 11.10, and we have once again included the full result for comparison.

The techniques introduced in this section will be applied to further ac circuits in the remaining parts of this book.

The frequency response of the simple R and C series combination is covered by a worked example, since the formulae development and calculations for the R and L series circuit provide a satisfactory guide to the necessary techniques.

11.4 R AND C HIGH PASS FILTER WITH PASSBAND ATTENTUATION

In the circuit given in Fig. 11.11,

$$\frac{V_{out}}{V_{in}} = \frac{R_2}{R_1 + Z_c + R_2} = \frac{R_2}{R_1 + R_2 + 1/j(\omega.C)}$$

Divide through by $(R_2 + R_2)$ gives:

$$\frac{V_{out}}{V_{in}} = \frac{R_2/(R_1 + R_2)}{1 + 1/[j(\omega.C).R_1 + R_2)]}$$

We can let $R_2/(R_1 + R_2) = \alpha$ (alpha), and since $C(R_1 + R_2) = \tau$ sec (the circuit time constant) we can let $1/C(R_1 + R_2) = \omega_0$ rad/s (the circuit frequency). Thus V_{out}/V_{in} can be rewritten as:

$$\frac{V_{out}}{V_{in}} = \frac{\alpha}{1 - j(\omega_0/\omega)} = \frac{\alpha}{1 - j(f_0/f)} \text{ ,}$$

which is recognizable as a similar solution to the result obtained in the series combination of L and R that gave us the basic high pass filter.

For the moment let us consider our circuit at high frequency only. In fact, let us consider it at such a high frequency that the capacitor could be considered to be a short-circuit. Our circuit would appear as given in Fig. 11.12.

We can use the potential divider theorem to state simply that at high frequency we can deduce that V_{out}/V_{in} is given by:

$$\frac{V_{out}}{V_{in}} = \frac{R_2}{R_1 + R_2} = \alpha \text{ (the passband attenuation)}$$

So this part of our filter result could have been deduced without reference to the necessary mathematics. From our chapters on transient analysis we have discovered the method for determining the time constants of simple R and C circuits. If we combine these deductions we can look at our calculated result and surmise that it is

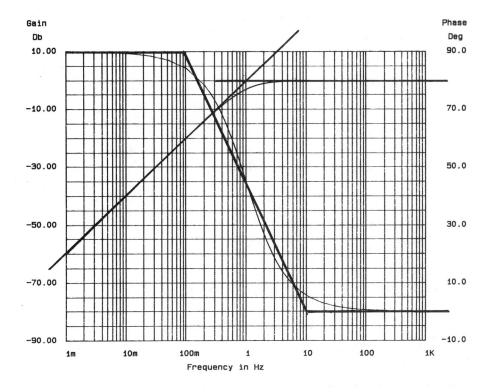

Fig. 11.10 — Asymptotic approximation of the circuit frequency response.

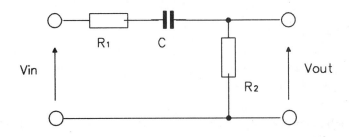

Fig. 11.11 — R and C high pass filter with passband attenuation.

correct and consistent with the results which we would expect at the limits of our circuits operation.

This kind of deductional proof of results is useful for acquiring confidence about the performance of ac circuits, and its use also helps to recognize the common

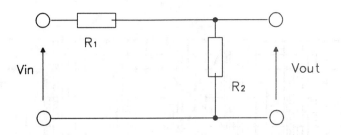

Fig. 11.12 — R and C high pass filter at high frequency.

threads running through linear circuit analysis in theorems and results, e.g. circuit time constants.

We can now develop the two forms of frequency response result already shown for the previous circuits: the full frequency response from the full equation and the approximate frequency response from the asymptotic deductions.

$$\frac{V_{out}}{V_{in}} = \frac{\alpha}{1 - j(f_0/f)} \ ,$$

which can be stated in magnitude and phase form:

$$\left|\frac{V_{out}}{V_{in}}\right| = \frac{\alpha}{\sqrt{[1 + (f_0/f)^2]}}$$

and

$$\angle V_{out}/V_{in} = -\tan^{-1}(-f_0/f) = \tan^{-1}(f_0/f) \ .$$

Once again we can use a computational technique to draw the actual frequency response, as given in Fig. 11.13.

11.4.1 Simplified deduction of transfer function magnitude and phase responses (asymptotic approximations)

We have:

$$\frac{V_{out}}{V_{in}} = \frac{\alpha}{1 - j(f_0/f)} \ .$$

As f tends to infinity:

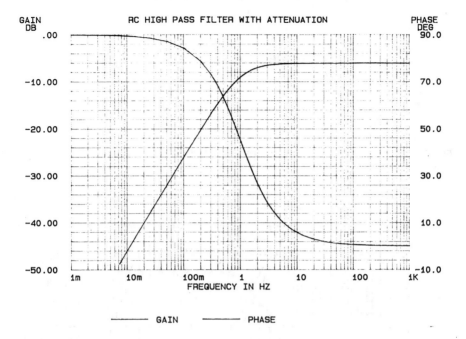

Fig. 11.13 — Frequency response of (V_{out}/V_{in}).

$\angle V_{out}/V_{in} \approx \alpha$, which is $20 \, \text{Log}_{10}(\alpha)$ dB.

Let $20 \, \text{Log}_{10}(\alpha) = \alpha_{dB}$ (our passband attentuation in dB).

and $\angle V_{out}/V_{in} \approx 0$ rad $(0°)$

At $f = f_0$:

$$\frac{V_{out}}{V_{in}} = \frac{\alpha}{1 - j(1)} = \left| \frac{V_{out}}{V_{in}} \right| - \frac{\alpha}{\sqrt{[1 + (1)^2]}} = \frac{\alpha}{\sqrt{2}} \, (\alpha_{dB} - 3 \text{ dB})$$

$$\angle V_{out}/V_{in} = -\tan^{-1}(-1) = \pi/4 \text{ rads } (45°)$$

and as f tends towards zero:

$$\frac{V_{out}}{V_{in}} \approx \frac{\alpha}{-j(f_0/f)} = +j(f/f_0)$$

$$\left|\frac{V_{\text{out}}}{V_{\text{in}}}\right| \approx \frac{\alpha}{\sqrt{[(f_0/f)^2]}} \quad [\alpha\text{dB} - 20\log_{10}(f/f_0)]$$

and $\angle V_{\text{out}}/V_{\text{in}} = +\pi/2$ rad (90°) (since $\dfrac{V_{\text{out}}}{V_{\text{in}}}$ is $+$ve and complex)

The asymptotic approximation is shown in Fig. 11.14, and we have once again

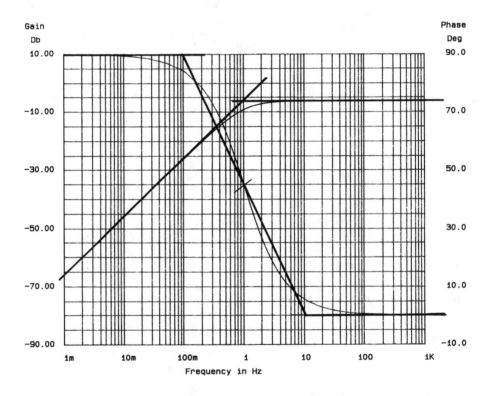

Fig. 11.14 — Frequency response of our R and C high pass filter (asymptotic approximation.)

included the full result for comparison. For the circuit given again ω_0 is normalised to 1 Hz. R_1 and R_2 are made equal and hence $\alpha = 0.5$ and α dB $= -6.02$ dB.

11.5 R AND C LOW PASS FILTER WITH PASSBAND ATTENTUATION

Using the non-analytical technique introduced in the previous section we can deduce the filter response of the Fig. 11.15 circuit in the following way.

    The circuit is a low pass filter since C is short-circuit at high frequencies and shunts the signal across the output. We can therefore assume that the response will be consistent with all our previous results, and be of the form:

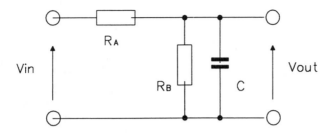

Fig. 11.15 — R and C low pass filter (passband attenuation).

$$\frac{V_{out}}{V_{in}} = \frac{\alpha}{1 + j(\omega/\omega_0)} = \frac{\alpha}{1 + j(f/f_0)} \ .$$

Now α is the passband attenuation, and this occurs at low frequency since the filter is a low pass filter. At a sufficiently low frequency our capacitor may be considered to be an open circuit to ac, and our filter circuit reduces to the circuit shown in Fig. 11.16.

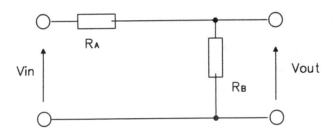

Fig. 11.16 — Low pass filter at low frequency.

From Fig. 11.16 we can see that the passband attenuation is given by the potential divider relationship between R_A and R_B.

$$\frac{V_{out}}{V_{in}} = \frac{R_B}{R_A + R_B} = \alpha \ .$$

The circuit time constant is determined by the method outlined in Chapter 6, and the effective resistance across our circuit capacitance is shown in Fig. 11.17.

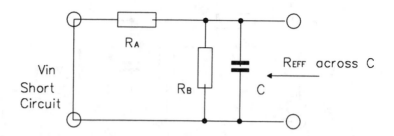

Fig. 11.17 — Time constant deduction for R and C low pass filter.

$$R_{\text{eff}} = R_A| \ |R_B = \frac{R_A \cdot R_B}{R_A + R_B} \ ,$$

thus

$$\tau = C \cdot R_{\text{eff}}, \text{ giving } \omega_0 = 1/\tau \text{ rad/s}$$

or

$$f_0 = 1/2(\cdot \pi \cdot \tau) \quad \text{Hz} \ ,$$

that is,

$$f_0 = 1/(2\pi C \cdot R_{\text{eff}}) \text{ Hz} \ ,$$

Thus our filter response is deduced to be:

$$\frac{V_{\text{out}}}{V_{\text{in}}} = \frac{\alpha}{1 + j(\omega/\omega_0)} = \frac{\alpha}{1 + j(f/f_0)}$$

where:

$$\alpha = \frac{R_B}{R_A + R_B} \text{ and } f_0 = 1/(2\pi C \cdot R_A| \ |R_B) \text{ Hz} \ .$$

For doubting students, the full analysis now follows. In Fig. 11.18,

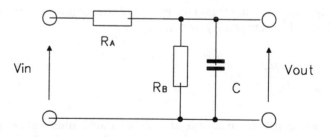

Fig. 11.18 — R and C filter, full analysis circuit.

$$\frac{V_{out}}{V_{in}} = \frac{Z_P}{Z_P + R_A} \text{ where } Z_P = R_B| \ |X_C \ .$$

But $Z_P = \dfrac{R_B . 1/(j\omega . C)}{R_B + j/(j\omega . C)}$ and if we multiply by $j\omega . C$

$$Z_P = \frac{R_B}{1 + j.\omega . CR_B} = R_B/(1 + j.\omega . CR_B) \ .$$

Therefore

$$\frac{V_{out}}{V_{in}} = \frac{R_B/(1 + j.\omega . CR_B)}{R_B/(1 + j.\omega . CR_B) + R_A}$$

Multiplying through by $(1 + j.\omega . CR_B)$ gives:

$$\frac{V_{out}}{V_{in}} = \frac{R_B}{R_B + R_A . (1 + j.\omega . CR_B)}$$

or

$$\frac{V_{out}}{V_{in}} = \frac{R_B}{R_B + R_A + j.\omega . CR_B R_A} \ .$$

Now divide through by $(R_A + R_B)$ to get:

$$\frac{V_{out}}{V_{in}} = \frac{R_B/(R_A + R_B)}{1 + j.\omega . CR_B R_A/(R_A + R_B)}$$

which finally gives:

$$\frac{V_{out}}{V_{in}} = \frac{\alpha}{1 + j(\omega/\omega_0)} = \frac{\alpha}{1 + j(f/f_0)} \ ,$$

where

$$\alpha = \frac{R_B}{R_A + R_B} \text{ and } f_0 = 1/(2\pi C . R_A| \ |R_B) \text{ Hz}$$

The simple deduction technique is of course applicable only if we have some idea about the transfer function of the circuit we are trying to analyze, and thus might appear a little pointless. If, however, we use these results to guide us about how we must form the transfer functions during analysis, we can begin to appreciate the very common patterns that are developed during ac circuit analysis.

We will now look at a band pass filter circuit that is commonly found in oscilloscope probes. These probes are used to compensate for the inherent distortion that occurs in oscilloscopes when their high input impedance is connected across a circuit under test.

11.6 THE FREQUENCY RESPONSE OF A COMPENSATED OSCILLOSCOPE PROBE

The leads of the cable connecting the scope to the circuit have an inherent capacitance, and this, together with the scope's input impedance, forms a parallel combination of R and C across the circuit under test. Fig. 11.19 outlines the problem and shows the probe circuit used to compensate for this effect.

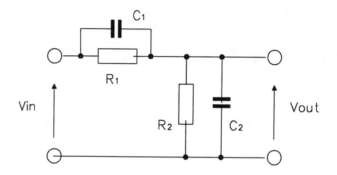

Fig. 11.19 — Oscilloscope probe compensation circuit.

In this circuit

$$\frac{V_{out}}{V_{in}} = \frac{Z_2}{Z_1 + Z_2} \text{ where } Z_1 = R_1|\ |X_{C1} \text{ and } Z_2 = R_2|\ |X_{C2} \ .$$

From our previous work we know that:

$$Z_P = R_P/(1 + j.\omega.C_P R_P)$$

Therefore

$$Z_1 = R_1/(1 + j.\omega.C_1 R_1)$$

and

$$Z_2 = R_2/(1 + j.\omega.C_2 R_2)$$

Therefore

$$\frac{V_{out}}{V_{in}} = \frac{R_1/(1+j.\omega.C_1R_1)}{R_1/(1+j.\omega.C_1R_1) + R_2/(1+j.\omega.C_2R_2)}$$

Now if we let $C_1R_1 = C_2R_2 = CR$ and multiply through by the factor $(1+j.\omega.CR)$ we get

$$\frac{V_{out}}{V_{in}} = \frac{R_1}{R_1+R_2}$$

This means that we have got no phase distortion and only resistive attenuation for all frequencies, thus we have the perfect reproduction of our measured signal. Thus on oscilloscope probes we can alter either R_1 or C_1, to achieve matching of signal measurement.

11.7 THE FREQUENCY RESPONSE OF THE SERIES *LCR* CIRCUIT

11.7.1 Second order low pass filter
The reason behind calling the circuit in Fig. 11.20 a second order low pass filter will

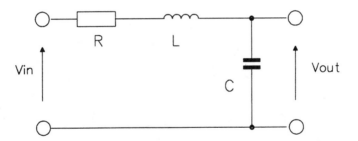

Fig. 11.20 — *LCR* low pass filter circuit V_c/V_{in}.

become apparent at the end of the full analysis. We will jump straight in and develop the transfer function from first principles.

$$\frac{V_{out}}{V_{in}} = \frac{1/j\omega C}{1/j\omega C + j\omega L + R}$$

$$= \frac{1}{1-\omega^2LC + j\omega CR}$$

$$\frac{1}{1-(\omega/\omega_0)^2 + j\omega/(\omega_0.Q_0)}$$

where

$$\omega_0 = \frac{1}{\sqrt{(LC)}} \text{ rad/s} \quad \text{and} \quad Q_0 = \frac{1}{\omega_0 \cdot CR} = \frac{1}{R}\frac{\sqrt{L}}{\sqrt{C}} \ .$$

$$\omega^2 LC = \frac{\omega^2}{\omega_0^2}, \quad \text{and} \quad \omega CR = \frac{\omega}{\omega_0}(\omega_0 CR) = \frac{\omega}{\omega_0 Q_0} \ .$$

For definitions of ω_0 and Q_0 see section 9.4

in cyclic frequency form

$$\frac{V_{OUT}}{V_{IN}} = \frac{1}{1 - (f/f_0)^2 + jf/(f_0 \cdot Q_0)}$$

where

$$f_0 = \frac{1}{2\pi\sqrt{(LC)}} \text{ Hz} \quad \text{and} \quad Q_0 = \frac{1}{2\pi \cdot f_0 \cdot CR} = \frac{1}{R}\frac{\sqrt{L}}{\sqrt{C}} \ .$$

The Micro-cap© circuit analysis package was employed to develop the gain and phase plots shown in Fig. 11.21 and from them we can see the effects of having different Q_0 for a set normalized resonant frequency of $f_0 = 1.0$ Hz.

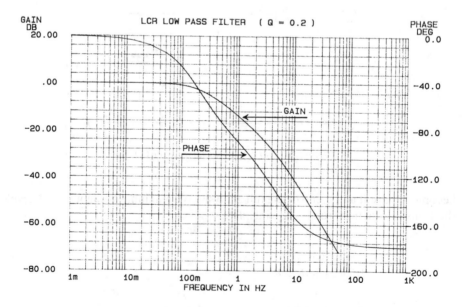

Fig. 11.21(a) — *LCR* low pass second order filter ($Q_0 = 0.2$).

If we look at the gain and phase responses given in Fig. 11.21 we can see that it is significantly different from the responses obtained for the first order *LR* low pass filter in section 11.3.

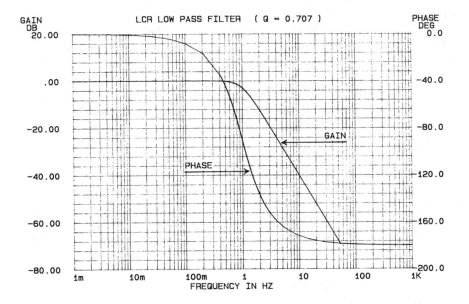

Fig. 11.21(b) — *LCR* low pass second order filter ($Q_0 = 0.707$ [$1/\sqrt{2}$]).

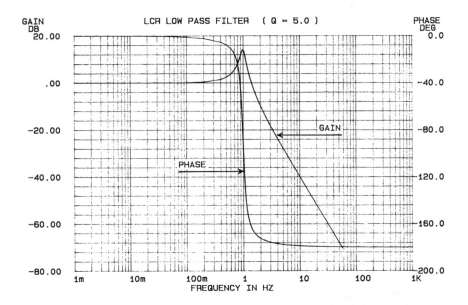

Fig. 11.21(c) — *LCR* low pass second order filter ($Q_0 = 5.0$).

In the first order responses there was no Q factor to take into account, and if we look at the attenmuation band roll-off we can see a 40 dB/dec reduction occurring as opposed to the first order 20 dB/dec found in the LR filter.

Similarly, we can see doubling effect upon the phase response range where we get a 0° to 180° change in phase as compared to the 90° range common in all first order systems.

The reason for the difference is not difficult to identify when we take note of the inclusion in our second order filter circuit to two reactive elements L and C and compare this to the first order filter circuits where only one reactive element occurred at any time.

Thus as an initial stab of defining a second order filter system we can say that it must include two reactive elements. We will see later that this has to be further qualified to take into account the reactive element's 'position' in the system, but we will do that when we are a little clearer about exactly how their position affects the responses.

We will now go on to look at another second order filter circuit to consolidate the considerations introduced in this section.

11.7.2   Second order high pass filter
In the circuit shown in Fig. 11.22,

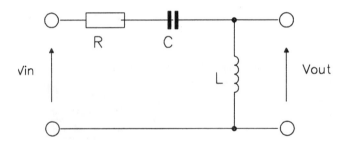

Fig. 11.22 — LCR high pass filter circuit V_L/V_{in}.

$$\frac{V_{out}}{V_{in}} = \frac{j\omega L}{1/j\omega C + j\omega L + R}$$

$$\frac{V_{out}}{V_{in}} = \frac{-\omega^2 LC}{1 - \omega^2 LC + j\omega CR}$$

$$\frac{V_{out}}{V_{in}} = \frac{-(\omega/\omega_0)^2}{1 - (\omega/\omega_0)^2 + j\omega/(\omega_0 \cdot Q_0)}$$

where

$$\omega_0 = \frac{1}{\sqrt{(LC)}} \text{ rad/s and } Q_0 = \frac{1}{\omega_0 \cdot CR} = \frac{1\sqrt{L}}{R\sqrt{C}}$$

or

$$\frac{V_{OUT}}{V_{IN}} = \frac{-(f/f_0)^2}{1 - (f/f_0)^2 + jf/(f_0 \cdot Q_0)}$$

where

$$f_0 = \frac{1}{2\pi\sqrt{(LC)}} \text{ Hz and } Q_0 = \frac{1}{2\pi \cdot f_0 \cdot CR} = \frac{1\sqrt{L}}{R\sqrt{C}} .$$

The Micro-cap© circuit analysis package was once again employed to develop the gain and phase plots shown in Fig. 11.23, and from them we can see the effects of

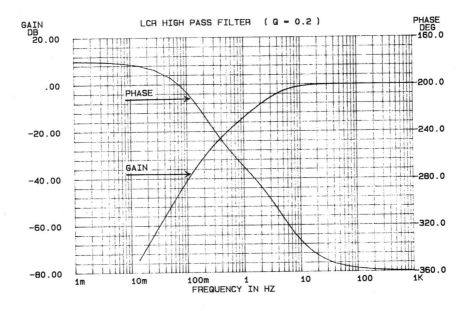

Fig. 11.23(a) — *LCR* high pass second order filter ($Q_0 = 0.2$).

having different Q_0 for a set normalized resonant frequency of $f_0 = 1.0$ Hz.

Significant second order effects are apparent once again in the 40 dB/dec attenuation band roll-off in gain and the 180° overall phase change. The Q factor is causing the same disruption in the high pass filter that it caused in the low pass case, and it is not difficult to see that we have in effect a mirror response to the low pass case.

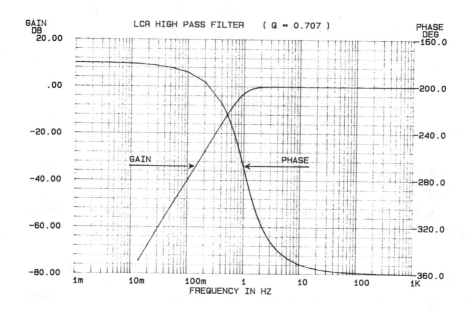

Fig. 11.23(b) — *LCR* high pass second order filter ($Q_0 = 1/\sqrt{2}$).

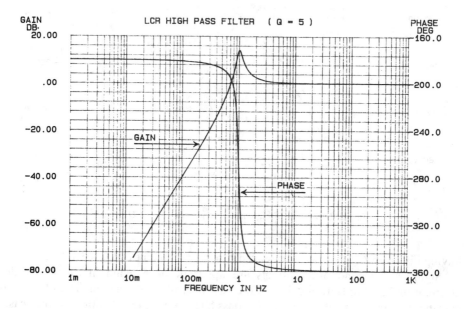

Fig. 11.23(c) — *LCR* high pass second order filter ($Q_0 = 5$).

All of these common factors could have been highlighted by investigating the asymptotic approximations for the filter responses, but with the progressively common occurrence of relatively cheap circuit analysis software like Micro-cap$^©$ it will become less necessary to seek these approximate techniques except in very simple cases.

However, at resonance in our low and high pass second order filters we get a clear indication of the overriding effect of the Q factor.

Low pass filter

At resonance: $\dfrac{V_C}{V_{in}} = \dfrac{1}{j/1Q} = -jQ$ $[20\,\mathrm{Log}_{10}(Q)\ \angle -90°]$

High pass filter

At resonance: $\dfrac{V_L}{V_{in}} = \dfrac{-1}{j1/Q} = +jQ$ $[20\,\mathrm{Log}_{10}(Q)\ \angle +90°]$.

This means that the phase is set at $\pm 90°$, and the gain at resonance is set by the Q factor. This should come as no real surprise to those who can remember the phasor diagram for resonance which we repeated in Fig. 11.24. Here we can see the $\pm 90°$

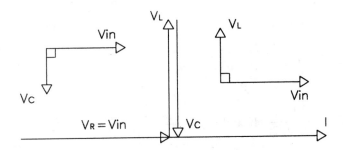

Fig. 11.24 — Phasor diagram for *LCR* series resonant circuit.

phase shift associated with V_C and V_L with respect to V_{in}. We can also see the Q factor or magnification effect associated with V_C and V_L when compared to V_{in}.

So in truth their are no surprises in the analysis except possibly how to choose to view the results of the analysis. To complete this chapter we will look at the series resonant circuit once more, but this time we will not get a second order response. It should become apparent why this is not altogether unexpected.

11.7.3   Band pass *LCR* filter (V_R/V_{in})
In the circuit given in Fig. 11.25.

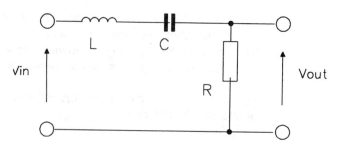

Fig. 11.25 — LCR bandpass filter circuit V_R/V_{in}.

$$\frac{V_{out}}{V_{in}} = \frac{R}{1/j\omega C + j\omega L + R}$$

$$= \frac{j\omega CR}{1 - \omega^2 LC + j\omega CR}$$

$$= \frac{j\omega/(\omega_0 . Q_0)}{1 - (\omega/\omega_0)^2 + j\omega/(\omega_0 . Q_0)}$$

where

$$\omega_0 = \frac{1}{\sqrt{(LC)}} \text{ rad/s} \quad \text{and} \quad Q_0 = \frac{1}{\omega_0 . CR} = \frac{1}{R}\frac{\sqrt{L}}{\sqrt{C}}$$

or

$$\frac{V_{OUT}}{V_{IN}} = \frac{jf/f_0 . Q_0}{1 - (f/f_0)^2 + jf/(Q_0 . f_0)}$$

where

$$f_0 = \frac{1}{2\pi\sqrt{(LC)}} \text{ Hz and } Q_0 = \frac{1}{2\pi . f_0 . CR} = \frac{1}{R}\frac{\sqrt{L}}{\sqrt{C}}$$

The Micro-cap© circuit analysis package was once again employed to develop the gain and phase plots shown in Figs 11.26, 27 and 28, and from them we can see the effects of having different Q_0 for a set normalized resonant frequency of $f_0 = 1.0$ Hz.

In all three results we can observe two attenuation bands of 20 dB/dec on the gain plot and an overall phase shift of 180° across the frequency range of interest. From this we can surmise that the cosy definition of filter order is in for a bit of revision. If we consider the band pass filter response for the case where $Q = 0.2$ we can point toward a better understanding of whats happening in our filter.

At low frequency we can consider our inductor to be tending towards a short circuit, and our capacitor could be considered to be tending toward an open circuit. So we can see that it is the capacitor that is directly causing the roll-off in filter gain, and we could simplify our circuit at low frequency to be a simple CR high pass filter;

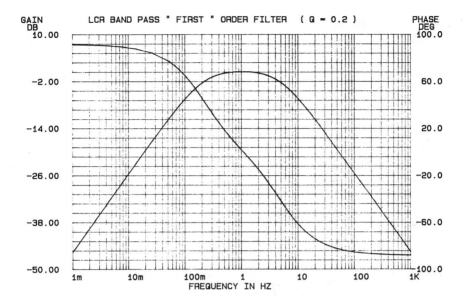

Fig. 11.26 — *LCR* bandpass first order filter ($Q_0 = 0.2$).

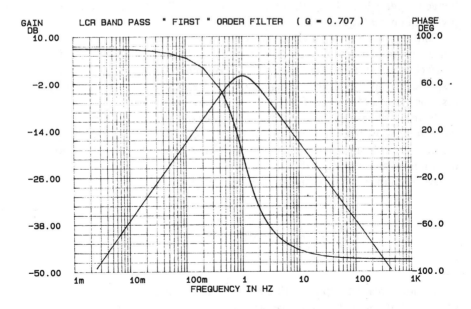

Fig. 11.27 — *LCR* bandpass first order filter ($Q_0 = 1/\sqrt{2}$).

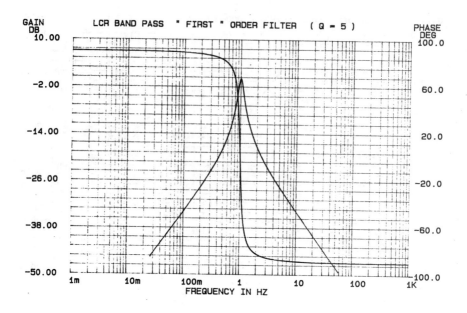

Fig. 11.28 — *LCR* band pass first order filter ($Q_0 = 5$).

hence we get a 20 dB/dec roll-off in gain and a $+90°$ to $0°$ change in phase over the low-frequency range.

Similar reasoning would allow us to say that at high frequency we could simplify our circuit to being a low pass *LR* filter circuit with a 20 dB/dec roll-off and a $0°$ to $-90°$ change in phase. This should show how our potential for a second order filter response is split between the high and low frequencies, hence we get an overall response that is effectively first order in appearance.

If we now consider the remaining two cases of $Q = 1/\sqrt{2}$ and 5.0 we can see that the high and low frequency effects are beginning to overlap, and in the $Q = 5.0$ case we can see an improved sharpness in attentuation which would become more pronounced as we increased our Q factor.

At resonance our response is given by:

$$\frac{V_{out}}{V_{in}} = \frac{j\omega/(\omega_0 \cdot Q_0)}{j\omega/(\omega_0 \cdot Q_0)} = 1.0 \ (0 \ \text{dB})$$

This is not dependent upon Q, thus all bandpass arrangements based upon the *LCR* series network have, at resonance, a peak gain of 1.0 (0 dB) and a phase response of $0°$. This, again, should not surprise those who are familiar with the phasor diagram of a series resonant network at resonance, where $V_R = V_{IN}$ and thus in our case $V_{OUT} = V_{IN}$. (See figure 11.24).

The chapter, and the book, is now formally and traditionally brought to an end with the now, we hope, compulsive worked examples and tutorial examples.

WORKED EXAMPLES

Example 11.1

Q. For the filter circuits shown in Fig. 11.29 prove that the transfer function for both

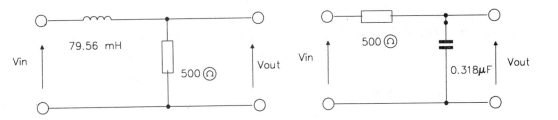

Fig. 11.29 — First order low pass filters.

circuits is given by:

$$\frac{V_{out}}{V_{in}} = \frac{1}{1 + jf/10^3} .$$

Plot the magnitude and phase responses in both full and approximate forms.

A. *Method* 1 *quick and dirty*

For both circuits it is easy to see that they are both low pass filters of the first order. Each circuit has only one reactive element, thus the filters are first order.

For the first circuit we can see that the inductor is short circuit at low frequencies, thus all the input passes straight through the filter (low pass filter).

For the second circuit we can see that the capacitor is short circuit at high frequencies and open circuit at low frequencies, thus all the input is shunted to ground at high frequency and unaffected at low frequency (low pass filter).

Thus both circuits have the transfer function frequency response given below.

$$\frac{V_{out}}{V_{in}} = \frac{1}{1 + j(f/f_0)}$$

(where $f_0 = \dfrac{1}{2 \cdot \pi \cdot \tau}$ Hz) and τ is the circuit time constant

For the inductor circuit, $\tau = L/R = 79.56 \times 10^{-3}/500$

$$= 0.1591 \times 10^3 \text{ s},$$

giving $f_0 = 1000$ Hz .

For the capacitor circuit, $\tau = CR = 0.318 \times 10^{-6} \times 500$

$$= 0.1591 \times 10^{-3} \text{ s },$$

giving $f_0 = 1000$ Hz .

Hence both circuits have the transfer function frequency response given by:

$$\frac{V_{out}}{V_{in}} = \frac{1}{1 + jf/1k}$$

The Bode plots for the above equation are given in Fig. 11.30.

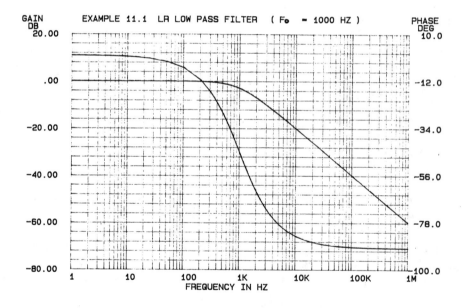

Fig. 11.30 — Bode plots for example 11.1.

Method 2   Full analysis

    Inductor circuit   *Capactor circuit*

$$\frac{V_{out}}{V_{in}} = \frac{R}{R + j\omega L} \qquad\qquad \frac{V_{out}}{V_{in}} = \frac{1/j\omega C}{1/j\omega C + R} .$$

$$= \frac{1}{1 + j\omega L/R}$$

$$= \frac{1}{1 + j\omega/\omega_1}$$

where

$$\omega_1 = R/L \text{ rad/s}$$

or

$$\frac{V_{out}}{V_{in}} = \frac{1}{1 + jf/f_1}$$

where

$$f_1 = \frac{1}{(2\pi\ L)/R}\ \text{Hz}$$

$$= \frac{1}{1 + j\omega CR}$$

$$= \frac{1}{1 + j\omega/\omega_2}$$

where

$$\omega_2 = 1/CR \text{ rad/s} ,$$

or

$$\frac{V_{out}}{V_{in}} = \frac{1}{1 + jf/f_2}$$

where

$$f_2 = \frac{1}{2\pi\ .\ CR}\ \text{Hz} .$$

The remainder of the full analysis follows the quick and dirty method from now on.

Example 11.2
Q. For the filter circuits shown in Fig. 11.31 prove that the transfer function for both

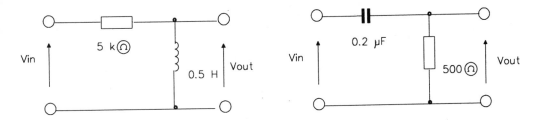

Fig. 11.31 — First order high pass filters.

circuits is given by:

$$\frac{V_{out}}{V_{in}} = \frac{1}{1 - j10^4/\omega}$$

Plot the magnitude and phase responses in both full and approximate forms.

Method 1   Quick and dirty
For both circuits it is easy to see that they are high pass filters of the first order. Each circuit has only one reactive element, thus the filters are first order.

For the first circuit we can see that the inductor is short circuit at low frequencies, thus all the input is shunted to ground at low frequencies. At high frequencies the inductor tends to present an open circuit to signal, and hence the signal is passed through to the output (high pass filter).

For the second circuit we can see that the capacitor is short circuit at high frequencies and open circuit at low frequencies, thus all the high frequency input is fed through to the output (high pass filter).

Thus both circuits have the transfer function frequency response given below.

$$\frac{V_{out}}{V_{in}} = \frac{1}{1 - j\omega_0/\omega} \quad \text{(where } \omega_0 = \frac{1}{\tau} \text{ rad/s)}$$

And 'τ' is the circuit time constant.

For the inductor circuit, $\tau = L/R = 500 \times 10^{-3}/5000$

$$= 0.1 \times 10^{-3} \text{ s},$$

giving $\omega_0 = 10000$ rad/s .

For the capacitor circuit, $\tau = CR = 0.2 \times 10^{-6} \times 500$

$$= 0.1 \times 10^{-3} \text{ s },$$

giving $\omega_0 = 10000$ rad/s .

Hence both circuits have the transfer function frequency response given by:

$$\frac{V_{out}}{V_{in}} = \frac{1}{1 - j10^4/\omega}$$

The Bode plots for the above equation are given in Fig. 11.32,

Method 2   Full analysis

Inductor circuit	*Capacitor circuit*
$$\frac{V_{out}}{V_{in}} = \frac{j\omega L}{j\omega L + R}$$	$$\frac{V_{out}}{V_{in}} = \frac{R}{R + 1/j\omega C}$$
$$= \frac{1}{1 + R/j\omega L}$$	$$= \frac{1}{1 + 1/j\omega CR}$$
$$= \frac{1}{1 - j\omega_1/\omega}$$	$$= \frac{1}{1 - j\omega_2/\omega}$$
where	where
$\omega_1 = R/L$ rad/s	$\omega_2 = \dfrac{1}{CR}$ rad/s

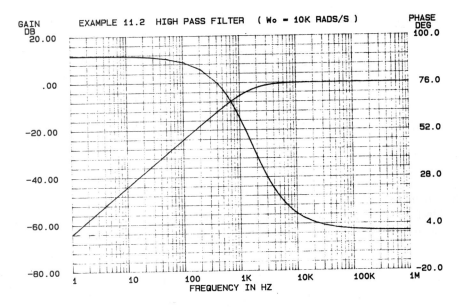

Fig. 11.32 — Bode plots.

Example 11.3

Q. Show that the filter circuit given in Fig. 11.33 has the transfer function frequency response given below.

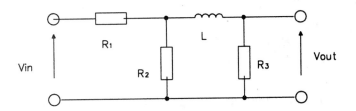

Fig. 11.33 — Low pass inductive filter with attentuation.

$$\frac{V_{out}}{V_{in}} = \frac{\alpha}{1 + j\omega/\omega_0}$$

where

$$\alpha = \frac{R_2 R_3}{R_1 R_2 + R_1 R_3 + R_2 R_3}$$

and

$$\omega_0 = 1/\tau \quad (\tau = L/R_\tau)$$

and

$$R_\tau = \frac{(R_1 R_2 + R_1 R_3 + R_2 R_3)}{(R_1 + R_2)}.$$

A. *Method 1   Quick and dirty*

At low frequency the inductor can be considered to be an effective short circuit. thus we can redraw our circuit as shown in Fig. 11.34. From which we can see that the low

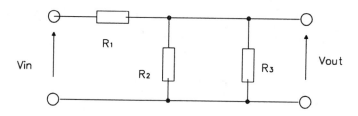

Fig. 11.34 — Filter at low frequency.

frequency attenuation is given by:

$$\alpha = \frac{R_2| \, |R_3}{R_1 + R_2| \, |R_3} = \frac{R_2 R_3/(R_2 + R_3)}{R_1 + R_2 R_3/(R_2 + R_3)}$$

$$= \frac{R_2 R_3}{(R_2 + R_3)R_1 + R_2 R_3}$$

Therefore

$$\alpha = \frac{R_2 R_3}{R_1 R_2 + R_1 R_3 + R_2 R_3}$$

The time constant of the inductor is given by $\tau = L/R_\tau$ where R_τ is the effective resistance connected across the inductors terminals. This is determined in the now familiar way shown in Fig. 11.35.

We can see that R_τ is given by:

$$R_\tau = R_1| \, |R_2 + R_3 = \frac{R_1 R_2}{R_1 + R_2} + R_3$$

$$= \frac{R_1 R_2 + R_3(R_1 + R_2)}{R_1 + R_2}$$

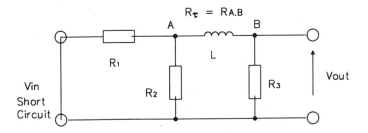

Fig. 11.35 — Determination of time constant.

$$= \frac{R_1 R_2 + R_3 R_1 + R_3 R_2}{R_1 + R_2} = \frac{R_1 R_2 + R_1 R_3 + R_2 R_3}{R_1 + R_2}$$

Now $\omega_0 = 1/\tau = R_\tau/L$ and since the filter is obviously a low pass filter we can write:

$$\frac{V_{out}}{V_{in}} = \frac{\alpha}{1 + j\omega/\omega_0}$$

where

$$\alpha = \frac{R_2 R_3}{R_1 R_2 + R_{1R3} + R_2 R_3}$$

and

$$\omega_0 = 1/\tau \ (\tau = L/R_1)$$

and

$$R_\tau = \frac{(R_1 R_2 + R_1 R_3 + R_2 R_3)}{(R_1 + R_2)}$$

Method 2   Full analysis
It is of advantage to reduce our circuit to a simpler form before launching into a full attack upon the development of the transfer function, and it is always a good policy to look for simplifications whenever possible. In this analysis we will first of all convert V_{in}, R_1 and R_2 into their equivalent Thévénin generator model as suggested by Fig. 11.36.

$$V_{TH} = V_{IN} \times \frac{R_2}{R_1 + R_2} \quad \text{and} \quad R_{TH} = R_1|\ |R_2 = \frac{R_1 R_2}{R_1 + R_2}$$

We can now write our transfer function as:

$$V_{out} = V_{TH} \times \frac{R_3}{R_{TH} + j\omega L + R_3}$$

$$= V_{IN} \times \frac{R_2}{(R_1 + R_2)} \times \frac{R_3}{(R_1 R_2/[R_1 + R_2] + j\omega L + R_3)}$$

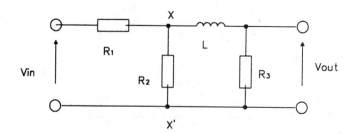

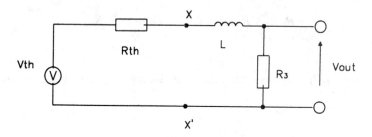

Fig. 11.36 — Thévénin model of V_{in}, R_1 and R_2.

$$\frac{V_{OUT}}{V_{IN}} = \frac{R_2 R_3}{(R_1 R_2 + j\omega L[R_1 + R_2] + R_3[R_1 + R_2])}$$

Therefore

$$\frac{V_{out}}{V_{in}} = \frac{R_2 R_3}{(R_1 R_2 + R_3 R_1 + R_3 R_2 + j\omega L[R_1 + R_2])}$$

$$= \frac{R_2 R_3/(R_1 R_2 + R_3 R_1 + R_3 R_2)}{(1 + j\omega L[R_1 + R_2]/(R_1 R_2 + R_3 R_2 + R_3 R_2))}$$

$$= \frac{\alpha}{(1 + j\omega L/R_\tau)} \ ,$$

and we can now write:

$$\frac{V_{out}}{V_{in}} = \frac{\alpha}{1 + j\omega/\omega_0}$$

where $\quad \alpha = \dfrac{R_2 R_3}{R_1 R_2 + R_1 R_3 + R_2 R_3}$

and

$$\omega_0 = 1/\tau \ (\tau = L/R_\tau)$$

and
$$R_\tau = \frac{(R_1 R_2 + R_1 R_3 + R_2 R_3)}{(R_1 + R_2)}$$

This example shows us that the approximation, (quick and dirty), method is relatively valid.

Example 4

Q. Using whatever method is appropriate determine the transfer function for the circuit given in Fig. 11.37.

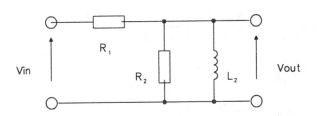

Fig. 11.37 — Filter network.

A *Method 1   Quick and dirty*
One reactive element means first order. At low frequency the inductor is a short circuit, therefore no output is allowed. At high frequency the inductor tends to be an open circuit, therefore the circuit reduces a potential divider R_1 and R_2, and high frequencies thus pass but with attenuation as a result of the potential divider. That is

$$\frac{V_{out}}{V_{in}} = \frac{\alpha}{1 - j\omega_0/\omega}$$

where
$$\alpha = R_2/(R_1 + R_2)$$

and
$$\omega_0 = R_T/L_2 \text{ rad/s}$$

and
$$R_T = \frac{R_1 R_2}{R_1 + R_2}$$

This suggested result will now be confirmed by a full analysis technique.

Method 2   Full analysis

$$\frac{V_{out}}{V_{in}} = \frac{Z_2}{Z_1 + Z_2}$$

where

$$Z_1 = R_1$$

and

$$Z_2 = \frac{R_2(j\omega L_2)}{R_2 + j\omega L_2} \ ,$$

therefore

$$\frac{V_{out}}{V_{in}} = \frac{R_2(j\omega L_2)/(R_2 + j\omega L_2)}{R_1 + R_2(j\omega L_2)/(R_2 + j\omega L_2)}$$

$$= \frac{R_2(j\omega L_2)}{R_1 \cdot (R_2 + j\omega L_2) + R_2(j\omega L_2)}$$

$$= \frac{j\omega L_2 R_2}{R_1 R_2 + j\omega L_2(R_1 + R_2)}$$

$$= \frac{j\omega L_2 R_2/(R_1 + R_2)}{R_1 R_2/(R_1 + R_2) + j\omega L_2}$$

$$= \frac{R_2/(R_1 + R_2)}{1/j\omega(L_2/R_T) + 1} \qquad \text{where } R_T = R_T| \ |R_2$$

$$= \frac{\alpha}{1 - j\omega_2/\omega} \qquad \text{where } \alpha = R_2/(R_1 + R_2)$$

$$= \frac{\alpha}{1 - j\omega_2/\omega} \qquad \text{and} \omega_2 = R_T/L_2 \text{ rad/s}$$

This confirms the quick and dirty method, but it is left to the student to decide which was the easiest and most informative.

Examples 11.5 to 11.7 give practice in working with the series resonant circuit and its three filter configurations. The Bode plot responses are given with the circuits, try to employ approximation techniques.

Example 11.5

Q. Draw the Bode plots for the circuit given in Fig. 11.38.

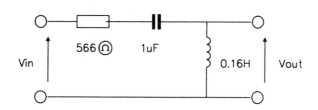

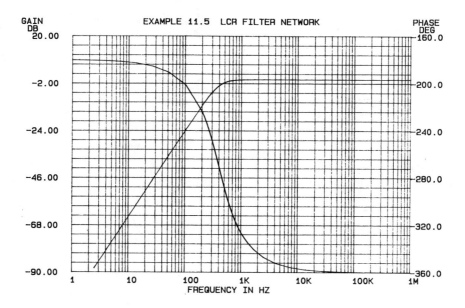

Fig. 11.38 — *LCR* filter network.

Example 11.6
Draw the Bode plots for the circuit given in Fig. 11.39

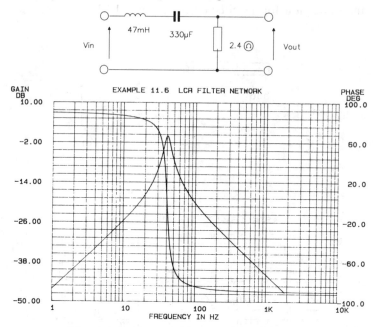

Fig. 11.39 — *LCR* filter network.

Example 11.7
Draw the Bode plots for the circuit given in Fig. 11.40.

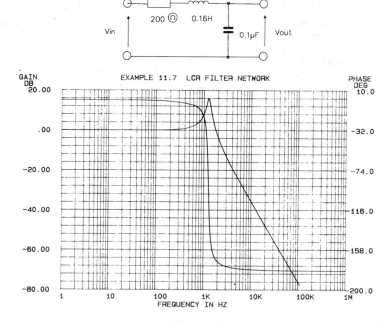

Fig. 11.40 — *LCR* filter network.

REVIEW QUESTIONS AND TUTORIAL EXAMPLES

(11.1) Derive the transfer function of a simple series LR network where the output is taken across a resistor of value 5 kΩ. $(L = 47$ mH). Repeat the example for an impure inductor which is found to have 100 Ω winding resistance.

$$(\text{TF}_1 = 1/(1 + jf/(16.92 \text{ kHz}), \text{TF}_2 = 0.98/(1 + jf/17.26 \text{ kHz}))$$

(11.2) Derive the transfer function of a simple series CR network where the output is taken across a capacitor of value 4700 pF $(R = 5$ kΩ). Repeat the example for an impure capacitor which is found to have 100 kΩ dielectric resistance.

$$(\text{TF}_1 = 1/(1 + jf/f_1) \quad f_1 = 6.77 \text{ kHz})$$

$$(\text{TF}_2 = 0.95/(1 + jf/f_2)) \quad f_2 = 7.11 \text{ kHz})$$

(11.3) Repeat example 11.1 for the output now being taken across the inductor.

$$[\text{TF}_1 = jf/f_1/(1 + jf/f_1) \quad f_1 = 16.92 \text{ kHz}]$$

$$[\text{TF}_2 = (0.02 + jf/f_2)/(1 + jf/f_2) \quad f_2 = 17.26 \text{ kHz}]$$

(11.4) Repeat example 11.2 for the output now being taken across the resistor.

$$[\text{TF}_1 = jf/f_1/(1 + jf/f_1) \quad f_1 = 6.77 \text{ kHz}]$$

$$[\text{TF}_2 = (0.05 + jf/f_2))/(1 + jf/f_2) \quad f_2 = 7.11 \text{ kHz}]$$

(Hint: for 11.3 and 11.4 is that $V_{\text{out}(2)} = V_{\text{in}} - V_{\text{out}(1)}$)

(11.5) Determine the transfer function and draw the Bode plots for the circuit given in Fig. 11.41. For the three possible resistor values given.

$$(\text{TF} = \frac{j\omega/(\omega_0)}{1 - (\omega/\omega_0)^2 + j\omega/(\omega_0 . Q)])}$$

$\omega_0 = 1.22$ M rad/s
$f_0 = 194$ kHz
$Q = 1/\sqrt{2}, 5, 0.2$.

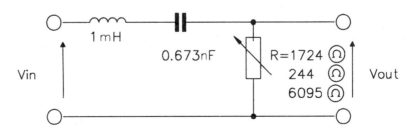

Fig. 11.41 — LCR bandpass filter.

(11.6) Use Micro-cap or some other software package to determine the frequency response of the forth order filter circuit given in Fig. 11.42.

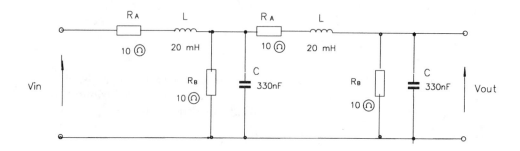

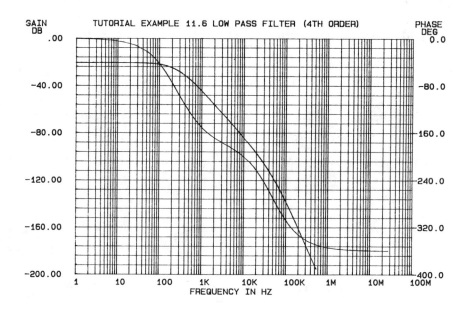

Fig. 11.42 — Fourth order filter network.

Appendix A:
Standard electrical quantity symbols and their units

Quantity	Quantity symbol	Unit	Unit symbol
Admittance	Y	siemen	S
Angular frequency	ω	radians per second	rad/s
Area	A	square metres	m²
Attenuation coefficient (or constant)	α	neper per metre	Np/m
Capacitance	C	farad	F
Charge	Q	coulomb	C
Charge density	σ	coulomb per square metre	C/m²
Conductance	G	siemen	S
Current	I	ampere	A
Current density	J	ampere per square metre	A/m²
Efficiency	η	per-unit or per cent	p.u. or %
Electric field strength	E	volt per metre	V/m
Electric flux	Ψ	coulomb	C
Electric flux density	D	coulomb per square metre	C/m²
Electromotive force	V	volt	V
Energy	W	joule	J
Field strength, electric	E	volt per metre	V/m
Field strength, magnetic	H	ampere per metre	A/m

Flux, electric	Ψ	coulomb	C
Flux, magnetic	Φ	weber	Wb
Flux density, electric	D	coulomb per square metre	C/m²
Flux density, magnetic	B	tesla	T
Force	F	newton	N
Frequency	f	hertz	Hz
Frequency, angular	ω	radians per second	rad/s
Frequency, rotational	n	revolutions per second	rev/s
Impedance	Z	ohm	Ω
Inductance, self	L	henry	H
Inductance, mutual	M	henry	H
Length	l	metre	m
Loss angle	δ	radian or degrees	rad or °
Magnetic field strength	H	ampere per metre	A/m
Magnetic flux	Φ	weber	Wb
Magnetic flux density	B	tesla	T
Magnetic flux linkage	Ψ	weber	Wb
Magnetising force	H	ampere per metre	A/m
Magnetomotive force	F_m	ampere	A
Mutual inductance	M	henry	H
Number of phases	m	—	—
Number of pole-pairs	p	—	—
Number of turns (of a winding	N	—	—
Period, Periodic time	T	second	s
Permeabnility, absolute	μ	henry per metre	H/m
Permeability of free space	μ_0	henry per metre	H/m
Permeability, relative	μ_r	—	—
Permeance	Λ	weber per ampere or per henry	Wb/A or /H
Permittivity, absolute	ε	farad per metre	F/m
Permittivity of free space	ε_0	farad per metre	F/m
Permittivity, relative	ε_r	—	—
Phase-change coefficient	β	radian per metre	rad/m
Potential, Potential difference	V	volt	V
Power, active	P	watt	W
Power, apparent	S	volt ampere	VA
Power, reactive	Q	volt ampere reactive	var
Propagation coefficient (or constant)	γ	—	—
Quality factor, magnification	Q	—	—
Quantity of electricity	Q	coulomb	C

Reactance	X	ohm	Ω
Reflection coefficient	ρ	—	—
Relative permeability	μ_r	—	—
Relative permittivity	ε_r	—	—
Reluctance	R_m	ampere per weber or per henry	A/Wb or /H
Resistance	R	ohm	Ω
Resistance,m temperature coefficient of	α	per degree Celsius or per kelvin	/°C or /K
Resistivity	ρ	ohm metre	Ωm
Slip	s	per unit or per cent	p.u. or %
Standing wave ratio	s	—	—
Susceptance	B	siemen	S
Temperature coefficient of resistance	α	per degree Celsius or per kelvin	/°C or /K
Temperature, thermodynamic	T	kelvin	K
Time	t	second	s
Torque	T	newton metre	Nm
Velocity	v	metre per second	m/s
Velocity, angular	ω	radian per second	rad/s
Volume	V	cubic metres	m^3
Wavelength	λ	metre	m

(Note that V/m may also be written as Vm^{-1}; A/m^2 as Am^{-2}; /K as K^{-1}, and so on.)

Appendix B:
Common prefixes

Prefix	Name	Meaning multiply by
E	exa	10^{18}
P	peta	10^{15}
T	tera	10^{12}
G	giga	10^9
M	mega	10^6
k	kilo	10^3
h	hecto	10^2
da	deca	10^1
d	deci	10^{-1}
c	centi	10^{-2}
m	milli	10^{-3}
μ	micro	10^{-6}
n	nano	10^{-9}
p	pico	10^{-12}
f	femto	10^{-15}
a	atto	10^{-18}

Appendix C:
Greek alphabet

Alpha	A	α	Nu	N	ν
Beta	B	β	Xi	Ξ	ξ
Gamma	Γ	γ	Omicron	O	o
Delta	Δ	δ	Pi	Π	π
Epsilon	E	ε	Rho	P	ρ
Zeta	Z	ζ	Sigma	Σ	σ
Eta	H	η	Tau	T	τ
Theta	Θ	θ	Upsilon	Y	υ
Iota	I	ι	Phi	Φ	ϕ
Kappa	K	κ	Chi	X	χ
Lambda	Λ	λ	Psi	Ψ	ψ
Mu	M	μ	Omega	Ω	ω

Appendix D:
Some basic definitions

Ampere   The ampere is that constant current which, if maintained in two straight parallel conductors of infinite length, of negligible circular cross-section, and placed 1 metre apart in vaccum, would produce between these conductors a force equal to 2×10^{-7} newton per metre of length.

Atom   An atom is the smallest part of an element which can take part in a chemical reaction and which retains the properties of the element. It contains subatomic particles called **electrons, protons,** and **neutrons.** Protons and neutrons are contained in the central part of an atom called the **nucleus.** Electrons constitute the other part of all atoms.

An electron has a mass of 9.11×10^{-31} kilogram and a negative charge of 1.602×10^{-19} coulomb.

A proton has a mass of 1.673×10^{-27} kilogram and a positive charge of 1.602×10^{-19} coulomb (i.e. equal to that of the electron).

An equal number of electrons and protons exist within an atom and it is said to be electrically balanced as the negtive and positive charges cancel each other out.

A neutron has a mass of 1.675×10^{-27} kilogram and carries no charge (i.e. it is neutral).

Charge   Charge is the quantity of electricity and is measured in coulombs.

Conductance   Conductance is the reciprocal of resistance and is measured in siemens.

Conductor   A conductor is a material which offers a low resistance to the passage of electric current.

Coulomb   The coulomb is the quantity of electricity which flows past a given point in an electric circuit when a current of one ampere is maintained for one second. The coulomb is the unit of electrical charge.

Current   Current is the rate of movement of charge.

Electromotive force   The elecromotive force (emf) is the driving influence which tends to produce an electric current in a closed circuit. It is provided by the source and its unit is the volt.

Energy Energy is the capacity of a system to do work. The unit of energy is the joule J.

Insulator An insulator is a material having a high resistance which prevents current flow.

Joule One joule is the work done or energy transferred when a force of one newton is exerted through a distance of one metre in the direction of the force. The joule is the unit of work done or energy.

Newton One newton is the force which, when applied to a mass of one kilogram, gives it an acceleration of one metre per second squared. The newton is the unit of force.

Ohm The unit of electrical resistance is the ohm, which is the resistance between two points of a conductor when a potential difference of one volt applied between these points, produces in the conductor a current of one ampere (the conductor not being a source of any electromotive force).

Potential The electric potential at a point is the potential difference between that point and earth, the latter being considered at zero potential.

Potential difference The potential difference (p.d.) between two points in a circuit is the energy transferred due to the passage of a unit of electrical charge. The unit of potential difference is the volt.

Power Power is the rate of doing work or transferring energy.

Resistance The resistance in an electric circuit is its opposition to the flow of electric current.

Resistivity The resistivity of a material is the resistance of a unit cube of the material measured between opposite faces of the cube.

Temperature coefficient of resistance The temperature coefficient of resistance of a material is the ratio of the change of resistance per degree change of termperature to the resistance at 0°C.

Volt One volt is the difference in potential between two points in a conductor when one joule of energy is required to transfer one coulomb of charge. The volt is the unit of electric potential.

Voltage Voltage is the value of an electromotive force or potential difference expressed in volts.

Watt One watt is one joule per second. The watt is the unit of power.

Appendix E
The full mathematical meaning of root mean square (RMS) when it is used to dictate a value for an ac sinusoidal waveform

If a sinusoid is given by, say, $i = I_{MAX} \sin(2\pi ft)$ A then its RMS value is given by the expression:

$$i_{(RMS)} = \sqrt{(\text{mean square of } i)}$$

where the

$$\text{'mean square of } i\text{'} = \frac{1}{(b-a)} \int_a^b (I_{MAX}^2 \sin^2(2\pi ft)) \, dt$$

For a sinusoidal waveform we need only integrate over one cycle since the averaging effect over this cycle is the same for all subsequent cycles. Therefore the

$$\text{'mean square of } i\text{'} = \frac{I_{(MAX)}^2}{T} \int_0^T \tfrac{1}{2}(1 - \cos 4\pi ft) \, dt$$

where $T = 1/f$ s

$$= \frac{I_{(MAX)}^2}{2T} \left[t - \frac{\sin 4\pi ft}{4\pi f} \right]_0^T$$

$$= \frac{I_{(MAX)}^2}{2T} \left[\left(T - \frac{\sin 4\pi}{4\pi} \right) - (0 - 0) \right]$$

$$= \frac{I_{(MAX)}^2}{2}$$

(Since $\sin 4\pi = 0$)

Now

$$i_{(RMS)} = \sqrt{(\text{mean square of } i)} = \frac{\sqrt{(I^2_{(MAX)})}}{\sqrt{2}}$$

Therefore

$$i_{(RMS)} = \frac{I_{(MAX)}}{\sqrt{2}}$$

This mathematical solution confirms the result arrived at by deduction in Chapter 8, section 8.1.3.

Bibliography

Books

B. A. Gregory, *An Introduction to Electrical Instrumentation,* Macmillan, 1973.
William Hayt, *Engineering Circuit Analysis,* McGraw-Hill, 1962.
Hughes, *Electrotechnology*, Longman.

Software

Electronic Workbench, Degem Systems Limited, IT Eduction Ltd, Rackery Lane, Llay, Wrexham LL12 0PB, United Kingdom.
Micro-cap III DATECH, Data Technology Datech Ltd, Sidcup Technology Centre, Maidstone Road, Sidcup, Kent DA14 5HT, United Kingdom. (American publishers: Spectrum Software, 1021 S. Wolfe Road, Sunnyvale, CA 94086, USA).

Index